WILEY SERIES IN PROBABILITY
AND MATHEMATICAL STATISTICS

ESTABLISHED BY WALTER A. SHEWHART AND SAMUEL S. WILKS

Probability and Mathematical Statistics

ALEXANDER · Elements of Mathematical Statistics
ANDERSON · An Introduction to Multivariate Statistical Analysis
BLACKWELL and GIRSHICK · Theory of Games and Statistical Decisions
CRAMÉR · The Elements of Probability Theory and Some of Its Applications
DOOB · Stochastic Processes
DWYER · Linear Computations
FELLER · An Introduction to Probability Theory and Its Applications, Volume I, *Second Edition*
FELLER · An Introduction to Probability Theory and Its Applications, Volume II
FISHER · Contributions to Mathematical Statistics
FISZ · Probability Theory and Mathematical Statistics, *Third Edition*
FRASER · Nonparametric Methods in Statistics
FRASER · Statistics—An Introduction
GRENANDER and ROSENBLATT · Statistical Analysis of Stationary Time Series
HANSEN, HURWITZ, and MADOW · Sample Survey Methods and Theory, Volume II
HOEL · Introduction to Mathematical Statistics, *Third Edition*
KEMPTHORNE · The Design and Analysis of Experiments
LEHMANN · Testing Statistical Hypotheses
PARZEN · Modern Probability Theory and Its Applications
RAO · Advanced Statistical Methods in Biometric Research
RAO · Linear Statistical Inference and Its Applications
RIORDAN · An Introduction to Combinatorial Analysis
SAVAGE · The Foundations of Statistics
SCHEFFÉ · The Analysis of Variance
WALD · Sequential Analysis
WALD · Statistical Decision Functions
WILKS · Mathematical Statistics

Applied Probability and Statistics

ACTON · Analysis of Straight-Line Data
ALLEN and ELY · International Trade Statistics
BAILEY · The Elements of Stochastic Processes with Applications to the Natural Sciences
BENNETT and FRANKLIN · Statistical Analysis in Chemistry and the Chemical Industry
BROWNLEE · Statistical Theory and Methodology in Science and Engineering, *Second Edition*

Applied Probability and Statistics (Continued)

BUSH and MOSTELLER · Stochastic Models for Learning
CHAKRAVARTI, LAHA and ROY · Handbook of Methods of Applied Statistics, Vol. I
CHAKRAVARTI, LAHA and ROY · Handbook of Methods of Applied Statistics, Vol. II
CHERNOFF and MOSES · Elementary Decision Theory
CHEW · Experimental Designs in Industry
CLARK · An Introduction to Statistics
CLELLAND, deCANI, BROWN, BURSK, and MURRAY · Basic Statistics with Business Applications
COCHRAN · Sampling Techniques, *Second Edition*
COCHRAN and COX · Experimental Designs, *Second Edition*
CORNELL · The Essentials of Educational Statistics
COX · Planning of Experiments
COX and MILLER · The Theory of Stochastic Processes
DEMING · Sample Design in Business Research
DEMING · Some Theory of Sampling
DODGE and ROMIG · Sampling Inspection Tables, *Second Edition*
DRAPER and SMITH · Applied Regression Analysis
FRYER · Elements of Statistics
GOLDBERGER · Econometric Theory
GOULDEN · Methods of Statistical Analysis, *Second Edition*
GUTTMAN and WILKS · Introductory Engineering Statistics
HALD · Statistical Tables and Formulas
HALD · Statistical Theory with Engineering Applications
HANSEN, HURWITZ, and MADOW · Sample Survey Methods and Theory, Volume I
HAUSER and LEONARD · Government Statistics for Business Use, *Second Edition*
HOEL · Elementary Statistics, *Second Edition*
JOHNSON and LEONE · Statistics and Experimental Design: In Engineering and the Physical Sciences, Volumes I and II
KEMPTHORNE · An Introduction to Genetic Statistics
MEYER · Symposium on Monte Carlo Methods
PRABHU · Queues and Inventories: A Study of Their Basic Stochastic Processes
RICE · Control Charts in Factory Management
SARHAN and GREENBERG · Contributions to Order Statistics
TIPPETT · Technological Applications of Statistics
WILLIAMS · Regression Analysis
WOLD and JURÉEN · Demand Analysis
YOUDEN · Statistical Methods for Chemists

Tracts on Probability and Statistics

BILLINGSLEY · Ergodic Theory and Information
CRAMÉR and LEADBETTER · Stationary and Related Stochastic Processes
TAKÁCS · Combinatorial Methods in the Theory of Stochastic Processes

Combinatorial Methods in the Theory of Stochastic Processes

Combinatorial Methods in the Theory of Stochastic Processes

LAJOS TAKÁCS
Professor of Mathematics
Case Institute of Technology

John Wiley & Sons, Inc.
New York · London · Sydney

Library of Congress Catalog Card Number: 67-13529
Printed in the United States of America

To Judith

Preface

In the theory of probability there are many problems whose solutions require the determination of the distribution of the maximum of random variables or the distribution of the supremum of stochastic processes. Such problems frequently arise in the theories of queues, dams, storage, insurance risk, physics, engineering, order statistics, games of chance, random walks, and elsewhere. In this book we shall show that for a wide class of random variables and for a wide class of stochastic processes we can obtain explicit results in a simple and elementary way by using a generalization of the classical ballot theorem. The classical ballot theorem originated in the year 1887 and is linked with the name of J. Bertrand. It is interesting to note, however, that Bertrand's theorem is equivalent to an earlier result of games of chance which was found in 1708 by A. De Moivre.

In this book we shall prove first some general theorems for the determination of the distribution of the maximum of random variables and the distribution of the supremum of stochastic processes. Then we shall give many examples for the applications of these general theorems. We shall cover a broad field of applications which includes the fields mentioned at the beginning of this preface. We shall give some problems for solution. Most of the problems are not merely exercises, but are intended to be extensions of the material covered in the book.

The book is divided into eight chapters. At the end of each chapter there is a list of references containing the papers and books mentioned in that chapter as well as other related material. The chapters are subdivided into sections. The numbering of the formulas and theorems starts anew in each section. The formulas and theorems mentioned in any one section refer to formulas and theorems in the same section. If there is reference made to formulas or theorems from another section, then this is stated explicitly.

The material covered in this book is based only on the elements of the theory of probability and stochastic processes. Most of the results presented here were achieved by the author in the past six years and some have already been published in a series of papers.

This book was written in the spring of 1966 at Stanford University while I was on sabbatical leave from Columbia University. I express my sincere thanks to the National Academy of Sciences for its partial support during the writing of this book.

LAJOS TAKÁCS

Palo Alto
May 1966

Contents

Combinatorial Methods in the Theory of Stochastic Processes

CHAPTER 1

Ballot Theorems

1. INTRODUCTION

In the theory of probability the problem frequently arises of finding the distribution of the maximum for random variables and the distribution of the supremum for stochastic processes. The aim of this book is to show that for a wide class of random variables and for a wide class of stochastic processes such problems can be solved in an elementary way by using the following generalization of the classical ballot theorem.

Theorem 1. *Let $\phi(u)$, $0 \leq u \leq t$, be a nondecreasing function for which $\phi'(u) = 0$ almost everywhere and $\phi(0) = 0$. Let $\phi(t + u) = \phi(t) + \phi(u)$ for $0 \leq u \leq t$. For $0 \leq u \leq t$ define $\delta(u) = 1$ if $\phi(v) - \phi(u) \leq v - u$ for $u \leq v \leq u + t$ and $\delta(u) = 0$ otherwise. Then*

$$\int_0^t \delta(u)\, du = t - \phi(t) \tag{1}$$

whenever $\phi(t) \leq t$.

If $\phi(u)$, $0 \leq u \leq t$, is a nondecreasing step function, then $\phi(u)$ has a finite or countably infinite number of jumps, $\phi'(u) = 0$ almost everywhere and Theorem 1 is applicable. If $\phi(u)$, $0 \leq u \leq t$, is a nondecreasing, continuous, singular function, then $\phi'(u) = 0$ almost everywhere and Theorem 1 is applicable also to such functions. An example for such functions is Lebesgue's singular function (E. Hewitt and K. Stromberg [21], p. 113). Another example is given by B. Sz.-Nagy [32], pp. 198–200, for a strictly increasing singular function.

Theorem 1 contains, as an interesting particular case, the following theorem.

Theorem 2. *If $k_1, k_2, \ldots, k_n$ are nonnegative integers with sum $k_1 + k_2 + \cdots + k_n = k \leq n$, then among the n cyclic permutations of $(k_1, k_2, \ldots, k_n)$ there are exactly $n - k$ for which the sum of the first r elements is less than r for all $r = 1, 2, \ldots, n$.*

If $t = n$ and $\phi(u) = k_1 + \cdots + k_r$ for $r \leq u < r + 1$ in Theorem 1, then we obtain Theorem 2. Conversely, we can deduce Theorem 1 from Theorem 2 by a suitable limiting procedure.

We shall use Theorem 1 in finding explicit formulas for the distribution of the maximum of random variables and for the distribution of the supremum of stochastic processes. In finding certain limiting distributions, we shall refer to additional theorems such as the weak law of large numbers, some Abelian theorems and some Tauberian theorems. All these theorems are mentioned in the Appendix. Occasionally we shall point out that some results can also be obtained by using the strong law of large numbers, some theorems for recurrent processes and the continuity theorem for Laplace-Stieltjes transforms. These theorems are also mentioned in the Appendix.

By using the mentioned methods we shall be able to find the distribution of the maximum of random variables and the distribution of the supremum for stochastic processes arising in the theories of queues, dams, storage, insurance risks, physics, engineering, order statistics, random walk, games of chance, and elsewhere.

2. A GENERALIZATION OF THE CLASSICAL BALLOT THEOREM

The following theorem, which it is proper to call the classical ballot theorem, originated in the year 1887.

Theorem 1. *If in a ballot candidate A scores a votes and candidate B scores b votes, and $a \geq \mu b$ where μ is a nonnegative integer, then the probability that throughout the counting the number of votes registered for A is always greater than μ times the number of votes registered for B is given by*

$$P = \frac{a - \mu b}{a + b}, \tag{1}$$

provided that all the possible voting records are equally probable.

We note that the probability that the number of votes registered for A is always at least μ times the number of votes registered for B is given by

$$Q = \frac{a + 1 - \mu b}{a + 1}. \tag{2}$$

By using (1) we can easily prove that (2) holds and conversely (2) implies (1).

Probability (1) for $\mu = 1$ was found in 1887 by J. Bertrand [8] and for $\mu \geq 1$, also in 1887, by É. Barbier [6]. The proof of (1) for $\mu = 1$ was given in 1887 by D. André [5] and for $\mu \geq 1$ in 1924 by A. Aeppli [2, 3]. Other proofs for (1) were given in 1947 by A. Dvoretzky and Th. Motzkin [13], in 1950 by H. D. Grossman [18], in 1961 by S. G. Mohanty and T. V. Narayana [29].

Actually, the particular case $\mu = 1$ can be traced back to 1708 when A. De Moivre [11] considered the following problem of duration of plays in the theory of games of chance.

Two players A and B play a sequence of games. In each game, independently of the others, either A wins a coin from B with probability p or B wins a coin from A with probability q where $p + q = 1$. Suppose that A has an initial capital of $a - b$ coins, and B has an infinite capital. What is the probability that A will be ruined at the $(a + b)$th game?

A. De Moivre found that the probability that the duration of game, ρ, is $a + b$ is given by

$$\mathbf{P}\{\rho = a + b\} = \frac{a - b}{a + b}\binom{a + b}{a} q^a p^b, \tag{3}$$

but he did not provide a proof. The problem was completely solved in 1775 by J. L. Lagrange [22] and in 1812 by P. S. Laplace [23], pp. 228–242. The probability that in the $a + b$ games A loses a games and B loses b games is

$$\binom{a + b}{a} q^a p^b.$$

The conditional probability that A will be ruined at the $(a + b)$th game, given that in the $(a + b)$ games A loses a games and B loses b games, is accordingly

$$P = \frac{a - b}{a + b}. \tag{4}$$

If we consider the $(a + b)$ games in reverse order and a loss for A corresponds to a vote for A, and a loss for B corresponds to a vote for B, then we can see immediately that $P = (a - b)/(a + b)$ is the probability that A is leading throughout the counting of the $a + b$ votes. In this way we obtained formula (1) for $\mu = 1$. It is interesting to recall A. M. Ampère [4] who comments formula (3) as it is remarkable for its simplicity and elegance.

In 1879 W. A. Whitworth [36, 37] showed that the number of ways in which a gains and b losses can be arranged in such a way that the losses are never in excess of the gains is

$$\frac{a + 1 - b}{a + 1}\binom{a + b}{a}. \tag{5}$$

This implies (2) for $\mu = 1$.

The classical ballot theorem is equivalent to the following theorem.

Theorem 2. *If an urn contains a cards each marked* 0 *and b cards each marked* $(\mu + 1)$, *and if all the $a + b$ cards are drawn without replacement* *from the urn, then the probability that for all* $r = 1, 2, \ldots, a + b$, *the sum of the first* r *numbers drawn is less than* r *is*

$$P = 1 - \frac{k}{n}, \tag{6}$$

where $n = a + b$ *is the number of the cards in the urn, and* $k = b(\mu + 1)$ *is the sum of the numbers on the cards, provided that* $k \leq n$ *and that all the possible results are equally probable.*

The equivalence of Theorem 1 and Theorem 2 can easily be seen. For if among the first r drawings there are α_r zeros and β_r $(\mu + 1)$'s, then $\alpha_r 0 + \beta_r(\mu + 1) < r = \alpha_r + \beta_r$ holds if and only if $\beta_r \mu < \alpha_r$.

The latter formulation of the classical ballot theorem suggests the following generalization.

Theorem 3. *Suppose that an urn contains* n *cards marked with nonnegative integers* $k_1, k_2, \ldots, k_n$ *respectively where* $k_1 + k_2 + \cdots + k_n = k \leq n$. *All the* n *cards are drawn without replacement from the urn. Denote by* ν_r, $r = 1, 2, \ldots, n$, *the number on the card drawn at the* r*th drawing. Then*

$$\mathbf{P}\{\nu_1 + \cdots + \nu_r < r \text{ for } r = 1, \ldots\ n\} = 1 - \frac{k}{n}, \tag{7}$$

provided that all the possible results are equally probable.

This is indeed true. It follows from the following more general theorem.

Theorem 4. *Let* $k_1, k_2, \ldots, k_n$ *be nonnegative integers with sum* $k_1 + k_2 + \cdots + k_n = k \leq n$. *Among the* n *cyclic permutations of* $(k_1, k_2, \ldots, k_n)$ *there are exactly* $n - k$ *for which the sum of the first* r *elements is less than* r *for all* $r = 1, 2, \ldots, n$.

Proof. Let $k_{r+n} = k_r$ for $r = 1, 2, \ldots$ and set $\phi_r = k_1 + \cdots + k_r$, $r = 1, 2, \ldots; \phi_0 = 0$. Define

$$\delta_r = \begin{cases} 1 & \text{if } \ i - \phi_i > r - \phi_r \quad \text{ for } \ i > r, \\ 0 & \text{otherwise,} \end{cases} \tag{8}$$

and

$$\psi_r = \inf \{i - \phi_i \text{ for } i > r\} \tag{9}$$

for $r = 0, 1, 2, \ldots$. Evidently $\delta_r = \psi_{r+1} - \psi_r$. Since $\phi_{r+n} = \phi_r + \phi_n$, we have $\delta_{r+n} = \delta_r$ and $\psi_{r+n} = \psi_r + n - k$ for $r = 0, 1, 2, \ldots$. Therefore among the n cyclic permutations of $(k_1, k_2, \ldots, k_n)$ there are exactly

$$\sum_{r=1}^{n} \delta_r = \psi_{n+1} - \psi_1 = n - k \tag{10}$$

for which the sum of the first r elements is less than r for $r = 1, 2, \ldots, n$.

Theorem 4 implies that among the $n!$ permutations of $(k_1, k_2, \ldots, k_n)$ there are exactly $(n-1)!\,(n-k)$ for which the sum of the first r elements is less than r for all $r = 1, 2, \ldots, n$. This proves Theorem 3.

Theorem 4 can also be formulated in the following way. Define $\phi(u) = \phi_i$ if $i \leq u < i+1$ and let

$$\delta(u) = \begin{cases} 1 & \text{if } \ v - \phi(v) \geq u - \phi(u) \quad \text{for } \ v \geq u, \\ 0 & \text{otherwise.} \end{cases} \tag{11}$$

Then (10) is equivalent to the following statement:

$$\int_0^n \delta(u)\,du = n - \phi(n) \tag{12}$$

if $\phi(n) \leq n$. For $\delta(u) = \delta_r$ if $r < u < r + 1$.

In the latter formulation of Theorem 4, $\phi(u)$, $0 \leq u \leq n$, is a nondecreasing step function which vanishes at $u = 0$. This raises the question of whether (12) remains also valid if $\phi(u)$, $0 \leq u \leq n$ is an arbitrary nondecreasing step function for which $\phi(0) = 0$. The answer is affirmative and we shall prove that the following theorem is valid.

Theorem 5. *Let $\phi(u)$, $0 \leq u \leq t$, be a nondecreasing step function satisfying the condition $\phi(0) = 0$. Define $\phi(u)$ for $0 \leq u < \infty$ by assuming that $\phi(u+t) = \phi(u) + \phi(t)$ for $u \geq 0$. Define*

$$\delta(u) = \begin{cases} 1 & \textit{if } \ v - \phi(v) \geq u - \phi(u) \quad \textit{for } \ v \geq u, \\ 0 & \textit{otherwise.} \end{cases} \tag{13}$$

Then

$$\int_0^t \delta(u)\,du = \begin{cases} t - \phi(t) & \textit{if } \ \phi(t) < t, \\ 0 & \textit{if } \ \phi(t) \geq t. \end{cases} \tag{14}$$

Proof. If $\phi(t) > t$, then $\delta(u) = 0$ for all $u \geq 0$ and thus the theorem is obviously true. Now let us consider the case $\phi(t) \leq t$. For $u \geq 0$ define

$$\psi(u) = \inf\{v - \phi(v) \text{ for } v \geq u\}. \tag{15}$$

Since $\phi(u+t) = \phi(u) + \phi(t)$ for $u \geq 0$, we have $\psi(u+t) = \psi(u) + t - \phi(t)$ for $u \geq 0$. Furthermore we have $0 \leq \psi(v) - \psi(u) \leq v - u$ for $0 \leq u \leq v$. Thus $\psi(u)$ is a monotone nondecreasing and absolutely continuous function of u. Consequently, $\psi'(u)$ exists for almost all u, $0 \leq \psi'(u) \leq 1$, and

$$\int_0^t \psi'(u)\,du = \psi(t) - \psi(0) = t - \phi(t). \tag{16}$$

Now we shall prove that $\psi'(u) = \delta(u)$ for almost all u, which implies the theorem. We note that $\delta(u) = 1$ if and only if $\psi(u) = u - \phi(u)$. The inequality $\psi(u) \leq u - \phi(u)$ always holds. Furthermore, we have $\phi(u + 0) = \phi(u)$ and $\phi'(u) = 0$ for almost all u.

First, we prove that

$$(17) \qquad \psi'(u) \leq \delta(u) \qquad \text{for almost all } u.$$

If $\psi'(u)$ exists, and if $\psi'(u) = 0$, then (17) obviously holds. Now we shall prove that if $\psi'(u)$ exists, if $\psi'(u) > 0$ and if $\phi(u + 0) = \phi(u)$, then $\delta(u) = 1$. If $\psi'(u) > 0$, then $\psi(v) > \psi(u)$ for $v > u$ and therefore $\psi(u) = \inf\{s - \phi(s) \text{ for } u \leq s \leq v\}$ holds for all $v > u$. Thus $u - \phi(v) \leq \psi(u) \leq u - \phi(u)$ for all $v > u$ and consequently $u - \phi(u + 0) \leq \psi(u) \leq u - \phi(u)$. If $\phi(u + 0) = \phi(u)$, then $\psi(u) = u - \phi(u)$ which implies that $\delta(u) = 1$. Since $\psi'(u) \leq 1$ always holds, (17) follows.

Second, we prove that

$$(18) \qquad \delta(u) \leq \psi'(u) \quad \text{for almost all } u.$$

If $\delta(u) = 0$ and $\psi'(u)$ exists, then (18) evidently holds. Now we shall prove that if $\delta(u) = 1$, if $\psi'(u)$ exists, if $\phi'(u) = 0$ and if u is an accumulation point of the set $D = \{u: \delta(u) = 1, 0 \leq u < \infty\}$, then $\psi'(u) = 1$. Suppose that $u \in D$ and $u = \lim_{n\to\infty} u_n$ where $u_n \in D$ and $u_n \neq u$. Then $\psi(u) = u - \phi(u)$ and $\psi(u_n) = u_n - \phi(u_n)$. Accordingly if $\psi'(u)$ exists and if $\phi'(u) = 0$, we have

$$(19) \qquad \psi'(u) = \lim_{n\to\infty} \frac{\psi(u) - \psi(u_n)}{u - u_n} = 1 - \lim_{n\to\infty} \frac{\phi(u) - \phi(u_n)}{u - u_n} = 1 - \phi'(u) = 1.$$

Since the isolated points of the set D form a countable set (possibly empty), (18) follows.

If we compare (17) and (18) then we obtain that $\psi'(u) = \delta(u)$ for almost all u. Hence by (16) we get (14) for $\phi(t) \leq t$. This completes the proof of the theorem.

In the proof of Theorem 5 we exploited only the fact that $\phi(u)$, $0 \leq u \leq t$, is a nondecreasing function for which $\phi(0) = 0$ and $\phi'(u) = 0$ almost everywhere. Thus it follows more generally that Theorem 1 of the Introduction also holds.

We note that if we alter the definition of $\delta(u)$ in such a way that $\delta(u) = 1$ when $v - \phi(v) > u - \phi(u)$ for all $v > u$ and $\delta(u) = 0$ otherwise, then (14) remains unchanged. Furthermore, if u is a discontinuity point of $\phi(u)$, then $\phi(u)$ may take any value in the interval $[\phi(u-0), \phi(u+0)]$.

The proof of Theorem 5 can be significantly simplified if we suppose that $\phi(u)$ has only a finite number of jumps in the interval $(0, t)$.

As we have seen, Theorem 5 is a step-by-step generalization of the classical ballot theorem. By using Theorem 5 we can deduce immediately the classical ballot theorem.

3. PROBLEMS

1. In a ballot candidate A scores a votes and candidate B scores b votes, and all the possible voting records are equally probable. Find $P(a, b)$, the probability that throughout the counting the number of votes registered for A is always greater than μ times the number of votes registered for B if μ is a nonnegative number.

2. In a ballot candidate A scores a votes and candidate B scores b votes, and all the possible voting records are equally probable. Find $Q(a, b)$, the probability that throughout the counting the number of votes registered for A is always at least μ times the number of votes registered for B if μ is a nonnegative integer.

3. In a ballot candidate A scores a votes and candidate B scores b votes, and all the possible voting records are equally probable. Let $b < a + c$ where c is a positive integer. Denote by α_r and β_r the number of votes registered for A and B respectively among the first r votes recorded. Find the probability $Q_c(a, b) = \mathbf{P}\{\beta_r < \alpha_r + c \text{ for } r = 1, 2, \ldots, a + b\}$.

4. In a ballot candidate A scores a votes and candidate B scores b votes, and all the possible voting records are equally probable. Let $c - d < b - a < c$ where $0 < c < d$ are integers. Denote by α_r and β_r the number of votes registered for A and B respectively among the first r votes recorded. Find the probability $P = \mathbf{P}\{c - d < \beta_r - \alpha_r < c \text{ for } r = 1, 2, \ldots, a + b\}$.

5. Prove Theorem 3 of Section 2 by mathematical induction on n.

6. Prove Theorem 5 of Section 2 for the case when $\phi(u)$ has only a finite number of jumps in the interval $(0, t)$.

7. The following three problems are questions 5669, 5744, 5804 in the *Educational Times* (1878) June, September, and November issues respectively. See W. A. Whitworth [36].

(*a*) A man drinks in random order n glasses of wine and n glasses of water (all of equal size). Prove that the probability that he never drinks throughout the process more wine than water is $1/(n + 1)$.

(*b*) If n men and their wives go over a bridge in single file and in random order, subject only to the condition that there are to be never more men than women gone over, prove that the probability that no man goes over before his wife is $(n + 1)/2^n$.

(*c*) If a man playing for a constant stake, wins $2n + 1$ games and loses $n + 1$ games, prove that the probability that he is never worse off than at the beginning and never better off than at the end is $n/(4n + 6)$.

8. Suppose that in a ballot candidates $A_1, A_2, \ldots, A_n$ score $a_1, a_2, \ldots, a_n$ votes respectively. Let $a_1 \geq a_2 \geq \cdots \geq a_n$. Denote by $\alpha_1^{(r)}, \alpha_2^{(r)}, \ldots, \alpha_n^{(r)}$ the number of votes registered for $A_1, A_2, \ldots, A_n$ respectively among the first r votes recorded. Find $\mathbf{P}\{\alpha_1^{(r)} \geq \alpha_2^{(r)} \geq \cdots \geq \alpha_n^{(r)}$ for $r = 1, 2, \ldots, a_1 + \cdots + a_n\}$, provided that all the possible voting records are equally probable. (P. A. MacMahon [26], p. 133.)

REFERENCES

[1] Aebly, J. "Démonstration du problème du scrutin par des considerations géometriques," *L'Enseignement Mathématique* **23** (1923), 185–186.

[2] Aeppli, A. "A propos de l'interprétation géometrique du problème du scrutin," *L'Enseignement Mathématique* **23** (1923), 328–329.

[3] Aeppli, A. *Zur Theorie verketteter Wahrscheinlichkeiten. Markoffsche Ketten höherer Ordnung*, Diss. Eidg. Techn. Hochschule, Zürich, 1924.

[4] Ampère, A. M. *Considerations sur la Théorie Mathématique de Jeu*, Lyon and Paris, 1802.

[5] André, D. "Solution directe du problème résolu par M. Bertrand," *C. R. Acad. Sci. Paris* **105** (1887), 436–437.

[6] Barbier, É. "Généralisation du problème résolu par M. J. Bertrand," *C. R. Acad. Sci. Paris* **105** (1887), 407 and 440 (errata).

[7] Barton, D. E. and C. L. Mallows, "Some aspects of the random sequence," *Ann. Math. Statist.* **36** (1965), 236–260.

[8] Bertrand, J. "Solution d'un problème," *C. R. Acad. Sci. Paris* **105** (1887) 369.

[9] Bizley, M. T. L. "Derivation of a new formula for the number of minimal lattice paths from (0, 0) to (km, kn) having just t contacts with the line $my = nx$ and having no points above this line; and a proof of Grossman's formula for the number of paths which may touch but do not rise above this line," *J. Inst. Actuar.* **80** (1954), 55–62.

[10] Bizley, M. T. L. and H. D. Grossman, "Fun with lattice-points 25. Paths having a given number of lattice points in a given region," *Scripta Math.* **20** (1954), 203–204.

[11] De Moivre, A. "De mensura sortis, seu, de probabilitate eventuum in ludis a casu fortuito pendentibus," *Philos. Trans. London* **27** (1711), 213–264.

[12] Dinges, H. "Eine kombinatorische Überlegung und ihre masstheoretische Erweiterung," *Zeitschr. Wahrscheinlichkeitstheorie* **1** (1963), 278–287.

[13] Dvoretzky, A. and Th. Motzkin, "A problem of arrangements," *Duke Math. J.* **14** (1947), 305–313.

[14] Erdös, P. and I. Kaplansky, "Sequences of plus and minus," *Scripta Math.* **12** (1946), 73–75.

[15] Göbel, F. *Some remarks on ballot problems*, Mathematisch Centrum, Amsterdam, August 1964.

[16] Graham, R. L. "A combinatorial theorem for partial sums," *Ann. Math. Statist.* **34** (1963), 1600–1602.

[17] Grossman, H. D. "Fun with lattice-points 4. The ballot-box problem," *Scripta Math.* **12** (1946), 223–225.

[18] Grossman, H. D. "Fun with lattice-points 21. Another extension of the ballot problem," *Scripta Math.* **16** (1950), 120–124.

[19] Grossman, H. D. "Fun with lattice-points 22. Paths in a lattice triangle," *Scripta Math.* **16** (1950), 207–212.

[20] Harper, L. H. "A family of combinatorial identities," *Ann. Math. Statist.* **37** (1966), 509–512.

[21] Hewitt, E. and K. Stromberg, *Real and Abstract Analysis*, Springer, New York, 1965.

[22] Lagrange, J. L. "Recherches sur les suites récurrentes dont les termes varient de plusieurs manières différentes, ou sur l'intégration des équations linéaires aux différences finies et partielles; et sur l'usage de ces équations dans la théorie des hazards," *Noveaux Mémoires de l'Académie des Sciences de Berlin*, (1775), 183–272. [*Oeuvres de Lagrange*, **IV**, pp. 151–251, Gauthier-Villars, Paris, 1869.]

[23] Laplace, P. S. *Théorie Analytique des Probabilités*, Courcier, Paris, 1812. [*Oeuvres complètes de Laplace*, **VII**, Gauthier-Villars, Paris, 1886.]

[24] Lucas, E. *Théorie des Nombres*. I, Gauthier-Villars, Paris, 1891.

[25] MacMahon, P. A. "Memoir on the theory of the partitions of numbers. Part IV. On the probability that the successful candidate at an election by ballot may never at any time have fewer votes than the one who is unsuccessful; on a generalisation of this question; and on its connexion with other questions of partition, permutation, and combination," *Phil. Trans. Roy. Soc. London Ser. A* **209** (1909), 153–175.

[26] MacMahon, P. A. *Combinatory Analysis*, I, Cambridge University Press, 1915.

[27] Mirimanoff, D. "A propos de l'interprétation géometrique du problème du scrutin," *L'Enseignement Mathématique* **23** (1923), 185–186.

[28] Mohanty, S. G. "An urn problem related to the ballot problem," *Amer. Math. Monthly* **73** (1966), 526–528.

[29] Mohanty, S. G. and T. V. Narayana, "Some properties of compositions and their application to probability and statistics," *Biometrische Zeitschrift* **3** (1961), 252–258, and **5** (1963), 8–18.

[30] Narayana, T. V. "A partial order and its applications to probability theory," *Sankhyā Ser. A* **21** (1959), 91–98.

[31] Riordan, J. "The enumeration of election returns by number of lead positions," *Ann. Math. Statist.* **35** (1964), 369–379.

[32] Sz.-Nagy, B. *Introduction to Real Functions and Orthogonal Expansions*, Oxford University Press, New York, 1965.

[33] Takács, L. "A generalization of the ballot problem and its application in the theory of queues," *J. Amer. Statist. Assoc.* **57** (1962), 327–337.

[34] Takács, L. "Ballot problems," *Zeitschr. Wahrscheinlichkeitstheorie* **1** (1962), 154–158.

[35] Takács, L. "The distribution of majority times in a ballot," *Zeitschr. Wahrscheinlichkeitstheorie* **2** (1963), 118–121.

[36] Whitworth, W. A. "Arrangements of m things of one sort and n things of another sort, under certain conditions of priority," *Messenger of Mathematics* **8** (1879), 105–114.

[37] Whitworth, W. A. *Choice and Chance*, 4th edition, Deighton Bell, Cambridge, 1886.

CHAPTER 2

Fluctuations of Sums of Random Variables

4. CYCLICALLY INTERCHANGEABLE RANDOM VARIABLES

We say that $\nu_1, \nu_2, \ldots, \nu_n$ are cyclically interchangeable random variables if all the n cyclic permutations of $(\nu_1, \nu_2, \ldots, \nu_n)$ have the same joint distribution. If $\nu_1, \nu_2, \ldots, \nu_n$ are interchangeable random variables or mutually independent and identically distributed random variables, then they are also cyclically interchangeable random variables.

Now we shall prove our fundamental theorem for cyclically interchangeable random variables.

Theorem 1. *Let $\nu_1, \nu_2, \ldots, \nu_n$ be cyclically interchangeable random variables taking on nonnegative integral values. Set $N_r = \nu_1 + \cdots + \nu_r$ for $r = 1, 2, \ldots, n$. Then we have*

$$(1)\quad \mathbf{P}\{N_r < r \text{ for } r = 1, \ldots, n \mid N_n = k\} = \begin{cases} (n-k)/n & \text{if } 0 \le k \le n, \\ 0 & \text{otherwise,} \end{cases}$$

where the conditional probability is defined up to an equivalence.

Proof. Define ν_{r+n} for $r = 1, 2, \ldots$ by assuming that $\nu_{r+n} = \nu_r$ for $r = 1, 2, \ldots.$ Set $N_r = \nu_1 + \cdots + \nu_r$ for $r = 1, 2, \ldots$ and $N_0 = 0$. Let

$$(2)\qquad \delta_r = \begin{cases} 1 & \text{if } i - N_i > r - N_r \quad \text{for } i > r, \\ 0 & \text{otherwise.} \end{cases}$$

Then δ_r is a random variable which has the same distribution for all $r = 0, 1, 2, \ldots.$ Evidently δ_0 is the indicator variable of the event $\{N_r < r \text{ for } r = 1, 2, \ldots, n\}$. Thus

$$(3)\quad \mathbf{P}\{N_r < r \text{ for } r = 1, \ldots, n \mid N_n\} = \mathbf{E}\{\delta_0 \mid N_n\} = \frac{1}{n}\sum_{r=1}^{n} \mathbf{E}\{\delta_r \mid N_n\}$$
$$= \frac{1}{n}\mathbf{E}\left\{\sum_{r=1}^{n} \delta_r \mid N_n\right\} = \begin{cases} (n - N_n)/n & \text{if } 0 \le N_n \le n, \\ 0 & \text{otherwise,} \end{cases}$$

with probability 1 because by (10) of Section 2

$$\sum_{r=1}^{n} \delta_r = \begin{cases} n - N_n & \text{if } 0 \leq N_n \leq n, \\ 0 & \text{otherwise} \end{cases} \tag{4}$$

holds for almost all realizations of $(\nu_1, \nu_2, \ldots, \nu_n)$. This completes the proof of the theorem.

From (1) it follows that

$$\mathbf{P}\{N_r < r \text{ for } r = 1, \ldots, n\} = \mathbf{E}\left\{\left[1 - \frac{N_n}{n}\right]^+\right\} \tag{5}$$

where $[x]^+ = x$ if $x \geq 0$ and $[x]^+ = 0$ if $x \leq 0$.

5. INTERCHANGEABLE RANDOM VARIABLES AND INDEPENDENT, IDENTICALLY DISTRIBUTED RANDOM VARIABLES

In the following sections of this chapter we are concerned with either a finite number of random variables $\nu_1, \nu_2, \ldots, \nu_n$ taking on nonnegative integral values or an infinite sequence of random variables $\nu_1, \nu_2, \ldots, \nu_r, \ldots$ taking on nonnegative integral values. We suppose that $\nu_1, \nu_2, \ldots, \nu_n$ are either interchangeable random variables or mutually independent and identically distributed random variables. Similarly for $\nu_1, \nu_2, \ldots, \nu_r, \ldots$ we suppose that they are either interchangeable random variables or mutually independent and identically distributed random variables.

In all cases the random variables $\{\nu_r\}$ have a common distribution. For the random variables $\{\nu_r\}$ we shall introduce a few notations which we shall use throughout this book. We shall write $N_r = \nu_1 + \cdots + \nu_r$ for $r = 1, 2, \ldots$ and $N_0 = 0$. Further,

$$\pi_j = \mathbf{P}\{\nu_r = j\}, \qquad j = 0, 1, 2, \ldots, \tag{1}$$

for the distribution of ν_r,

$$\gamma = \mathbf{E}\{\nu_r\} = \sum_{j=0}^{\infty} j\pi_j \tag{2}$$

for the expectation of ν_r (possibly $\gamma = \infty$),

$$\gamma_2 = \mathbf{E}\{\nu_r(\nu_r - 1)\} = \sum_{j=0}^{\infty} j(j-1)\pi_j \tag{3}$$

for the second factorial moment of ν_r (possibly $\gamma_2 = \infty$), and

$$\pi(z) = \mathbf{E}\{z^{\nu_r}\} = \sum_{j=0}^{\infty} \pi_j z^j \tag{4}$$

for the generating function of ν_r which is necessarily convergent if $|z| \leq 1$. We have $\gamma = \pi'(1-0)$ and $\gamma_2 = \pi''(1-0)$.

If $\nu_1, \nu_2, \ldots, \nu_r, \ldots$ is an infinite sequence of interchangeable random variables, then there exists a distribution function $G(x)$ such that

$$\lim_{n\to\infty} \mathbf{P}\left\{\frac{N_n}{n} \le x\right\} = G(x). \tag{5}$$

If, in particular, $\nu_1, \nu_2, \ldots, \nu_r, \ldots$ are mutually independent and identically distributed random variables, then $G(x) = 1$ if $x \ge \gamma$ and $G(x) = 0$ if $x < \gamma$. That is, in this case

$$\lim_{n\to\infty} \frac{N_n}{n} = \gamma \tag{6}$$

in probability. This is the weak law of large numbers.

Now we shall prove the following fundamental theorem.

Theorem 1. *If $\nu_1, \nu_2, \ldots, \nu_r, \ldots$ is an infinite sequence of mutually independent and identically distributed random variables taking on nonnegative integral values, then*

$$\mathbf{P}\{N_r < r \text{ for } r = 1, 2, \ldots\} = \begin{cases} 1 - \gamma & \textit{if } \gamma < 1, \\ 0 & \textit{if } \gamma \ge 1. \end{cases} \tag{7}$$

Proof. By the continuity theorem for probabilities

$$\mathbf{P}\{N_r < r \text{ for } r = 1, 2, \ldots\} = \lim_{n\to\infty} \mathbf{P}\{N_r < r \text{ for } r = 1, 2, \ldots, n\}. \tag{8}$$

Now for every finite n, $\nu_1, \nu_2, \ldots, \nu_n$ are cyclically interchangeable random variables for which (5) of Section 4 is applicable. Thus

$$\mathbf{P}\{N_r < r \text{ for } r = 1, 2, \ldots\} = \lim_{n\to\infty} \mathbf{E}\left\{\left[1 - \frac{N_n}{n}\right]^+\right\}. \tag{9}$$

Now by (6) $\lim_{n\to\infty} [(n - N_n)/n]^+ = [1 - \gamma]^+$ in probability, and since $[(n - N_n)/n]^+$ is bounded, it follows that

$$\lim_{n\to\infty} \mathbf{E}\left\{\left[1 - \frac{N_n}{n}\right]^+\right\} = [1 - \gamma]^+. \tag{10}$$

This proves (7).

Theorem 2. *If $\nu_1, \nu_2, \ldots, \nu_r, \ldots$ is an infinite sequence of interchangeable random variables taking on nonnegative integral values, then*

$$\mathbf{P}\{N_r < r \text{ for } r = 1, 2, \ldots\} = \int_0^1 (1 - x)\, dG(x) \tag{11}$$

where $G(x)$ is defined by (5).

Proof. Now (9) holds unchangeably. Since $[(n - N_n)/n]^+$ is bounded, by (5) it follows that

$$\lim_{n\to\infty} \mathbf{E}\left\{\left[1 - \frac{N_n}{n}\right]^+\right\} = \int_0^1 (1 - x)\, dG(x) \tag{12}$$

which proves (11).

In what follows we shall also make use of the following two theorems.

Theorem 3. *Let $w = \delta$ be the smallest nonnegative real root of the equation*

$$\pi(w) = w. \tag{13}$$

If $\gamma \le 1$, and $\pi_1 \ne 1$, then $\delta = 1$. If $\gamma > 1$ or $\pi_1 = 1$, then $0 \le \delta < 1$. The equation (13) *has no other root in the domain $|w| \le \delta$.*

Proof. In the interval $0 \le w \le 1$ both $\pi(w)$ and $\pi'(w)$ are nondecreasing functions of w. $\pi(1) = 1$ and $\pi'(1) = \gamma$. If $\gamma = \pi'(1) \le 1$ and $\pi_1 \ne 1$, then (13) has one and only one root $w = 1$ in the interval [0, 1]. If $\gamma > 1$, then (13) has exactly two roots in the interval [0, 1], $w = 1$ and $w = \delta$ where $0 \le \delta < 1$. If $\pi_1 = 1$, then all $w \in [0, 1]$ satisfy (13). This proves the first part of the theorem. To prove the second part we note that always $\pi'(\delta) \le 1$ and hence $|\pi'(w)| < \pi'(\delta) \le 1$ if $|w| < \delta$. Accordingly, if $|w| \le \delta$ and $w \ne \delta$ we have

$$|\pi(w) - \pi(\delta)| = \left|\int_\delta^w \pi'(z)\, dz\right| < |w - \delta|$$

which shows that $\pi(w) = w$ is impossible if $|w| \le \delta$ and $w \ne \delta$.

Theorem 4. *If $0 \le z < 1$, then*

$$w = z\pi(w) \tag{14}$$

has exactly one real root $w = \delta(z)$ in the interval $0 \le w < 1$ and $\lim_{z\to 1-0} \delta(z) = \delta$ where δ is the smallest nonnegative real root of $\pi(w) = w$.

Proof. Since both $\pi(w)$ and $\pi'(w)$ are nondecreasing functions of w in the interval [0, 1], it follows that (14) has exactly one root $w = \delta(z)$ in [0, 1]. Further, evidently $\delta(z)$ is a nondecreasing function of z. Since $\delta(z) < \delta$ for $0 \le z < 1$ and $\lim_{z\to 1-0} \delta(z) = \delta^*$ is a root of $\pi(w) = w$, it follows that $\delta^* = \delta$.

NOTE. If $|z| < 1$, then

$$w = z\pi(w) \tag{15}$$

has exactly one root $w = \delta(z)$ in the domain $|w| < 1$ and we have

$$\delta(z) = \sum_{j=1}^{\infty} \frac{z^j}{j!}\left(\frac{d^{j-1}[\pi(w)]^j}{dw^{j-1}}\right)_{w=0}. \tag{16}$$

For if $|w| = 1$, then $|z\pi(w)| < |w|$ and by Rouché's theorem it follows that (15) has exactly one root in the domain $|w| < 1$. The explicit form (16) can be obtained by Lagrange's expansion. (See Appendix.)

6. THE DISTRIBUTION OF THE MAXIMUM OF $\{N_r - r\}$

We are now interested in finding the distribution of the random variable $\max_{1 \le r \le n} (N_r - r)$ for finite n as well as the distribution of $\sup_{1 \le r < \infty} (N_r - r)$.

Theorem 1. *If $\nu_1, \nu_2, \ldots, \nu_n$ are interchangeable random variables taking on nonnegative integral values, then*

$$(1)\quad \mathbf{P}\{\max_{1 \le r \le n} (N_r - r) < k\} = \mathbf{P}\{N_n < n + k\} - \sum_{j=1}^{n-1} \sum_{l=0}^{n-j} \left(1 - \frac{l}{n-j}\right) \mathbf{P}\{N_j = j + k, N_n = j + k + l\}$$

for $k = 0, \pm 1, \pm 2, \ldots$. If $k < 0$, then both sides of (1) *are* 0.

Proof. We shall prove a slightly more general formula from which (1) follows. If $i = 1, 2, \ldots$ and $k = 0, \pm 1, \pm 2, \ldots$, then

$$(2)\quad \mathbf{P}\{N_r < r + k \text{ for } r = 1, 2, \ldots, n \text{ and } N_n \le n + k - i\} = \mathbf{P}\{N_n \le n + k - i\} - \sum_{j=1}^{n-i} \sum_{l=0}^{n-i-j} \left(1 - \frac{l}{n-j}\right) \cdot \mathbf{P}\{N_j = j + k, N_n = j + k + l\}.$$

It is sufficient to prove that the subtrahend on the right-hand side of (2) is the probability that $N_r \ge r + k$ for some $r = 1, 2, \ldots, n - 1$ and $N_n \le n + k - i$. This event can occur in the following mutually exclusive ways: the greatest r for which $N_r \ge r + k$ is $r = j$ ($j = 1, 2, \ldots, n - i$). Then $N_j = j + k$ and $N_r < r + k$ for $r = j + 1, \ldots, n$, or equivalently, $N_r - N_j < r - j$ for $r = j + 1, \ldots, n$. By Theorem 1 of Section 4

$$(3)\quad \mathbf{P}\{N_r - N_j < r - j \text{ for } r = j + 1, \ldots, n \mid N_j = j + k, N_n = j + k + l\} = \left(1 - \frac{l}{n-j}\right)$$

if $0 \le l \le n - j$ and if the left hand side is defined. If we multiply (3) by $\mathbf{P}\{N_j = j + k, N_n = j + k + l\}$ and add for all (j, l) satisfying $1 \le j \le j + l \le n - i$, then we get the subtrahend on the right-hand side of (2). If $i = 1$ in (2), then we get (1).

If $k = 0$ in (2), then by (1) of Section 4 we can also write

$$(4)\quad \mathbf{P}\{N_r < r \text{ for } r = 1, 2, \ldots, n \text{ and } N_n \le n - i\} = \sum_{j=1}^{n-i} \left(1 - \frac{j}{n}\right) \mathbf{P}\{N_n = j\}.$$

Theorem 2. *If $\nu_1, \nu_2, \ldots, \nu_n$ are interchangeable random variables taking on nonnegative integral values, then*

$$\mathbf{E}\left\{\max_{0\le r\le n}(N_r - r)\right\} = \sum_{j=1}^{n}\frac{1}{j}\,\mathbf{E}\{[N_j - j]^+\}. \tag{5}$$

Proof. Since

$$\mathbf{E}\left\{\max_{0\le r\le n}(N_r - r)\right\} = \sum_{k=1}^{\infty}\left[1 - \mathbf{P}\left\{\max_{1\le r\le n}(N_r - r) < k\right\}\right], \tag{6}$$

we get (5) by (1). If γ is finite, then (5) is finite. If $\gamma = \infty$, then (5) is also ∞.

If, in particular, $\nu_1, \nu_2, \ldots, \nu_n$ are mutually independent and identically distributed random variables, then in (1) and in (2) we can use the following substitution

$$\begin{aligned}\mathbf{P}\{N_j = j + k, N_n = j + k + l\} &= \mathbf{P}\{N_j = j + k\}\mathbf{P}\{N_n - N_j = l\}\\ &= \mathbf{P}\{N_j = j + k\}\mathbf{P}\{N_{n-j} = l\}.\end{aligned} \tag{7}$$

In this particular case (1) can also be written in the following form

$$\begin{aligned}&\mathbf{P}\left\{\max_{1\le r\le n}(N_r - r) < k\right\}\\ &\quad= \mathbf{P}\{N_n < n + k\} - \sum_{j=1}^{n-1}\mathbf{P}\{N_j = j + k\}\mathbf{E}\left\{\left[1 - \frac{N_{n-j}}{n-j}\right]^+\right\}.\end{aligned} \tag{8}$$

Theorem 3. *Let $\nu_1, \nu_2, \ldots, \nu_r, \ldots$ be mutually independent and identically distributed random variables taking on nonnegative integers. If $\gamma < 1$, then*

$$\mathbf{P}\left\{\sup_{1\le r<\infty}(N_r - r) < k\right\} = 1 - (1-\gamma)\sum_{j=1}^{\infty}\mathbf{P}\{N_j = j + k\} \tag{9}$$

for all $k = 0, \pm 1, \pm 2, \ldots$. If $\gamma \ge 1$, and $\pi_1 \ne 1$, then

$$\mathbf{P}\left\{\sup_{1\le r<\infty}(N_r - r) < k\right\} = 0 \tag{10}$$

for all $k = 0, \pm 1, \pm 2, \ldots$. If $\pi_1 = 1$, then

$$\mathbf{P}\left\{\sup_{1\le r<\infty}(N_r - r) = 0\right\} = 1. \tag{11}$$

Proof. By the continuity theorem for probabilities we have

$$\mathbf{P}\left\{\sup_{1\le r<\infty}(N_r - r) < k\right\} = \lim_{n\to\infty}\mathbf{P}\left\{\max_{1\le r\le n}(N_r - r) < k\right\}, \tag{12}$$

and the right-hand side can be obtained by (8).

First, consider the case $\gamma < 1$. Then by the weak law of large numbers

$$\lim_{n\to\infty} \frac{N_n}{n} = \gamma$$

in probability. Hence $\lim_{n\to\infty} \mathbf{P}\{N_n < n + k\} = 1$ for $k = 0, \pm 1, \pm 2, \ldots$ and

$$\lim_{n\to\infty} \mathbf{E}\left\{\left[1 - \frac{N_{n-j}}{n-j}\right]^+\right\} = 1 - \gamma \tag{13}$$

for $j = 1, 2, \ldots$. We shall show that

$$\sum_{j=1}^{\infty} \mathbf{P}\{N_j = j + k\} \leq \frac{1}{1-\gamma} \tag{14}$$

for $k = 0, \pm 1, \pm 2, \ldots$. If we form the limit $n \to \infty$ in (8), then we get (9). It remains to prove (14). If we take into consideration that the right-hand side of (8) is nonnegative, $\mathbf{P}\{N_n < n + k\} \leq 1$, and

$$\mathbf{E}\left\{\left[1 - \frac{N_{n-j}}{n-j}\right]^+\right\} \geq \mathbf{E}\left\{1 - \frac{N_{n-j}}{n-j}\right\} = 1 - \gamma, \tag{15}$$

then we get the inequality

$$(1-\gamma)\sum_{j=1}^{n-1} \mathbf{P}\{N_j = j + k\} \leq 1 \tag{16}$$

which holds for all $k = 0, \pm 1, \pm 2, \ldots$ and $n = 1, 2, \ldots$. This proves (14).

Second, if $\gamma > 1$, then $\lim_{n\to\infty} \mathbf{P}\{N_n < n + k\} = 0$ for all k and the inequality

$$0 \leq \mathbf{P}\left\{\max_{1\leq r\leq n} (N_r - r) < k\right\} \leq \mathbf{P}\{N_n < n + k\} \tag{17}$$

implies (10).

Finally, if $\gamma = 1$, then by (7) of Section 5

$$\mathbf{P}\left\{\sup_{1\leq r<\infty} (N_r - r) < 0\right\} = 0. \tag{18}$$

Hence (10) holds if $k \leq 0$. If $k > 0$ and $\pi_1 \neq 1$, when necessarily $\pi_0 > 0$, then the obvious inequality

$$\pi_0{}^k \mathbf{P}\left\{\sup_{1\leq r<\infty} (N_r - r) < k\right\} \leq \mathbf{P}\left\{\sup_{1\leq r<\infty} (N_r - r) < 0\right\} \tag{19}$$

implies (10) for $k > 0$. If $\pi_1 = 1$, then $\mathbf{P}\{N_r = r\} = 1$ for all $r = 1, 2, \ldots$, whence (11) follows.

NOTE. If $\nu_1, \nu_2, \ldots, \nu_r, \ldots$ are interchangeable random variables, then we can define a random variable θ such that $\nu_1, \nu_2, \ldots, \nu_r, \ldots$ are conditionally independent and identically distributed random variables for given θ. That is $\nu_1, \nu_2, \ldots, \nu_r, \ldots$ can be obtained by randomization of a parameter from a sequence of mutually independent and identically distributed random variables. Thus $\mathbf{P}\left\{\sup_{1 \le r < \infty} (N_r - r) < k \mid \theta\right\}$ can be obtained by (9) and forming its expectation with respect to θ we get $\mathbf{P}\left\{\sup_{1 \le r < \infty} (N_r - r) < k\right\}$.

Theorem 4. *If $\nu_1, \nu_2, \ldots, \nu_r, \ldots$ are mutually independent and identically distributed random variables taking on nonnegative integers and if $\gamma < 1$, then*

$$\mathbf{P}\left\{\sup_{1 \le r < \infty} (N_r - r) < k\right\} = Q_k \tag{20}$$

where $Q_k = 0$ if $k < 0$, $Q_0 = 1 - \gamma$ and

$$Q(z) = \sum_{k=0}^{\infty} Q_k z^k = \frac{Q_0 \pi(z)}{\pi(z) - z} \tag{21}$$

for $|z| < 1$.

Proof. By the theorem of total probability we can write for $k = 0, 1, 2, \ldots$ that

$$\begin{aligned} \text{(22)}\quad & \mathbf{P}\{N_r < r + k \text{ for } r = 1, \ldots, n + 1\} \\ &= \sum_{j=0}^{k} \pi_j \mathbf{P}\{N_r < r + k + 1 - j \text{ for } r = 1, \ldots, n\} \end{aligned}$$

if we take into consideration that ν_1 may take on the values $0, 1, 2, \ldots$. If $n \to \infty$ in (22), then we obtain that

$$Q_k = \sum_{j=0}^{k} \pi_j Q_{k+1-j} \tag{23}$$

holds for $k = 0, 1, 2, \ldots$. Now by (7) of Section 5, $Q_0 = 1 - \gamma$ and starting from Q_0 the probabilities $Q_1, Q_2, \ldots$ can be obtained recursively by (23). If $k < 0$, then evidently $Q_k = 0$. By introducing generating functions we get (21) which is convergent for $|z| < 1$.

Since $0 \le Q_0 \le Q_1 \le \cdots \le Q_k \le \cdots \le 1$, the limit $\lim_{k \to \infty} Q_k$ exists and by Abel's theorem (see Appendix)

$$\lim_{k \to \infty} Q_k = \lim_{z \to 1-0} (1 - z) Q(z) = \frac{Q_0}{1 - \pi'(1 - 0)} = \frac{Q_0}{1 - \gamma} = 1. \tag{24}$$

Accordingly, if $\gamma < 1$, then $\sup_{1 \le r < \infty} (N_r - r)$ is a proper random variable which with probability 1 takes on only finite values. By using the weak law of large numbers we showed that $Q_0 = 1 - \gamma$ and hence by Abel's theorem we concluded that $\lim_{k\to\infty} Q_k = 1$. If we use the strong law of large numbers, we can conclude directly that $\lim_{k\to\infty} Q_k = 1$, and then by Abel's theorem it follows that $Q_0 = 1 - \gamma$.

It is interesting to note that if $\pi(z) = z$ has a root $z = a$ for $|z| > 1$ and no other roots for $1 < |z| \leq a$, then

$$1 - Q_k \sim \frac{1-\gamma}{\pi'(a) - 1} a^{-k} \tag{25}$$

as $k \to \infty$.

NOTE. If we compare (9) and (20), we get an interesting identity. If $\gamma < 1$, then

$$\sum_{j=1}^{\infty} \mathbf{P}\{N_j = j + k\} = \frac{1 - Q_k}{1 - \gamma} \tag{26}$$

where $Q_k = 0$ if $k < 0$, $Q_0 = 1 - \gamma$ and Q_k for $k > 0$ is given by (21).

7. A DISCRETE GENERALIZATION OF THE CLASSICAL RUIN THEOREM

The classical ruin theorem is as follows.

Theorem 1. *Two players A and B are playing a sequence of games. In each game either A wins a coin from B with probability p or B wins a coin from A with probability q* $(0 < p < 1, p + q = 1)$. *The games are independent of each other. Suppose that initially A has a coins and B has b coins. The games are continued until one of the two players is ruined. The probability that ultimately A will be ruined is given by*

$$P_A = \begin{cases} [1 - (p/q)^b]/[1 - (p/q)^{a+b}] & \text{if } p \neq q, \\ b/(a+b) & \text{if } p = q. \end{cases} \tag{1}$$

The probability that ultimately B will be ruined, P_B, is given by an analogous formula.

In 1657 C. Huygens [11] found P_A/P_B in the particular case when $a = b = 12$ and $p/q = 5/9$. About 1680 or so J. Bernoulli [4] found P_A/P_B in the general case and its proof was given in 1711 by A. De Moivre [7].

Now we shall prove the following generalization of Theorem 1.

Theorem 2. *Let* $\nu_1, \nu_2, \ldots, \nu_r, \ldots$ *be mutually independent, and identically distributed random variables taking on nonnegative integral values. For* $i \geq 1$ *denote by* $\rho(i)$ *the smallest r such that* $N_r = r - i$. *If there is no such r, then* $\rho(i) = \infty$. *If* $\pi_0 > 0$, *then for* $1 \leq i \leq k$

$$\mathbf{P}\left\{\sup_{1\leq r\leq \rho(i)} (N_r - r) < k - i\right\} = \frac{Q_{k-i}}{Q_k} \tag{2}$$

where $Q_0 \neq 0$ is chosen arbitrarily and Q_k, $k = 1, 2, \ldots,$ can be obtained by the following recurrence formula

$$Q_k = \sum_{j=0}^{k} \pi_j Q_{k+1-j}, \qquad k = 0, 1, 2, \ldots. \tag{3}$$

Proof. Let

$$Q(k, i) = \mathbf{P}\{N_r < r + k - i \text{ for } r = 1 \ \ldots, \rho(i)\}. \tag{4}$$

If $\pi_0 > 0$, then the probabilities $Q(k, i)$, $1 \leq i \leq k < \infty$, are positive. Since $\rho(i)$ may be represented as a sum of mutually independent and identically distributed random variables as follows: $\rho(i) = \rho(1) + [\rho(2) - \rho(1)] + \cdots + [\rho(i) - \rho(i-1)]$, we obtain easily that

$$Q(k, i) = \prod_{l=k+1-i}^{k} Q(l, 1). \tag{5}$$

Let $Q(k, 1) = Q_{k-1}/Q_k$ for $k = 1, 2, \ldots,$ where $Q_0 \neq 0$ is chosen arbitrarily. Then $Q(k, i) = Q_{k-i}/Q_k$ for $1 \leq i \leq k$. If we take into consideration that ν_1 may take on the values $j = 0, 1, 2, \ldots,$ then we can write

$$Q(k + i, i) = \sum_{j=0}^{k} \pi_j Q(k + i, i + j - 1). \tag{6}$$

Hence

$$Q_k = \sum_{j=0}^{k} \pi_j Q_{k+1-j} \tag{7}$$

for $k = 0, 1, 2, \ldots.$ This proves the theorem.

It is interesting to observe that the system (3) is exactly the same as (23) of Section 6.

The system of linear equations (3) can be solved explicitly by using generating functions. By (3) we obtain that

$$Q(z) = \sum_{k=0}^{\infty} Q_k z^k = \frac{Q_0 \pi(z)}{\pi(z) - z} \tag{8}$$

for $|z| < \delta$ where δ is the smallest nonnegative real root of $\pi(z) = z$. If $\gamma \leq 1$, then $\delta = 1$, whereas if $\gamma > 1$, then $0 < \delta < 1$.

If $|z|$ is small enough, then we can write

$$\begin{aligned} Q(z) &= Q_0 + \frac{Q_0 z}{\pi_0 - [\pi_0 + z - \pi(z)]} \\ &= Q_0 + Q_0 z \sum_{k=0}^{\infty} \frac{1}{\pi_0^{k+1}} [\pi_0 + z - \pi(z)]^k. \end{aligned} \tag{9}$$

Hence

$$Q_1 = \frac{Q_0}{\pi_0} \tag{10}$$

and for $k = 1, 2, \ldots$

$$Q_{k+1} = Q_0 \sum_{\nu=1}^{k} \frac{(-1)^\nu \nu!}{\pi_0^{\nu+1}} \sum_{\substack{i_1+i_2+\cdots+i_k=\nu \\ i_1+2i_2+\cdots+ki_k=k}} \frac{(\pi_1 - 1)^{i_1} \pi_2^{i_2} \cdots \pi_k^{i_k}}{i_1!\ i_2! \cdots \cdot i_k!}. \tag{11}$$

NOTE. If γ is a finite positive number, then Q_k, $k = 0, 1, 2, \ldots$, can also be obtained in the following way. Introduce the following probability distribution

$$\pi_j^* = \frac{1}{\gamma}(1 - \pi_0 - \pi_1 - \cdots - \pi_j), \qquad j = 0, 1, 2, \ldots, \tag{12}$$

which has the generating function

$$\pi^*(z) = \sum_{j=0}^{\infty} \pi_j^* z^j = \frac{1 - \pi(z)}{\gamma(1 - z)}. \tag{13}$$

If we define $P_0 = Q_0$ and $P_k = Q_k - Q_{k-1}$, $k = 1, 2, \ldots$, then

$$P(z) = \sum_{k=0}^{\infty} P_k z^k = Q(z)(1 - z) = P_0(1 - z) + \frac{P_0 z}{1 - \gamma\pi^*(z)}. \tag{14}$$

From (14) it follows that

$$P_1 = P_0 \frac{\gamma\pi_0^*}{1 - \gamma\pi_0^*} \tag{15}$$

and for $k = 1, 2, \ldots$

$$P_{k+1} = P_0 \sum_{\nu=1}^{k} \frac{\nu!\,\gamma^\nu}{(1 - \gamma\pi_0^*)^{\nu+1}} \sum_{\substack{i_1+i_2+\cdots+i_k=\nu \\ i_1+2i_2+\cdots+ki_k=k}} \frac{(\pi_1^*)^{i_1}(\pi_2^*)^{i_2} \cdots (\pi_k^*)^{i_k}}{i_1!\, i_2! \cdots i_k!}. \tag{16}$$

Now we shall give another expression for Q_k, $k = 0, 1, 2, \ldots$.

Theorem 3. *If $\gamma \neq 1$, then*

$$Q_k = Q_0 \left[\frac{(1/\delta)^k}{1 - \pi'(\delta)} - \sum_{j=1}^{\infty} \mathbf{P}\{N_j = j + k\}\right] \tag{17}$$

for all $k = 0, \pm 1, \pm 2, \ldots$ where δ is the smallest nonnegative real root of $\pi(z) = z$. If $\gamma < 1$, then $\delta = 1$, whereas if $\gamma > 1$ then $0 < \delta < 1$. If $k < 0$, then the right-hand side of (17) *is* 0.

Proof. In the case of $\gamma < 1$ we already proved (17) in Theorem 3 of Section 6. There it was $Q_0 = 1 - \gamma$. Since Q_0 is a factor of proportionality, this does not restrict the generality.

Now we shall prove (17) for $\gamma > 1$. Without loss of generality, we may suppose that $Q_0 = 1$. In this case by (8)

$$\sum_{k=-\infty}^{\infty} Q_k z^k = \frac{\pi(z)}{\pi(z) - z} \tag{18}$$

for $|z| < \delta$ and $Q_k = 0$ if $k < 0$. Furthermore, we have

$$\sum_{k=-\infty}^{\infty} \left(\sum_{j=1}^{\infty} \mathbf{P}\{N_j = j + k\} \right) z^k = \frac{\pi(z)}{z - \pi(z)} \tag{19}$$

for $\delta < |z| < 1$.

If we subtract $1/(1 - \pi'(\delta))\delta^k$ from Q_k for $k \geq 0$, then the resulting sequence has the generating function

$$\frac{\pi(z)}{\pi(z) - z} - \frac{\delta}{(1 - \pi'(\delta))(\delta - z)} \tag{20}$$

and this generating function is convergent for $|z| \leq \delta$. Similarly, if we subtract $1/(1 - \pi'(\delta))\delta^k$ from $\sum_{j=1}^{\infty} \mathbf{P}\{N_j = j + k\}$ for $k < 0$, then the resulting sequence has the generating function

$$\frac{\pi(z)}{z - \pi(z)} + \frac{\delta}{(1 - \pi'(\delta))(\delta - z)} \tag{21}$$

and this generating function is convergent for $\delta \leq |z| < 1$.

If $|z| = \delta$, then the sum of the generating functions (20) and (21) is 0 and consequently the sum of the corresponding elements in the two sequences is also 0, that is,

$$Q_k + \sum_{j=1}^{\infty} \mathbf{P}\{N_j = j + k\} = \frac{1}{(1 - \pi'(\delta))\delta^k} \tag{22}$$

for all $k = 0, \pm 1, \pm 2, \ldots$. This proves (17) for $\gamma > 1$. If $\gamma < 1$, then $\delta = 1$ and both (20) and (21) are convergent generating functions for $|z| = 1$. Thus (22) holds in this case too. This proves (17) for $\gamma < 1$ too.

If $k < 0$, then $Q_k = 0$ and by using this fact we can obtain interesting identities by choosing particular sequences of random variables $\{\nu_1, \nu_2, \ldots, \nu_r, \ldots\}$.

Theorem 4. *If $\pi_0 > 0$, then for $i \geq 1$ we have*

$$\mathbf{E}\left\{ \sup_{1 \leq r \leq \rho(i)} (N_r - r) \right\} = \sum_{k=i}^{\infty} \left(\frac{Q_k - Q_{k-i}}{Q_k} \right) - 1. \tag{23}$$

Proof. The random variable $\sup_{1 \leq r \leq \rho(i)} (N_r - r)$ may take on the values $-1, 0, 1, 2, \ldots$ and therefore its expectation is

$$\mathbf{E}\left\{ \sup_{1 \leq r \leq \rho(i)} (N_r - r) \right\} = \sum_{j=0}^{\infty} \mathbf{P}\left\{ \sup_{1 \leq r \leq \rho(i)} (N_r - r) \geq j \right\} - 1. \tag{24}$$

By (2) we obtain (23).

Finally, we prove a theorem concerning the asymptotic behavior of Q_k as $k \to \infty$.

Theorem 5. *Let $\pi_0 > 0$. If $\gamma < 1$, then*

$$\lim_{k\to\infty} Q_k = \frac{Q_0}{1-\gamma}. \tag{25}$$

If $\gamma = 1$, then

$$\lim_{k\to\infty} \frac{Q_k}{k} = \frac{2Q_0}{\gamma_2} \tag{26}$$

where $\gamma_2 = \pi''(1-0)$. If $\gamma > 1$, then

$$\lim_{k\to\infty} Q_k\delta^k = \frac{Q_0}{1-\pi'(\delta)} \tag{27}$$

where δ is the smallest nonnegative real root of $\pi(z) = z$. We have $0 < \delta < 1$.

Proof. If Q_0 is positive, then $Q_1, Q_2, \ldots, Q_k, \ldots$ form a nondecreasing sequence of positive numbers and thus the limit $\lim_{k\to\infty} Q_k$ exists (possibly ∞). If $\gamma < 1$, then by Abel's theorem we obtain that

$$\lim_{k\to\infty} Q_k = \lim_{z\to 1-0} (1-z)Q(z) = \frac{Q_0}{1-\pi'(1-0)} = \frac{Q_0}{1-\gamma} \tag{28}$$

which proves (25).

We note that if $\gamma < 1$, then $\lim_{k\to\infty} Q_k$ is finite and we can choose Q_0 such that $\lim_{k\to\infty} Q_k = 1$. However, if $\gamma \geq 1$, then $\lim_{k\to\infty} Q_k = \infty$ for all $Q_0 > 0$, and we cannot choose Q_0 such that $\lim_{k\to\infty} Q_k = 1$.

If $\gamma = 1$, then by a Tauberian theorem of G. H. Hardy and J. E. Littlewood (see Appendix) it follows that

$$\lim_{k\to\infty} \frac{Q_k}{k} = \lim_{z\to 1-0} (1-z)^2 Q(z) = \frac{2Q_0}{\pi''(1-0)} = \frac{2Q_0}{\gamma_2} \tag{29}$$

which proves (26). This result can also be obtained by the theory of recurrent events. If we observe the occurrences of a recurrent event at times $t = 1, 2, \ldots$ and suppose that the recurrent event occurred initially at time $t = 1$ and the recurrence time has the distribution π_j^*, $j = 0, 1, 2, \ldots$, defined by (12), then Q_k/Q_0 is the expected number of the occurrences of the recurrent event up to time $t = k$. Thus by the theory of recurrent events

$$\lim_{k\to\infty} \frac{Q_k}{k} = \frac{Q_0}{\pi^{*\prime}(1-0)} \tag{30}$$

which is in agreement with (29).

If $\gamma_2 = \infty$, then the right-hand side of (26) is 0. In this case we can use another Tauberian theorem of G. H. Hardy and J. E. Littlewood to find the asymptotic behavior of Q_k as $k \to \infty$. (See Appendix.) Accordingly if

$$Q(z) \sim \frac{1}{(1-z)^{\alpha+1}} L\left(\frac{1}{1-z}\right) \tag{31}$$

as $z \to 1$ $(0 < z < 1)$ where $\alpha \geq 0$ and $L(cx) \sim L(x)$ for every positive c as $x \to \infty$, then

$$Q_k \sim \frac{k^\alpha}{\Gamma(\alpha+1)} L(k) \tag{32}$$

as $k \to \infty$.

If $\gamma > 1$, then by Abel's theorem we can conclude that

$$\lim_{k\to\infty} Q_k \delta^k = \lim_{z\to 1-0} (1-z)Q(z\delta) = \frac{Q_0}{1-\pi'(\delta)} \tag{33}$$

provided that $\lim\limits_{k\to\infty} Q_k \delta^k$ exists. The existence of this limit can be proved directly as follows. Since $Q(z\delta)$ is convergent for $|z| \leq 1$ and since the only singularity of $Q(z\delta)$ in the unit circle $|z| \leq 1$ is a simple pole at $z = 1$, it follows that

$$Q(z\delta) = \frac{Q_0}{(1-\pi'(\delta))(1-z)} + \sum_{k=0}^{\infty} c_k z^k \tag{34}$$

where $\lim\limits_{k\to\infty} c_k = 0$. Hence (27) immediately follows.

NOTE. If we use the explicit formula (17) for Q_k, then (27) can be sharpened as follows

$$\lim_{k\to\infty}\left[Q_k - \frac{Q_0(1/\delta)^k}{1-\pi'(\delta)}\right] = -\frac{Q_0}{\gamma-1}. \tag{35}$$

For by a theorem of K. L. Chung (see Appendix) we have

$$\lim_{k\to\infty} \sum_{j=1}^{\infty} \mathbf{P}\{N_j = j + k\} = \frac{1}{\gamma - 1} \tag{36}$$

if $\gamma > 1$, and thus (35) follows from (17).

If $\gamma < 1$, then by the same theorem of K. L. Chung it follows that

$$\lim_{k\to\infty} \sum_{j=1}^{\infty} \mathbf{P}\{N_j = j + k\} = 0. \tag{37}$$

Thus by (17) we obtain that

$$\lim_{k\to\infty} Q_k = \frac{Q_0}{1-\gamma} \tag{38}$$

if $\gamma < 1$ which is in agreement with (25).

8. THE DISTRIBUTION OF THE MAXIMUM OF $\{r - N_r\}$

We are now interested in finding the distribution of the random variable $\max_{1\le r\le n} (r - N_r)$ for finite n as well as the distribution of $\sup_{1\le r<\infty} (r - N_r)$.

Theorem 1. *If $\nu_1, \nu_2, \ldots, \nu_n$ are interchangeable random variables taking on nonnegative integral values, then for $k > 0$*

$$\mathbf{P}\{\max_{1\le r\le n} (r - N_r) < k\} = 1 - \sum_{j=k}^{n} \frac{k}{j} \mathbf{P}\{N_j = j - k\}. \tag{1}$$

Proof. We shall find the probability of the complementary event of $\{\max_{1\le r\le n} (r - N_r) < k\}$, that is, the probability that $N_r \le r - k$ for some $r = 1, 2, \ldots, n$. This latter event can occur in the following mutually exclusive ways: the smallest r such that $N_r = r - k$ is $r = j$ $(j = k, \ldots, n)$. Then $N_j = j - k$ and $N_r > r - k$ for $r = 1, \ldots, j - 1$, or equivalently, $N_j - N_r < j - r$ for $r = 1, \ldots, j - 1$. By Theorem 1 of Section 4

$$\mathbf{P}\{N_j - N_r < j - r \text{ for } r = 1, \ldots, j - 1 \mid N_j = j - k\} = \frac{k}{j} \tag{2}$$

for $0 < k \le j$ where the conditional probability is defined up to an equivalence. If we multiply (2) by $\mathbf{P}\{N_j = j - k\}$ and add for $k \le j \le n$, then we get the probability of the complementary event. This proves (1).

In a similar way as (1) we can also prove the following more general formula

$$\begin{aligned} &\mathbf{P}\{r - N_r < k \text{ for } r = 1, \ldots, n - 1 \text{ and } n - N_n < k - i\} \\ &= \mathbf{P}\{N_n > n + i - k\} - \sum_{j=k}^{n} \frac{k}{j} \mathbf{P}\{N_j = j - k, N_n > n + i - k\} \end{aligned} \tag{3}$$

for $k > 0$, $n \ge 1$ and $i > 0$.

Theorem 2. *If $\nu_1, \nu_2, \ldots, \nu_n$ are interchangeable random variables taking on nonnegative integral values, then*

$$\mathbf{E}\left\{\max_{0\le r\le n} (r - N_r)\right\} = \sum_{j=1}^{n} \frac{1}{j} \mathbf{E}\{[j - N_j]^+\}. \tag{4}$$

Proof. Now the random variable $\max_{0\le r\le n} (r - N_r)$ may take on the values $0, 1, \ldots, n$ and thus

$$\mathbf{E}\left\{\max_{0\le r\le n} (r - N_r)\right\} = \sum_{k=1}^{n} \mathbf{P}\left\{\max_{1\le r\le n} (r - N_r) \ge k\right\} \tag{5}$$

and the right-hand side can be obtained by (1). Thus (4) follows.

We note that if $\nu_1, \nu_2, \ldots, \nu_r, \ldots$ is an infinite sequence of interchangeable random variables taking on nonnegative integral values, then letting $n \to \infty$ in (1) we get

$$\mathbf{P}\left\{\sup_{1 \le r < \infty} (r - N_r) < k\right\} = 1 - \sum_{j=k}^{\infty} \frac{k}{j} \mathbf{P}\{N_j = j - k\} \tag{6}$$

for $k > 0$.

If $\nu_1, \nu_2, \ldots, \nu_r, \ldots$ is an infinite sequence of mutually independent and identically distributed random variables, then $\sup_{1 \le r < \infty} (r - N_r)$ has a geometric distribution given by the following theorem.

Theorem 3. *Let $\nu_1, \nu_2, \ldots, \nu_r, \ldots$ be mutually independent and identically distributed random variables taking on nonnegative integers. If $k > 0$, then*

$$\mathbf{P}\left\{\sup_{1 \le r < \infty} (r - N_r) < k\right\} = 1 - \delta^k \tag{7}$$

where δ is the smallest nonnegative real root of the equation

$$\pi(w) = w. \tag{8}$$

If $\gamma \le 1$ and $\pi_1 \ne 1$, then $\delta = 1$ and if $\gamma > 1$ or $\pi_1 = 1$, then $\delta < 1$.

Proof. For $i \ge 1$ define $\rho(i)$ as the smallest r such that $N_r = r - i$. If there is no such r, then $\rho(i) = \infty$. Now $\rho(i)$ can be represented as a sum of i mutually independent and identically distributed random variables as follows: $\rho(i) = \rho(1) + [\rho(2) - \rho(1)] + \cdots + [\rho(i) - \rho(i-1)]$. Let

$$\mathbf{E}\{z^{\rho(1)}\} = \delta(z) \tag{9}$$

for $|z| < 1$. Then

$$\mathbf{E}\{z^{\rho(i)}\} = [\delta(z)]^i \tag{10}$$

for $|z| < 1$. Now if we suppose that $N_i = j$, then $\rho(i) = i + \rho^*(j)$ where $\rho^*(j)$ has the same distribution as $\rho(j)$ and $\{\rho^*(j)\}$ is independent of $\{N_i\}$. Thus we get

$$\mathbf{E}\{z^{\rho(i)}\} = z^i[\pi(\delta(z))]^i \tag{11}$$

for $|z| < 1$. If we compare (10) and (11), then we get

$$\delta(z) = z\pi(\delta(z)) \tag{12}$$

for $|z| < 1$. If $0 < z < 1$, then

$$w = z\pi(w) \tag{13}$$

has one and only one real root in the interval $0 < w < 1$ and thus necessarily $w = \delta(z)$. If $z \to 1$, $0 < z < 1$, then $\delta(z) \to \delta$ where δ is the smallest nonnegative real root of $w = \pi(w)$. If $\gamma \leq 1$ and $\pi_1 \neq 1$, then $\delta = 1$, whereas if $\gamma > 1$ or $\pi_1 = 1$, then $\delta < 1$.

By the definition of $\rho(i)$ we have

$$\mathbf{P}\left\{\max_{1\leq r\leq n}(r - N_r) < k\right\} = 1 - \mathbf{P}\{\rho(k) \leq n\} \tag{14}$$

for $k > 0$ and by Abel's theorem

$$\lim_{n\to\infty} \mathbf{P}\{\rho(k) \leq n\} = \lim_{z\to 1} [\delta(z)]^k = \delta^k. \tag{15}$$

This proves (7).

Accordingly, if $\gamma > 1$ or $\pi_1 = 1$, then $\sup_{1\leq r<\infty} (r - N_r)$ is a proper random variable which is finite with probability 1. If $\gamma \leq 1$ and $\pi_1 \neq 1$, then $\sup_{1\leq r<\infty} (r - N_r)$ is infinite with probability 1.

The random variable $\rho(k)$, $k = 1, 2, \ldots$, plays an important role in the theory of games of chance. It can be interpreted as the duration of game. The distribution of $\rho(k)$, $k = 1, 2, \ldots$, is given by the following theorem.

Theorem 4. *Let $\nu_1, \nu_2, \ldots, \nu_r, \ldots$ be interchangeable random variables taking on nonnegative integers. For $k \geq 1$ define $\rho(k)$ as the smallest r such that $N_r = r - k$. Then*

$$\mathbf{P}\{\rho(k) = n\} = \frac{k}{n}\mathbf{P}\{N_n = n - k\} \tag{16}$$

for $1 \leq k \leq n$.

Proof. We have evidently

$$\mathbf{P}\{\rho(k) \leq n\} = 1 - \mathbf{P}\left\{\max_{1\leq r\leq n}(r - N_r) < k\right\} \tag{17}$$

and the right-hand side can be obtained by (1). Hence (16) follows.

It is interesting to note that formula (3) of Section 2 is a particular case of formula (16). It is surprising that the original simplicity is preserved for this more general case too.

In what follows we suppose that, in particular, $\nu_1, \nu_2, \ldots, \nu_r, \ldots$ are mutually independent and identically distributed random variables taking on nonnegative integers.

If $\gamma \leq 1$ and $\pi_1 \neq 1$, then $\lim_{n\to\infty} \mathbf{P}\{\rho(k) \leq n\} = 1$, that is, $\rho(k)$ is a proper random variable. If $\gamma > 1$ or $\pi_1 = 1$, then $\mathbf{P}\{\rho(k) = \infty\} = 1 - \delta^k > 0$.

If $\gamma < 1$, then the expectation of $\rho(k)$ is

$$\mathbf{E}\{\rho(k)\} = k\sum_{n=k}^{\infty} \mathbf{P}\{N_n = n - k\} = \frac{k}{1 - \gamma} \tag{18}$$

which follows from (26) of Section 6. If $\gamma = 1$ and $\pi_1 \neq 1$, then $\mathbf{E}\{\rho(k)\} = \infty$. It is interesting to observe that by (18) we have also

(19) $$\mathbf{E}\{\rho(k)\} = \sum_{n=1}^{\infty} \mathbf{P}\{0 < n - N_n \leq k\}$$

for $\gamma < 1$.

If $|z| < 1$, then by (16) we get

(20) $$\mathbf{E}\{z^{\rho(k)}\} = [\delta(z)]^k = k \sum_{n=k}^{\infty} \frac{z^n}{n} \mathbf{P}\{N_n = n - k\}$$

and $w = \delta(z)$ is the only root of $w = z\pi(w)$ in the domain $|w| < 1$.

NOTE. If $\nu_1, \nu_2, \ldots, \nu_r, \ldots$ are mutually independent and identically distributed random variables taking on nonnegative integers, then by comparing (6) and (7) we obtain the following interesting identity:

(21) $$\sum_{j=k}^{\infty} \frac{k}{j} \mathbf{P}\{N_j = j - k\} = \delta^k$$

for $k > 0$ where δ is the smallest nonnegative real root of $\pi(w) = w$.

9. THE DISTRIBUTION OF THE MAXIMUM FOR DUAL SEQUENCES

With every sequence of random variables $\nu_1, \nu_2, \ldots, \nu_r, \ldots$ taking on nonnegative integers we associate a sequence of random variables $\nu_1^*, \nu_2^*, \ldots, \nu_r^*, \ldots$ taking on nonnegative integers as follows: Let $N_0 = 0$ and $N_r = \nu_1 + \cdots + \nu_r$ for $r = 1, 2, \ldots$ and similarly $N_0^* = 0$ and $N_r^* = \nu_1^* + \cdots + \nu_r^*$ for $r = 1, 2, \ldots$. Suppose that

(1) $$N_n^* = \sup\{r : N_r < n \text{ and } r = 0, 1, 2, \ldots\}$$

for $n = 1, 2, \ldots$. In this case we say that $\{\nu_r^*\}$ is the dual sequence of $\{\nu_r\}$. Then, conversely, $\{\nu_r\}$ is the dual sequence of $\{\nu_r^*\}$.

We have the obvious relation

(2) $$\{N_n^* < k\} \equiv \{N_k \geq n\}$$

for $n + k > 0$. This implies that

(3)
$$\{N_r^* - r < k \text{ for } r = 1, \ldots, n\} \equiv \{r - N_r \leq k \text{ for } r = 1, \ldots, n + k\}$$

and

(4)
$$\{r - N_r^* \leq k \text{ for } r = 1, \ldots, n\} \equiv \{N_r - r < k \text{ for } r = 1, \ldots, n - k\}.$$

Accordingly, if we know the distribution of the maximum for the sequences $\{N_r - r\}$ and $\{r - N_r\}$, then by using the relations (3) and (4) we can obtain immediately the distribution of the maximum for the dual sequences $\{N_r^* - r\}$ and $\{r - N_r^*\}$ and conversely.

10. EXAMPLES

In this section we consider some particular sequences of random variables $\{\nu_1, \nu_2, \ldots, \nu_r, \ldots\}$ and determine all those quantities which make it possible to apply the general theorems proved in this chapter.

1. *Bernoulli Sequence.* Suppose that $\nu_1, \nu_2, \ldots, \nu_r, \ldots$ are mutually independent and identically distributed random variables with distribution $\mathbf{P}\{\nu_r = 0\} = q$, $\mathbf{P}\{\nu_r = 2\} = p$, where $p + q = 1$ and $0 < p < 1$. In this case

$$\mathbf{P}\{N_n = 2j\} = \binom{n}{j} p^j q^{n-j} \tag{1}$$

for $j = 0, 1, \ldots, n$. Now $\pi(z) = q + pz^2$ and by (8) of Section 7

$$Q(z) = \frac{Q_0(q + pz^2)}{(1 - z)(q - pz)}. \tag{2}$$

Hence

$$Q_k = \frac{Q_0}{q}\left(\frac{1 - (p/q)^k}{1 - p/q}\right) \quad \text{if} \quad p \neq q \quad \text{and} \quad k \geq 1, \tag{3}$$

and

$$Q_k = 2Q_0 k \quad \text{if} \quad p = q \quad \text{and} \quad k \geq 1. \tag{4}$$

Now $\gamma = 2p$. If $\gamma \leq 1$, then $\delta = 1$ and if $\gamma > 1$, then $\delta = q/p$.

2. *Pascal Sequence.* Suppose that $\nu_1, \nu_2, \ldots, \nu_r, \ldots$ are mutually independent and identically distributed random variables with distribution $\mathbf{P}\{\nu_r = j\} = pq^j, j = 0, 1, 2, \ldots,$ where $p + q = 1$ and $0 < p < 1$. Then $\pi_j = pq^j$ for $j = 0, 1, \ldots,$ and $\pi(z) = p/(1 - qz)$. In this case

$$\mathbf{P}\{N_n = j\} = \binom{n + j - 1}{n - 1} p^n q^j \tag{5}$$

for $j = 0, 1, 2, \ldots$. By (8) of Section 7

$$Q(z) = \frac{Q_0 p}{(1 - z)(p - qz)} \tag{6}$$

whence

$$Q_k = Q_0\left(\frac{1 - (q/p)^{k+1}}{1 - q/p}\right) \quad \text{if} \quad p \neq q \quad \text{and} \quad k \geq 0, \tag{7}$$

and

$$Q_k = Q_0(k+1) \quad \text{if} \quad p = q \quad \text{and} \quad k \geq 0. \tag{8}$$

Now $\gamma = q/p$. If $\gamma \leq 1$, then $\delta = 1$, and if $\gamma > 1$, then $\delta = p/q$.

3. *Poisson Sequence.* Suppose that $\nu_1, \nu_2, \ldots, \nu_r, \ldots$ are mutually independent and identically distributed random variables with distribution

$$\mathbf{P}\{\nu_r = j\} = e^{-a}\frac{a^j}{j!}, \qquad j = 0, 1, 2, \ldots. \tag{9}$$

Then $\pi(z) = e^{-a(1-z)}$ and

$$\mathbf{P}\{N_n = j\} = e^{-an}\frac{(an)^j}{j!}, \qquad j = 0, 1, 2, \ldots. \tag{10}$$

By (8) of Section 7

$$Q(z) = \frac{Q_0}{1 - e^{a(1-z)}z} \tag{11}$$

whence

$$Q_k = Q_0 \sum_{j=0}^{k} (-1)^j e^{a(k-j)} \frac{[a(k-j)]^j}{j!} \tag{12}$$

for $k = 0, 1, 2, \ldots$.

Now $\gamma = a$. If $\gamma \leq 1$, then $\delta = 1$. If $\gamma > 1$, then δ is the only root of $e^{-a(1-\delta)} = \delta$ in $(0, 1)$.

4. *Pólya Sequence.* (F. Eggenberger and G. Pólya [9].) Suppose that an urn originally contains a white balls and b black balls. We perform a sequence of drawings. After each drawing the ball is returned and c balls of the color drawn are added to the urn. Let $\nu_r = h$ if the rth ball drawn is white and $\nu_r = 0$ if the rth ball drawn is black. h is a positive integer.

In this case $\nu_1, \nu_2, \ldots, \nu_r, \ldots$ are interchangeable random variables. We have $\mathbf{P}\{\nu_r = h\} = a/(a+b)$, $\mathbf{P}\{\nu_r = 0\} = b/(a+b)$ and $\mathbf{E}\{\nu_r\} = ah/(a+b)$ for $r = 1, 2, \ldots$. Furthermore,

$$\mathbf{P}\{N_n = jh\} = \frac{\dbinom{\alpha+j-1}{j}\dbinom{\beta+n-j-1}{n-j}}{\dbinom{\alpha+\beta+n-1}{n}} \tag{13}$$

if $j = 0, 1, \ldots, n$ where $\alpha = a/c$ and $\beta = b/c$, and

$$\mathbf{P}\{N_n = jh, N_{n+m} = (j+k)h\} = \tag{14}$$

$$\frac{\dbinom{\alpha+j-1}{j}\dbinom{\beta+n-j-1}{n-j}\dbinom{\alpha+j+k-1}{k}\dbinom{\beta+n-j+m-k-1}{m-k}}{\dbinom{\alpha+\beta+n-1}{n}\dbinom{\alpha+\beta+n+m-1}{m}}$$

for $j = 0, 1, \ldots, n$ and $k = 0, 1, \ldots, m$.

Now we can define a random variable θ such that given θ the random variables $\nu_1, \nu_2, \ldots, \nu_r, \ldots$ are mutually independent and identically distributed. If we suppose that $\mathbf{P}\{\nu_r = h\} = \theta$ and $\mathbf{P}\{\nu_r = 0\} = 1 - \theta$ where θ has the distribution function

$$(15)\quad \mathbf{P}\{\theta \le x\} = \frac{\Gamma(\alpha+\beta)}{\Gamma(\alpha)\Gamma(\beta)}\int_0^x y^{\alpha-1}(1-y)^{\beta-1}\,dy \qquad (0 \le x \le 1),$$

then $\nu_1, \nu_2, \ldots, \nu_r, \ldots$ is a Pólya sequence as defined above. Accordingly a Pólya sequence can be represented as a randomized Bernoulli sequence.

In this case $\mathbf{E}\{\nu_r \mid \theta\} = h\theta$ with probability 1 and by Theorem 1 of Section 5

$$(16)\qquad \mathbf{P}\{N_r < r \text{ for } r = 1, 2, \ldots \mid \theta = x\} = [1 - hx]^+,$$

therefore unconditionally

$$(17)\qquad \mathbf{P}\{N_r < r \text{ for } r = 1, 2, \ldots\} = \int_0^{1/h} (1 - hx)\, d\mathbf{P}\{\theta \le x\}.$$

Since

$$(18)\qquad \mathbf{P}\{N_n = jh \mid \theta = x\} = \binom{n}{j} x^j (1-x)^{n-j}$$

for $j = 0, 1, \ldots, n$, we obtain by Theorem 3 of Section 6 that

$$(19)\quad \mathbf{P}\left\{\sup_{1\le r<\infty} (N_r - r) < k \mid \theta = x\right\} = 1 - (1 - hx) \sum_{l \ge (k+1)/h} \binom{lh - k}{l} x^l (1-x)^{l(h-1)-k}$$

if $0 \le x < 1/h$ and 0 if $x \ge 1/h$. Hence unconditionally

$$(20)\quad \mathbf{P}\left\{\sup_{1\le r<\infty} (N_r - r) < k\right\} = \mathbf{P}\{\theta < 1/h\} - \sum_{l \ge (k+1)/h} \binom{lh-k}{l} \int_0^{1/h} (1 - hx) x^l (1-x)^{l(h-1)-k}\, d\mathbf{P}\{\theta \le x\}.$$

By (6) of Section 8

$$(21)\qquad \mathbf{P}\left\{\sup_{1\le r<\infty} (r - N_r) < k\right\} = 1 - \sum_{j=k}^{\infty} \frac{k}{j} \mathbf{P}\{N_j = j - k\}$$

holds for all $k > 0$.

11. OTHER METHODS

In this chapter we have determined the distribution of the random variable $\eta_n = \max(0, \xi_1, \xi_1 + \xi_2, \ldots, \xi_1 + \cdots + \xi_n)$ where $\xi_1, \xi_2, \ldots,$

$\xi_r, \ldots$ are either interchangeable random variables or mutually independent, and identically distributed random variables in the cases where $\xi_1, \xi_2, \ldots, \xi_r, \ldots$ may take either on the values $-1, 0, 1, 2, \ldots$ or on the values $1, 0, -1, -2, \ldots$. If we suppose that $\xi_1, \xi_2, \ldots, \xi_r, \ldots$ are mutually independent and identically distributed random variables with an arbitrary distribution, then we can apply the method of F. Pollaczek [16], E. Sparre-Andersen [1], F. Spitzer [17] and W. Feller [10] to find the distribution of the random variable $\eta_n = \max(0, \xi_1, \xi_1 + \xi_2, \ldots, \xi_1 + \cdots + \xi_n)$. To present this method we shall introduce an operator **A** and record its basic properties.

Let $G(x)$ be a monotone nondecreasing function of bounded variation in $(-\infty, \infty)$. Then

$$\gamma(s) = \int_{-\infty}^{\infty} e^{-sx}\, dG(x) \tag{1}$$

is convergent for $\mathrm{Re}(s) = 0$. Knowing $\gamma(s)$, the function

$$\gamma^+(s) = \int_{-0}^{\infty} e^{-sx}\, dG(x) \tag{2}$$

is determined uniquely for $\mathrm{Re}(s) \geq 0$. Now define an operator **A** such that

$$\gamma^+(s) = \mathbf{A}\gamma(s). \tag{3}$$

The operator **A** is linear and $\mathbf{A}^2 = \mathbf{A}$. Now suppose that

$$G(x) = \sum_{n=0}^{\infty} \frac{a^n}{n!} F_n(x) \tag{4}$$

where $F_n(x)$ is the nth iterated convolution of a distribution function $F(x)$ with itself; $F_0(x) = 1$ if $x \geq 0$ and $F_0(x) = 0$ if $x < 0$. If

$$\phi(s) = \int_{-\infty}^{\infty} e^{-sx}\, dF(x) \tag{5}$$

for $\mathrm{Re}(s) = 0$, then the Laplace-Stieltjes transform of $G(x)$ is given by

$$\gamma(s) = e^{a\phi(s)} \tag{6}$$

for $\mathrm{Re}(s) = 0$. In what follows we shall make use of the following two statements, the truth of which can be seen immediately.

(i) If $\mathbf{A}\phi(s) = \phi(s)$, then $\mathbf{A}\gamma(s) = e^{a\phi(s)}$.

(ii) If $\mathbf{A}\phi(s) = 0$, then $\mathbf{A}\gamma(s) = 1$.

Theorem 1. *Let $\xi_1, \xi_2, \ldots, \xi_r, \ldots$ be mutually independent and identically distributed random variables for which*

$$\mathbf{E}\{e^{-s\xi_r}\} = \phi(s) \tag{7}$$

when Re$(s) = 0$. *Let* $\eta_n = \max(0, \xi_1, \xi_1 + \xi_2, \ldots, \xi_1 + \cdots + \xi_n)$ *and*

$$\mathbf{E}\{e^{-s\eta_n}\} = \Phi_n(s) \tag{8}$$

for Re$(s) \geq 0$. *If* $0 \leq w < 1$ *and* Re$(s) \geq 0$, *then we have*

$$\sum_{n=0}^{\infty} \Phi_n(s) w^n = \exp\left(\sum_{n=1}^{\infty} \frac{w^n}{n} \mathbf{A}\{[\phi(s)]^n\}\right), \tag{9}$$

or equivalently,

$$\sum_{n=0}^{\infty} \Phi_n(s) w^n = \exp(-\mathbf{A}\{\log[1 - w\phi(s)]\}). \tag{10}$$

Proof. Now we can write

$$\eta_n = \max(0, \xi_1 + \eta_{n-1}^*) \tag{11}$$

where η_{n-1}^* has the same distribution as η_{n-1} and is independent of ξ_1. Thus $\Phi_0(s) \equiv 1$ and

$$\Phi_n(s) = \mathbf{A}\{\phi(s)\Phi_{n-1}(s)\} \tag{12}$$

for $n = 1, 2, \ldots$ and Re$(s) \geq 0$. The solution of this recurrence relation is given by the generating function (9). This can be proved as follows:

First, (9) and (i) imply that

$$\mathbf{A}\left\{\sum_{n=0}^{\infty} \Phi_n(s) w^n\right\} = \exp\left(\sum_{n=1}^{\infty} \frac{w^n}{n} \mathbf{A}\{[\phi(s)]^n\}\right) = \sum_{n=0}^{\infty} \Phi_n(s) w^n. \tag{13}$$

Second, (9) and (ii) imply that

$$\begin{aligned} &\mathbf{A}\left\{[1 - w\phi(s)] \sum_{n=0}^{\infty} \Phi_n(s) w^n\right\} \\ &\qquad = \mathbf{A}\left\{\exp\left(-\sum_{n=1}^{\infty} \frac{w^n}{n} [(\phi(s))^n - \mathbf{A}(\phi(s))^n]\right)\right\} = 1. \end{aligned} \tag{14}$$

Thus by (13) and (14) we obtain

$$\mathbf{A}\left\{w\phi(s) \sum_{n=0}^{\infty} \Phi_n(s) w^n\right\} = \sum_{n=0}^{\infty} \Phi_n(s) w^n - 1 \tag{15}$$

for $0 \leq w < 1$ and Re$(s) \geq 0$. Hence it follows that $\Phi_0(s) \equiv 1$ and that $\Phi_n(s)$, $n = 1, 2, \ldots$, satisfies (12). This completes the proof of the theorem.

From (9) it follows that

$$\Phi_n(s) = \sum_{k_1 + 2k_2 + \cdots + nk_n = n} \frac{[\mathbf{A}(\phi(s))]^{k_1} [\mathbf{A}(\phi(s))^2]^{k_2} \ldots [\mathbf{A}(\phi(s))^n]^{k_n}}{k_1!\, k_2! \ldots k_n!\, 1^{k_1}\, 2^{k_2} \ldots n^{k_n}} \tag{16}$$

and the distribution of η_n can be obtained by inversion.

Theorem 1 has been proved by F. Pollaczek [16] in form (10). However, Pollaczek made the restriction that $\phi(\epsilon) < \infty$ for some $\epsilon > 0$ and in this case he defined the operator **A** in the following way

$$\mathbf{A}\phi(s) = \frac{s}{2\pi i}\int_{\epsilon-i\infty}^{\epsilon+i\infty} \frac{\phi(z)}{z(s-z)}\,dz. \tag{17}$$

It should be noted that we can use (17) also for $\epsilon = 0$ if we define the integral by its Cauchy's principal value. Form (9) of Theorem 1 has been given by F. Spitzer [17].

In many cases the generating function (9) can be obtained in the following way. If we suppose that

$$1 - w\phi(s) = [\Phi^+(s, w)]^\alpha [\Phi^-(s, w)]^\beta \tag{18}$$

for $\mathrm{Re}(s) = 0$ where $\alpha = \pm 1$, $\beta = \pm 1$, $\Phi^+(s, w)$ is regular and free from zeros in the domain $\mathrm{Re}(s) > 0$ and continuous for $\mathrm{Re}(s) \geq 0$, $\Phi^-(s, w)$ is regular and free from zeros in the domain $\mathrm{Re}(s) < 0$ and continuous for $\mathrm{Re}(s) \leq 0$, furthermore

$$\lim_{|s|\to\infty} \frac{\log \Phi^+(s, w)}{s} = 0 \qquad [\mathrm{Re}(s) > 0]$$

and

$$\lim_{|s|\to\infty} \frac{\log \Phi^-(s, w)}{s} = 0 \qquad [\mathrm{Re}(s) < 0],$$

then

$$\mathbf{A}\{\log [1 - w\phi(s)]\} = \alpha \log \Phi^+(s, w) + \beta \log \Phi^-(0, w) \tag{19}$$

and

$$(1 - w)\sum_{n=0}^{\infty} \Phi_n(s) w^n = \left[\frac{\Phi^+(0, w)}{\Phi^+(s, w)}\right]^\alpha \tag{20}$$

for $0 < w < 1$ and $\mathrm{Re}(s) \geq 0$.

If we define

$$\eta = \sup(0, \xi_1, \xi_1 + \xi_2, \ldots, \xi_1 + \cdots + \xi_r, \ldots), \tag{21}$$

then η is a proper random variable if $\mathbf{E}\{\xi_1\} < 0$. If $\mathbf{E}\{\xi_1\} \geq 0$ and $\mathbf{P}\{\xi_1 = 0\} \neq 1$, then $\mathbf{P}\{\eta = \infty\} = 1$. (See Appendix.) If $\mathbf{E}\{\xi_1\} < 0$, then

$$\Phi(s) = \mathbf{E}\{e^{-s\eta}\} \tag{22}$$

exists for $\mathrm{Re}(s) \geq 0$ and $\Phi(s) = \lim_{n\to\infty} \Phi_n(s)$. By using Abel's theorem it follows from (9) that

$$\Phi(s) = \lim_{w\to 1}(1 - w)\sum_{n=0}^{\infty}\Phi_n(s)w^n = \exp\left(-\sum_{n=1}^{\infty}\frac{1}{n}[1 - \mathbf{A}(\phi(s))^n]\right). \tag{23}$$

This result has been found by S. Täcklind [27] and F. Spitzer [17]. By (20) we can also write

$$\Phi(s) = \lim_{w\to 1} \left[\frac{\Phi^+(0, w)}{\Phi^+(s, w)}\right]^\alpha. \tag{24}$$

Evidently η has the same distribution as max $(0, \xi + \eta)$ where ξ is independent of η and $\mathbf{P}\{\xi \leq x\} = F(x)$ where $F(x)$ is the common distribution function of the random variables ξ_r, $r = 1, 2, \ldots$. In the case when $\mathbf{E}\{\xi_1\} < 0$, the distribution function $W(x) = \mathbf{P}\{\eta \leq x\}$ satisfies the following integral equation of Wiener-Hopf type

$$W(x) = \begin{cases} \int_{-\infty}^{x} W(x - y)\, dF(y) & \text{for } x \geq 0, \\ 0 & \text{for } x < 0. \end{cases} \tag{25}$$

12. PROBLEMS

1. In a ballot candidate A scores a votes and candidate B scores b votes and all the possible voting records are equally probable. Suppose that $\mu b < a + c$ where μ and c are positive integers. Denote by α_r and β_r the number of votes registered for A and B respectively among the first r votes recorded. Find the probability $P = \mathbf{P}\{\mu\beta_r < \alpha_r + c \text{ for } r = 1, 2, \ldots, a + b\}$.

2. Two players A and B are playing a sequence of games. In each game either A wins a coin from B with probability p or B wins a coin from A with probability q $(p + q = 1, 0 < p < 1)$. The games are independent of each other. Suppose that initially A has a coins and B has b coins. The games are continued until one of the two players is ruined. Find P_A, the probability that ultimately A will be ruined.

3. Consider the previous problem in the case when initially B has an infinite capital. Find the distribution and the expectation of $\rho(a)$, the duration of the game.

4. Two players A and B are playing a sequence of games. The games are independent of each other. Suppose that initially A has a coins and B has b coins. In each game either A wins k coins $(k = 0, 1, 2, \ldots)$ from B with probability pq^{k+1} or B wins a coin from A with probability p $(p + q = 1, 0 < p < 1)$. The games are continued until one of the two players is ruined. Find P_A, the probability that ultimately A will be ruined.

5. Consider the previous problem in the case when initially B has an infinite capital. Find the distribution and the expectation of $\rho(a)$, the duration of the game.

6. Suppose that $\nu_1, \nu_2, \ldots, \nu_r, \ldots$ are mutually independent and identically distributed random variables with distribution $\mathbf{P}\{\nu_r = 0\} = q$, $\mathbf{P}\{\nu_r = 2\} = p$ where $p + q = 1$ and $0 < p < 1$. Find the distributions of the random variables $\sup_{1\leq r<\infty} (N_r - r)$ and $\sup_{1\leq r<\infty} (r - N_r)$.

7. Suppose that an urn originally contains a white balls and b black balls. We perform a sequence of drawings. After each drawing the ball is returned and c balls of the color drawn are added to the urn. Define ν_r as 2 if the rth ball drawn is white and as 0 if the rth ball drawn is black. Find the distributions of the random variables $\sup_{1 \le r < \infty} (N_r - r)$ and $\sup_{1 \le r < \infty} (r - N_r)$.

8. Suppose that $\nu_1, \nu_2, \ldots, \nu_r, \ldots$ are mutually independent and identically distributed random variables with distribution $\mathbf{P}\{\nu_r = j\} = e^{-a} a^j/j!$ for $j = 0, 1, 2, \ldots$. Write down the identities (26) of Section 6 and (21) of Section 8 in this case.

9. Prove that

$$\sum_{j=1}^{n} \frac{1}{j} \binom{n-1}{j-1} \left(\frac{j}{n}\right)^{j-1} \left(1 - \frac{j}{n}\right)^{n-j} = 1$$

for $n = 1, 2, \ldots$.

10. Let $\xi_1, \xi_2, \ldots, \xi_r, \ldots$ be a sequence of mutually independent random variables having a common distribution function

$$\mathbf{P}\{\xi_r \le x\} = \begin{cases} e^{-\lambda(\alpha - x)} & \text{if } x \le \alpha, \\ 1 & \text{if } x \ge \alpha, \end{cases}$$

where α is a positive constant. Find the distribution function of the random variable $\eta_n = \max(0, \xi_1, \xi_1 + \xi_2, \ldots, \xi_1 + \cdots + \xi_n)$.

REFERENCES

[1] Andersen, E. S. "On the fluctuations of sums of random variables," I and II. *Math. Scand.* **1** (1953), 263–285, and **2** (1954), 195–223.

[2] Baxter, G. "An operator identity," *Pacific J. Math.* **4** (1958), 649–663.

[3] Baxter, G. "An analytic problem whose solution follows from a simple algebraic identity," *Pacific J. Math.* **10** (1960), 731–742.

[4] Bernoulli, J. *Ars Conjectandi*, (Opus posth.), Basileae, 1713.

[5] Borovkov, A. A. "New limit theorems in boundary problems for sums of independent terms," (Russian) *Sibirsk. Mat. Zhur.* **3** (1962), 645–694. [English translation: *Selected Translations in Mathematical Statistics and Probability, IMS and AMS*, **5** (1965), 315–372.]

[6] Darling, D. A. "The maximum of sums of stable random variables," *Trans. Amer. Math. Soc.* **83** (1956), 164–169.

[7] De Moivre, A. "De mensura sortis, seu, de probabilitate eventuum in ludis a casu fortuito pendentibus," *Philos. Trans. London* **27** (1711), 213–264.

[8] Dwass, M. "A fluctuation theorem for cyclic random variables," *Ann. Math. Statist.* **33** (1962), 1450–1454.

[9] Eggenberger, F. and G. Pólya, "Über die Statistik verketteter Vorgänge," *Zeitschr. ang. Math. und Mech.* **3** (1923), 279–289.

[10] Feller, W. "On combinatorial methods in fluctuation theory," *Probability and Statistics*, The Harald Cramér Volume, Edited by U. Grenander. Almqvist and Wiksell, Stockholm and John Wiley and Sons, New York, 1959, pp. 75–91.

[11] Huygens, C. "Opera Varia C. Hugenius," *Lugdunum Batavorum*, 1724, pp. 723–744.

[12] Kac, M. and H. Pollard, "The distribution of the maximum of partial sums of independent random variables," *Canadian J. Math.* **2** (1950), 375–384.

[13] Kemperman, J. H. B. *The Passage Problem for a Stationary Markov Chain*, The University of Chicago Press, 1961.

[14] Kingman, J. F. C. "Spitzer's identity and its use in probability theory," *J. London Math. Soc.* **37** (1962), 309–316.

[15] Kinney, J. R. "First passage times of a generalized random walk," *Ann. Math. Statist.* **32** (1961), 235–243.

[16] Pollaczek, F. "Fonctions caractéristiques de certaines répartitions définies au moyen de la notion d'ordre," *C. R. Acad. Sci. Paris* **234** (1952), 2334–2336.

[17] Spitzer, F. "A combinatorial lemma and its application to probability theory," *Trans. Amer. Math. Soc.* **82** (1956), 323–339.

[18] Spitzer, F. "A Tauberian theorem and its probability interpretation," *Trans. Amer. Math. Soc.* **94** (1960), 150–169.

[19] Spitzer, F. *Principles of Random Walk*, D. Van Nostrand, Princeton, New Jersey, 1964.

[20] Takács, L. "The probability law of the busy period for two types of queuing processes," *Operations Res.* **9** (1961), 402–407.

[21] Takács, L. "Combinatorial methods in the theory of queues," *Rev. Inst. Internat. Statist.* **32** (1964), 207–219.

[22] Takács, L. "Combinatorial methods in the theory of dams," *J. Appl. Prob.* **1** (1964), 69–76.

[23] Takács, L. "A combinatorial method in the theory of Markov chains," *J. Math. Anal. Appl.* **9** (1964), 153–161.

[24] Takács, L. "Application of ballot theorems in the theory of queues," *Proceedings of the Symposium on Congestion Theory*, Chapel Hill, North Carolina, August 24–26, 1964. Edited by W. L. Smith and W. E. Wilkinson, University of North Carolina Press, Chapel Hill, North Carolina, 1965, pp. 337–398.

[25] Takács, L. "From ballot theorems to the theory of queues," *Columbia University Report CU*-41-64-*Nonr*-266 (**59**), MS, March, 1964. [Abstract: *Post Office Telecommunications Journal, Special Issue, Report of the Proceedings of the Fourth International Teletraffic Congress*, London, 1964, pp. 25–26.]

[26] Tanner, J. C. "A derivation of the Borel distribution," *Biometrika* **48** (1961), 222–224.

[27] Täcklind, S. "Sur le risque de ruine dans des jeux inéquitables," *Skand. Aktuarietids.* **25** (1942), 1–42.

[28] Vogel, W. "Die kombinatorische Lösung einer Operator-Gleichung," *Zeitschr. Wahrscheinlichkeitstheorie* **2** (1963), 122–134.

[29] Wendel, J. G. "Spitzer's formula: a short proof," *Proc. Amer. Math. Soc.* **9** (1958), 905–908.

[30] Wendel, J. G. "Brief proof of a theorem of Baxter," *Math. Scand.* **11** (1962), 107–108.

CHAPTER 3

Fluctuations of Sample Functions of Stochastic Processes

13. STOCHASTIC PROCESSES WITH CYCLICALLY INTERCHANGEABLE INCREMENTS

We say that a stochastic process $\{\chi(u), 0 \le u \le t\}$ has cyclically interchangeable increments if for all $n = 2, 3, \ldots$

$$\chi\left(\frac{rt}{n}\right) - \chi\left(\frac{rt - t}{n}\right), \qquad r = 1, 2, \ldots, n, \tag{1}$$

are cyclically interchangeable random variables, that is, for $n = 2, 3, \ldots$ all the n cyclic permutations of the random variables (1) have the same joint distribution.

If for all $n = 2, 3, \ldots$ the random variables (1) are interchangeable or mutually independent and identically distributed, then they are also cyclically interchangeable.

Now we shall prove our fundamental theorem for processes with cyclically interchangeable increments.

Theorem 1. *If $\{\chi(u), 0 \le u \le t\}$ is a real-valued separable stochastic process with cyclically interchangeable increments almost all of whose sample functions are nondecreasing step functions vanishing at $u = 0$, then*

$$\mathbf{P}\{\chi(u) \le u \text{ for } 0 \le u \le t \mid \chi(t) = y\} = \begin{cases} (t - y)/t & \text{if } 0 \le y \le t, \\ 0 & \text{otherwise,} \end{cases} \tag{2}$$

where the conditional probability is defined up to an equivalence.

Proof. Define $\chi(u)$ for $0 \le u < \infty$ by assuming that $\chi(u + t) = \chi(u) + \chi(t)$ for $u \ge 0$. Let

$$\delta(u) = \begin{cases} 1 & \text{if } \chi(v) - \chi(u) \le v - u \quad \text{for } v \ge u, \\ 0 & \text{otherwise.} \end{cases} \tag{3}$$

Then $\delta(u)$ is a random variable which has the same distribution for all $u \geq 0$. Evidently $\delta(0)$ is the indicator variable of the event $\{\chi(u) \leq u$ for $0 \leq u \leq t\}$. Thus we have

$$(4)\quad \mathbf{P}\{\chi(u) \leq u \text{ for } 0 \leq u \leq t \mid \chi(t)\} = \mathbf{E}\{\delta(0) \mid \chi(t)\}$$
$$= \frac{1}{t}\int_0^t \mathbf{E}\{\delta(u) \mid \chi(t)\}\, du = \mathbf{E}\left\{\frac{1}{t}\int_0^t \delta(u)\, du \mid \chi(t)\right\}$$
$$= \begin{cases} \left(1 - \dfrac{\chi(t)}{t}\right) & \text{if } 0 \leq \chi(t) \leq t, \\ 0 & \text{otherwise,} \end{cases}$$

with probability 1 because by Theorem 5 of Section 2

$$(5)\qquad \int_0^t \delta(u)\, du = \begin{cases} t - \chi(t) & \text{if } 0 \leq \chi(t) \leq t, \\ 0 & \text{otherwise,} \end{cases}$$

holds for almost all sample functions. This completes the proof of the theorem.

We note that in (2) the left-hand side can be replaced by $\mathbf{P}\{\chi(u) < u$ for $0 < u \leq t \mid \chi(t) = y\}$ without changing the right-hand side.

From (2) it follows that

$$(6)\qquad \mathbf{P}\{\chi(u) \leq u \text{ for } 0 \leq u \leq t\} = \mathbf{E}\left\{\left[1 - \frac{\chi(t)}{t}\right]^+\right\}$$

where $[x]^+$ denotes the positive part of x.

14. STOCHASTIC PROCESSES WITH INTERCHANGEABLE INCREMENTS AND STOCHASTIC PROCESSES WITH STATIONARY INDEPENDENT INCREMENTS

A stochastic process $\{\chi(u), 0 \leq u \leq T\}$ is said to have *interchangeable increments* if for all $n = 2, 3, \ldots$ and for all finite $t \in (0, T]$

$$(1)\qquad \chi\left(\frac{rt}{n}\right) - \chi\left(\frac{rt - t}{n}\right), \qquad r = 1, 2, \ldots, n,$$

are interchangeable random variables, that is, all the $n!$ permutations of the random variables (1) have a common joint distribution.

If, in particular, for all $n = 2, 3, \ldots$ and for all finite $t \in (0, T]$ the random variables (1) are mutually independent and identically distributed, then the stochastic process $\{\chi(u), 0 \leq u \leq T\}$ is said to have *stationary independent increments.*

If $\mathbf{P}\{\chi(0) = 0\} = 1$, then in both cases the stochastic process $\{\chi(u), 0 \leq u \leq t\}$ has cyclically interchangeable increments for all finite $t \in (0, T]$.

In all subsequent considerations of this chapter we are concerned with real-valued stochastic processes $\{\chi(u), 0 \leq u \leq T\}$ having either interchangeable increments or stationary independent increments, for which almost all sample functions are nondecreasing step functions vanishing at $u = 0$. The parameter range may be either finite or infinite. The trivial case $\mathbf{P}\{\chi(u) = 0\} = 1$ for $u > 0$ will be excluded.

First we shall mention a few basic properties of the considered processes $\{\chi(u), 0 \leq u \leq T\}$.

For both types of processes

$$\mathbf{E}\{\chi(u)\} = \rho u \tag{2}$$

if $0 \leq u \leq T$ where ρ is a nonnegative number (possibly ∞). If $\rho = 0$, then $\mathbf{P}\{\chi(u) = 0\} = 1$ for $0 \leq u \leq T$ which case is excluded.

Now suppose that $T = \infty$. If $\{\chi(u), 0 \leq u < \infty\}$ has interchangeable increments, then there is a distribution function $G(x)$ such that

$$\lim_{t \to \infty} \mathbf{P}\left\{\frac{\chi(t)}{t} \leq x\right\} = G(x). \tag{3}$$

If, in particular, $\{\chi(u), 0 \leq u < \infty\}$ has stationary independent increments and $\mathbf{E}\{\chi(u)\} = \rho u$, then $G(x) = 0$ if $x < \rho$ and $G(x) = 1$ if $x \geq \rho$. That is, in this case

$$\lim_{t \to \infty} \frac{\chi(t)}{t} = \rho \tag{4}$$

in probability. This is the weak law of large numbers.

Now we shall prove the following fundamental theorem.

Theorem 1. *If $\{\chi(u), 0 \leq u < \infty\}$ is a real-valued separable stochastic process with stationary independent increments for which almost all sample functions are nondecreasing step functions vanishing at $u = 0$, then*

$$\mathbf{P}\{\chi(u) \leq u \text{ for } 0 \leq u < \infty\} = \begin{cases} 1 - \rho & \text{if } \rho < 1, \\ 0 & \text{if } \rho \geq 1. \end{cases} \tag{5}$$

Proof. By the continuity theorem for probabilities

$$\mathbf{P}\{\chi(u) \leq u \text{ for } 0 \leq u < \infty\} = \lim_{t \to \infty} \mathbf{P}\{\chi(u) \leq u \text{ for } 0 \leq u \leq t\}. \tag{6}$$

For any finite t, $\{\chi(u), 0 \leq u \leq t\}$ has cyclically interchangeable increments for which Theorem 1 of Section 13 is applicable. Thus by (6) of Section 13

$$\mathbf{P}\{\chi(u) \leq u \text{ for } 0 \leq u < \infty\} = \lim_{t \to \infty} \mathbf{E}\left\{\left[1 - \frac{\chi(t)}{t}\right]^+\right\}. \tag{7}$$

Now by (4) $\lim_{t\to\infty}\left[1-\frac{\chi(t)}{t}\right]^+ = [1-\rho]^+$ in probability. Since $\left[1-\frac{\chi(t)}{t}\right]^+$ is bounded, it follows that

$$\lim_{t\to\infty} \mathbf{E}\left\{\left[1-\frac{\chi(t)}{t}\right]^+\right\} = [1-\rho]^+. \tag{8}$$

This proves (5).

Theorem 2. *If $\{\chi(u), 0 \le u < \infty\}$ is a real-valued, separable stochastic process with interchangeable increments for which almost all sample functions are nondecreasing step functions vanishing at $u = 0$, then*

$$\mathbf{P}\{\chi(u) \le u \text{ for } 0 \le u < \infty\} = \int_0^1 (1-x)\, dG(x) \tag{9}$$

where $G(x)$ is defined by (3).

Proof. Now (7) holds unchangeably. Since $[(t-\chi(t))/t]^+$ is bounded, by (3) it follows that

$$\lim_{t\to\infty} \mathbf{E}\left\{\left[1-\frac{\chi(t)}{t}\right]^+\right\} = \int_0^1 (1-x)\, dG(x) \tag{10}$$

which proves (9).

If we suppose that $\{\chi(u), 0 \le u < \infty\}$ is a real-valued stochastic process with stationary independent increments almost all of whose sample functions are nondecreasing step functions vanishing at $u = 0$, then we have

$$\mathbf{E}\{e^{-s\chi(u)}\} = e^{-u\Phi(s)} \tag{11}$$

for all $u \ge 0$ and for $\text{Re}(s) \ge 0$ where

$$\Phi(s) = \int_{+0}^{\infty} (1-e^{-sx})\, dN(x) \tag{12}$$

and $N(x), 0 < x < \infty$, is a nondecreasing function for which $\lim_{x\to\infty} N(x) = 0$ and

$$\int_{+0}^{1} x\, dN(x) < \infty. \tag{13}$$

There is no restriction in supposing that (Nx) is continuous on the right. Then the expected number of jumps of magnitude $>x$ occurring in the interval $(0, t)$ is $t[N(\infty) - N(x)]$. Define $\lambda = N(\infty) - N(0) = -N(0)$ (possibly ∞). We have $\lambda = \lim_{s\to\infty} \Phi(s)$. If $\lambda = 0$, then $\mathbf{P}\{\chi(u) = 0\} = 1$ for $u \ge 0$ which case is excluded.

The expected number of jumps occurring in the interval $(0, t)$ is λt, and $\mathbf{P}\{\chi(t) = 0\} = e^{-\lambda t}$ for $t \ge 0$.

If λ is a finite positive number, then

$$H(x) = \frac{N(0) - N(x)}{N(0)} \tag{14}$$

is the distribution function of a nonnegative random variable and

$$\psi(s) = \int_0^\infty e^{-sx}\, dH(x) = 1 - \frac{\Phi(s)}{\lambda} \tag{15}$$

for $\operatorname{Re}(s) \geq 0$.

Let

$$\rho = \int_{+0}^\infty x\, dN(x). \tag{16}$$

If $\operatorname{Re}(s) > 0$, then $\Phi'(s)$ exists and

$$\Phi'(s) = \int_{+0}^\infty e^{-sx} x\, dN(x). \tag{17}$$

We have $\rho = \lim_{s \to +0} \Phi'(s)$ and

$$\mathbf{E}\{\chi(t)\} = \rho t \tag{18}$$

for all $t \geq 0$.

If ρ is a finite positive number, then

$$H^*(x) = \frac{\int_0^x N(y)\, dy}{\int_0^\infty N(y)\, dy}, \qquad 0 \leq x < \infty, \tag{19}$$

is the distribution function of a nonnegative random variable and

$$\psi^*(s) = \int_0^\infty e^{-sx}\, dH^*(x) = \frac{\Phi(s)}{\rho s} \tag{20}$$

for $\operatorname{Re}(s) > 0$. If both λ and ρ are finite positive numbers, then

$$\psi^*(s) = \frac{\lambda[1 - \psi(s)]}{\rho s} \tag{21}$$

for $\operatorname{Re}(s) > 0$.

Throughout this chapter we shall use the notation $H_n(x)$ for the nth iterated convolution of $H(x)$ with itself; $H_0(x) = 1$ if $x \geq 0$ and $H_0(x) = 0$ if $x < 0$. Similarly, we shall denote by $H_n^*(x)$ the nth iterated convolution of $H^*(x)$ with itself; $H_0^*(x) = 1$ if $x \geq 0$ and $H_0^*(x) = 0$ if $x < 0$.

We note also that

$$\mathbf{Var}\,\{\chi(t)\} = \sigma^2 t \tag{22}$$

where

(23) $$\sigma^2 = \int_{+0}^{\infty} x^2 \, dN(x) = -\Phi''(+0).$$

Finally, we shall prove three theorems for $\Phi(s)$ defined by (12).

Theorem 3. *If* $\text{Re}(s) > 0$, *then*

(24) $$\lim_{|s| \to \infty} \frac{\Phi(s)}{s} = 0.$$

Proof. If $\text{Re}(s) > 0$, then $|1 - e^{-sx}| \leq |s| \, x$ for $x \geq 0$ and also $|1 - e^{-sx}| \leq 2$ for $x \geq 0$. Hence by (12)

(25) $$|\Phi(s)| \leq |s| \int_0^{\epsilon} x \, dN(x) - 2N(\epsilon)$$

for any $\epsilon > 0$ if $\text{Re}(s) \geq 0$. By (25)

(26) $$\lim_{|s| \to \infty} \left| \frac{\Phi(s)}{s} \right| \leq \int_0^{\epsilon} x \, dN(x)$$

for any $\epsilon > 0$. If $\epsilon \to 0$, then by (13) the right-hand side of (26) tends to 0. This proves (24).

Theorem 4. *Let* $s = \omega$ *be the largest nonnegative real root of*

(27) $$\Phi(s) = s.$$

If $\rho \leq 1$, *then* $\omega = 0$, *and if* $\rho > 1$, *then* $\omega > 0$. *The equation* (27) *has no other root in the domain* $\text{Re}(s) > \omega$.

Proof. In the interval $[0, \infty)$, $\Phi(s)$ is monotone increasing and $\Phi'(s)$ is monotone decreasing. $\Phi(0) = 0$, $\Phi'(+0) = \rho$, and $\lim_{s \to \infty} \Phi(s)/s = 0$. Accordingly if $\rho \leq 1$, then $s = 0$ is the only root of $\Phi(s) = s$ in the interval $[0, \infty)$. If $\rho > 1$, then $\Phi(s) = s$ has exactly two roots in $[0, \infty)$, $s = 0$ and $s = \omega$ where $0 < \omega < \infty$. This proves the first part of the theorem. To prove the second part we note that $|\Phi'(\omega)| \leq 1$ always holds and hence $|\Phi'(s)| < |\Phi'(\omega)| \leq 1$ if $\text{Re}(s) > \omega$. Accordingly if $\text{Re}(s) > \omega$, then we have

(28) $$|\Phi(s) - \Phi(\omega)| = \left| \int_{\omega}^{s} \Phi'(z) \, dz \right| < |s - \omega|$$

which shows that $\Phi(s) = s$ is impossible if $\text{Re}(s) > \omega$.

Theorem 5. *If* z *is a real positive number, then*

(29) $$\Phi(s) = s - z$$

has exactly one nonnegative real root $s = \omega(z)$ *and* $\lim_{z \to +0} \omega(z) = \omega$ *where* ω *is the largest nonnegative real root of* $\Phi(s) = s$.

Proof. Since $\Phi(s)$ is monotone increasing and $\Phi'(s)$ is monotone decreasing in the interval $(0, \infty)$ and $\lim_{s\to\infty} \Phi(s)/s = 0$, it follows that (29) has exactly one root $s = \omega(z)$ in the interval $(0, \infty)$. Evidently $\omega(z)$ is a nondecreasing function of z and $\omega(z) > \omega$ for all $z > 0$. Thus $\lim_{z\to+0} \omega(z) = \omega^*$ exists and $\Phi(\omega^*) = \omega^*$. Therefore necessarily $\omega^* = \omega$. This proves the statement.

We note that if z is a complex number and $\text{Re}(z) > 0$, then (29) has exactly one root $s = \omega(z)$ in the domain $\text{Re}(s) \geq 0$.

Throughout this chapter we shall make frequent use of the following type of integral:

$$\int_a^b g(u)\mathbf{P}\{u + x < \chi(u) < u + x + du\}. \tag{30}$$

For simplicity we shall use the notation

$$\int_a^b g(u)\, d_u\mathbf{P}\{\chi(u) \leq u + x\} \tag{31}$$

for (30). If the random variable $\chi(u)$ has a density function, then (30) reduces to

$$\int_a^b g(u) \frac{\partial \mathbf{P}\{\chi(u) \leq u + x\}}{\partial x}\, du. \tag{32}$$

If $\chi(u)$ is a discrete random variable, then (30) reduces to

$$\sum_{a\leq u\leq b} g(u)\mathbf{P}\{\chi(u) = u + x\}. \tag{33}$$

15. THE DISTRIBUTION OF THE SUPREMUM FOR THE PROCESS $\{\chi(u) - u\}$

First we consider the case when $\{\chi(u), 0 \leq u \leq T\}$ has interchangeable increments, and then we shall show that further results can be obtained if $\{\chi(u), 0 \leq u \leq T\}$ has stationary independent increments.

In what follows we shall use the notation $d_x\mathbf{P}\{\chi(u) \leq x\} = P\{x < \chi(u) < x + dx\}$ regardless of whether u depends on x or not.

Theorem 1. *If* $\{\chi(u), 0 \leq u \leq T\}$ *is a separable stochastic process with interchangeable increments almost all of whose sample functions are nondecreasing step functions vanishing at* $u = 0$, *then*

$$\mathbf{P}\left\{\sup_{0\leq u\leq t} [\chi(u) - u] \leq x\right\} = \mathbf{P}\{\chi(t) \leq t + x\} - \iint_{0<y\leq z\leq t} \left(\frac{t - z}{t - y}\right) d_y\, d_z\mathbf{P}\{\chi(y) \leq y + x, \chi(t) \leq z + x\} \tag{1}$$

for all x *and finite* $t \in (0, T]$.

Proof. We shall prove a slightly more general formula from which (1) follows. If $c \geq 0$, then

$$(2)\quad \mathbf{P}\{\chi(u) \leq u + x \text{ for } 0 \leq u \leq t \text{ and } \chi(t) \leq t + x - c\}$$
$$= \mathbf{P}\{\chi(t) \leq t + x - c\} - \iint_{0<y\leq z\leq t-c} \left(\frac{t-z}{t-y}\right) d_y d_z \mathbf{P}\{\chi(y) \leq y + x, \chi(t) \leq z + x\}$$

for all x and finite $t \in (0, T.]$ It is sufficient to prove that the subtrahend on the right-hand side of (2) is the probability that $\chi(t) \leq t + x - c$ and $\chi(u) > u + x$ for some $u \in (0, t]$. Let $y = \sup \{u : \chi(u) > u + x$ and $0 \leq u \leq t - c\}$. Then $\chi(y) = y + x$ and $\chi(u) \leq u + x$ for $y \leq u \leq t - c$, or equivalently, $\chi(u) - \chi(y) \leq u - y$ for $y \leq u \leq t - c$. Under the condition that $\chi(y) = y + x$ and $\chi(t) = z + x$, the probability that $\chi(u) - \chi(y) \leq u - y$ for $y \leq u \leq t - c$ is $(t - z)/(t - y)$ for $0 \leq y \leq z \leq t - c$. This follows from Theorem 1 of Section 13 if we apply it to the process $\chi(y + u) - \chi(y), 0 \leq u \leq t - y$. If we integrate $(t - z)/(t - y)$ with respect to $d_y d_z \mathbf{P}\{\chi(y) \leq y + x, \chi(t) \leq z + x\} = \mathbf{P}\{y + x < \chi(y) < y + x + dy, z - y < \chi(t) - \chi(y) < z - y + dz\}$ over the domain $0 < y \leq z \leq t - c$, then we get the subtrahend on the right-hand side of (2). This proves (2). If $c = 0$ in (2), then we get (1) which was to be proved.

If $x = 0$, then (2) reduces to

$$(3)\quad \mathbf{P}\{\chi(u) \leq u \text{ for } 0 \leq u \leq t \text{ and } \chi(t) \leq t - c\}$$
$$= \int_0^{t-c} \left(1 - \frac{y}{t}\right) d_y \mathbf{P}\{\chi(t) \leq y\}$$

where $0 \leq c \leq t$. This follows from (2) of Section 13.

Theorem 2. *If $\{\chi(u), 0 \leq u \leq T\}$ is a separable stochastic process with interchangeable increments almost all of whose sample functions are non-decreasing step functions vanishing at $u = 0$, then*

$$(4)\qquad \mathbf{E}\left\{\sup_{0\leq u\leq t} [\chi(u) - u]\right\} = \int_0^t \frac{1}{y} \mathbf{E}\{[\chi(y) - y]^+\}\, dy$$

for $t \in (0, T]$.

Proof. Since

$$(5)\qquad \mathbf{E}\left\{\sup_{0\leq u\leq t} [\chi(u) - u]\right\} = \int_0^\infty \mathbf{P}\left\{\sup_{0\leq u\leq t} [\chi(u) - u] > x\right\} dx,$$

we get (4) by (1). If ρ is finite, then (4) is also finite. If $\rho = \infty$, then (4) is also ∞.

If, in particular, the process $\{\chi(u), 0 \leq u \leq T\}$ has stationary independent increments, then in (1) and in (2) we can use the following substitution $d_y d_z \mathbf{P}\{\chi(y) \leq y + x, \chi(t) \leq z + x\} = \mathbf{P}\{y + x < \chi(y) < y + x + dy\}\, \mathbf{P}\{z - y < \chi(t) - \chi(y) < z - y + dz\}$. In this case (1) can also be written in the following form

$$\text{(6)}\quad \mathbf{P}\left\{\sup_{0\le u\le t} [\chi(u) - u] \le x\right\} = \mathbf{P}\{\chi(t) \le t + x\} - \int_{+0}^{t} \mathbf{E}\left\{\left[1 - \frac{\chi(t-y)}{t-y}\right]^{+}\right\} d_y\mathbf{P}\{\chi(y) \le y + x\}.$$

If we introduce the notation

$$\text{(7)}\qquad W(t, x) = \mathbf{P}\left\{\sup_{0\le u\le t} [\chi(u) - u] \le x\right\},$$

then (6) can be written in the following equivalent form,

$$\text{(8)}\quad W(t, x) = \mathbf{P}\{\chi(t) \le t + x\} - \int_{+0}^{t} W(t - y, 0)\, d_y\mathbf{P}\{\chi(y) \le y + x\}.$$

This equation makes it possible to find $W(t, x)$ by using Laplace-Stieltjes transforms. Define

$$\text{(9)}\qquad \Omega(t, s) = \int_0^\infty e^{-sx}\, d_xW(t, x)$$

which is convergent for $\mathrm{Re}(s) \ge 0$. If

$$\text{(10)}\qquad \mathbf{E}\{e^{-s\chi(u)}\} = e^{-u\Phi(s)}$$

for $\mathrm{Re}(s) \ge 0$ and we form the Laplace-Stieltjes transform of (8), then we get

$$\text{(11)}\qquad \Omega(t, s) = e^{[s-\Phi(s)]t} - s\int_0^t W(t - y, 0)e^{[s-\Phi(s)]y}\, dy.$$

Hence

$$\text{(12)}\quad \int_0^\infty e^{-zt}\Omega(t, s)\, dt = \frac{1}{z - s + \Phi(s)}\left[1 - s\int_0^\infty e^{-zt}W(t, 0)\, dt\right]$$

for $\mathrm{Re}(z) > 0$. The left-hand side of (12) is bounded for $\mathrm{Re}(s) \ge 0$ if $\mathrm{Re}(z) > 0$. In this domain the denominator of the right-hand side of (12) has one and only one root $s = \omega(z)$ and consequently this must be also a root of the numerator. Thus

$$\text{(13)}\qquad \int_0^\infty e^{-zt}W(t, 0)\, dt = \frac{1}{\omega(z)}$$

for $\mathrm{Re}(z) > 0$ where $s = \omega(z)$ is the only root of $\Phi(s) = s - z$ in the domain $\mathrm{Re}(s) \ge 0$. Accordingly

$$\text{(14)}\qquad \int_0^\infty e^{-zt}\Omega(t, s)\, dt = \frac{1}{z - s + \Phi(s)}\left(1 - \frac{s}{\omega(z)}\right)$$

if $\mathrm{Re}(z) > 0$ and $\mathrm{Re}(s) \geq 0$. Finally $W(t, x)$ can be obtained by inversion.

Theorem 3. *Suppose that $\{\chi(u), 0 \leq u \leq \infty\}$ is a separable stochastic process with stationary independent increments for which almost all sample functions are nondecreasing step functions vanishing at $u = 0$. If $\rho < 1$, then*

$$(15)\quad \mathbf{P}\left\{\sup_{0 \leq u < \infty} [\chi(u) - u] \leq x\right\} = 1 - (1 - \rho)\int_{+0}^{\infty} d_y \mathbf{P}\{\chi(y) \leq y + x\}$$

for all x. If $\rho \geq 1$, then

$$(16)\quad \mathbf{P}\left\{\sup_{0 \leq u < \infty} [\chi(u) - u] \leq x\right\} = 0$$

for all x.

Proof. By the continuity theorem for probabilities we have

$$(17)\quad \mathbf{P}\left\{\sup_{0 \leq u < \infty} [\chi(u) - u] \leq x\right\} = \lim_{t \to \infty} \mathbf{P}\left\{\sup_{0 \leq u \leq t} [\chi(u) - u] \leq x\right\}$$

and the right-hand side can be obtained by (6).

First, consider the case $\rho < 1$. Then by the weak law of large numbers

$$\lim_{t \to \infty} \frac{\chi(t)}{t} = \rho$$

in probability. Hence $\lim_{t \to \infty} \mathbf{P}\{\chi(t) < t + x\} = 1$ for all x and

$$(18)\quad \lim_{t \to \infty} \mathbf{E}\left\{\left[1 - \frac{\chi(t - y)}{t - y}\right]^{+}\right\} = 1 - \rho$$

for any $y \geq 0$. We shall show that

$$(19)\quad \int_{+0}^{\infty} d_y \mathbf{P}\{\chi(y) \leq y + x\} \leq \frac{1}{1 - \rho}$$

for all x. If we form the limit $t \to \infty$ in (6), then we get (15). It remains to prove (19). If we take into consideration that the right-hand side of (6) is nonnegative, $\mathbf{P}\{\chi(t) \leq t + x\} \leq 1$ and

$$(20)\quad \mathbf{E}\left\{\left[1 - \frac{\chi(t - y)}{t - y}\right]^{+}\right\} \geq \mathbf{E}\left\{1 - \frac{\chi(t - y)}{t - y}\right\} = 1 - \rho,$$

then we get the inequality

$$(21)\quad (1 - \rho)\int_{+0}^{t} d_y \mathbf{P}\{\chi(y) \leq y + x\} \leq 1$$

which holds for all $t \geq 0$ and x. This proves (19).

Second, if $\rho > 1$, then $\lim_{t\to\infty} \mathbf{P}\{\chi(t) \le t + x\} = 0$ for all x and the inequality

$$(22) \qquad 0 \le \mathbf{P}\left\{\sup_{0\le u\le t} [\chi(u) - u] \le x\right\} \le \mathbf{P}\{\chi(t) \le t + x\}$$

implies (16).

Finally, if $\rho = 1$, then by (5) of Section 14

$$(23) \qquad \mathbf{P}\left\{\sup_{0\le u<\infty} [\chi(u) - u] \le 0\right\} = 0.$$

Hence (16) holds if $x \le 0$. If $x > 0$, then we can find a y such that $0 < x < y$ and $\mathbf{P}\{\chi(y) < y - x\} > 0$ and the obvious inequality

$$(24) \quad \mathbf{P}\{\chi(y) < y - x\}\mathbf{P}\left\{\sup_{0\le u<\infty} [\chi(u) - u] \le x\right\} \le \mathbf{P}\left\{\sup_{0\le u<\infty} [\chi(u) - u] \le 0\right\} = 0$$

implies (16) for $x > 0$. This completes the proof of the theorem.

NOTE. If $\{\chi(u), 0 \le u < \infty\}$ has interchangeable increments, then it can be represented as a process with conditionally stationary independent increments. Then the conditional distribution of $\sup_{0\le u<\infty} [\chi(u) - u]$ can be obtained by (15) and forming the expectation of the conditional distribution, we obtain the distribution of $\sup_{0\le u<\infty} [\chi(u) - u]$.

Theorem 4. *If $\{\chi(u), 0 \le u < \infty\}$ is a separable stochastic process with stationary independent increments for which almost all sample functions are nondecreasing step functions vanishing at $u = 0$ and if $\rho < 1$, then*

$$(25) \qquad \mathbf{P}\left\{\sup_{0\le u<\infty} [\chi(u) - u] \le x\right\} = W(x)$$

where $W(x) = 0$ for $x < 0$, $W(0) = 1 - \rho$, and

$$(26) \qquad \Omega(s) = \int_0^\infty e^{-sx}\, dW(x) = \frac{W(0)s}{s - \Phi(s)}$$

for $\operatorname{Re}(s) > 0$.

Proof. By (5) of Section 14, $W(0) = 1 - \rho$ and evidently $W(x) = 0$ if $x < 0$. Now we shall find $W(x)$ for $x > 0$. If $0 < y$ and $0 \le y + x$, then we have

$$(27) \quad W(x) = \int_0^{y+x} W(y+x-z)\, d_z\mathbf{P}\{\chi(y)\le z\} - W(0)\int_0^y d_z\mathbf{P}\{\chi(z)\le z+x\}.$$

The first term on the right-hand side of (27) is the probability that $\chi(y) = z$ $(0 \leq z \leq y + x)$ and $\chi(v) - v \leq x$ for $y \leq v < \infty$. The second term on the right-hand side of (27) is the probability that $\chi(v) - v \leq x$ is violated for some v in the interval $(0, y)$ and $\chi(v) - v \leq x$ for $y \leq v < \infty$. If $z = \sup \{v : \chi(v) - v > x \text{ and } 0 \leq v < y\}$, then $\chi(z) - z = x$ and the event $\{\chi(v) - v \leq x \text{ for } z \leq v < \infty\}$ has the same probability as $\{\chi(v) - \chi(z) \leq v - z \text{ for } 0 \leq v - z < \infty\}$, that is, $W(0)$. Thus we obtain the second term on the right-hand side of (27). If $-y \leq x < 0$, then the right-hand side of (27) is 0 because it is the probability of the impossible event.

Let

$$\Omega(s) = \int_0^\infty e^{-sx}\, dW(x) \tag{28}$$

for $\text{Re}(s) \geq 0$ and form the Laplace-Stieltjes transform of (27). Then we get

$$\Omega(s) = e^{y[s-\Phi(s)]}\,\Omega(s) - W(0)s\int_0^y e^{z[s-\Phi(s)]}\, dz \tag{29}$$

for all $y > 0$. Since

$$\int_0^y e^{z[s-\Phi(s)]}\, dz = \frac{e^{y[s-\Phi(s)]} - 1}{s - \Phi(s)} \tag{30}$$

for $\text{Re}(s) > 0$, we get

$$\Omega(s) = \frac{W(0)s}{s - \Phi(s)} \tag{31}$$

for $\text{Re}(s) > 0$. This proves (26).

We defined $W(x)$ as a function continuous on the right and thus $W(x)$ is uniquely determined by its Laplace-Stieltjes transform (26). $W(x)$ is a monotone nondecreasing function of x and $0 \leq W(x) \leq 1$. Thus $\lim_{x\to\infty} W(x)$ exists and by an Abelian theorem (see Appendix)

$$\lim_{x\to\infty} W(x) = \lim_{s\to+0} \Omega(s) = \frac{W(0)}{1 - \Phi'(+0)} = \frac{W(0)}{1 - \rho} = 1. \tag{32}$$

Accordingly if $\rho < 1$, then $\sup_{0\leq u<\infty} [\chi(u) - u]$ is a proper random variable which with probability 1 takes on only finite values. By using the weak law of large numbers we showed that $W(0) = 1 - \rho$ and hence by an Abelian theorem we concluded that $\lim_{x\to\infty} W(x) = 1$. If we use the strong law of large numbers, then we can prove directly that $\lim_{x\to\infty} W(x) = 1$ and then by the above mentioned Abelian theorem it follows that $W(0) = 1 - \rho$.

Since $\rho < 1$, we can write that $\Phi(s) = \rho s\, \psi^*(s)$ where $\psi^*(s)$ is the Laplace-Stieltjes transform of the distribution function $H^*(x)$ defined by (19) of Section 14. Thus by (26)

$$\Omega(s) = \frac{1 - \rho}{1 - \rho\psi^*(s)} = (1 - \rho)\sum_{n=0}^{\infty} \rho^n [\psi^*(s)]^n \tag{33}$$

for $\mathrm{Re}(s) \geq 0$, whence by inversion we obtain

$$W(x) = (1 - \rho)\sum_{n=0}^{\infty} \rho^n H_n^*(x) \tag{34}$$

where $H_n^*(x)$ is the nth iterated convolution of $H^*(x)$ with itself; $H_0^*(x) = 1$ if $x \geq 0$ and $H_0^*(x) = 0$ if $x < 0$.

Now $W(x)$ is the unique solution of the following integral equation

$$W(x) = (1 - \rho)H_0^*(x) + \rho H^*(x) * W(x). \tag{35}$$

It is interesting to note that if $\Phi(s) = s$ has a root $s = -\alpha$ in the domain $\mathrm{Re}(s) < 0$ and no other roots in the domain $-\alpha \leq \mathrm{Re}(s) < 0$, then

$$1 - W(x) \sim \frac{1 - \rho}{\Phi'(-\alpha) - 1}\, e^{-\alpha x} \tag{36}$$

as $x \to \infty$.

NOTE. If we compare (15) and (25), we obtain an interesting identity. If $\rho < 1$, then

$$\int_{+0}^{\infty} d_y \mathbf{P}\{\chi(y) \leq y + x\} = \frac{1 - W(x)}{1 - \rho} \tag{37}$$

where $W(x) = 0$ if $x < 0$, $W(0) = 1 - \rho$ and $W(x)$ for $x > 0$ is given by (26) or (34).

16. A CONTINUOUS GENERALIZATION OF THE CLASSICAL RUIN THEOREM

In Section 7 we gave a discrete generalization of the classical ruin theorem. Now we shall prove a continuous analogy of that theorem.

Theorem 1. *Let $\{\chi(u), 0 \leq u \leq \infty\}$ be a separable stochastic process with stationary independent increments for which almost all sample functions are nondecreasing step functions vanishing at $u = 0$ For $c \geq 0$ define $\theta(c) = \inf \{u: \chi(u) \leq u - c$ and $0 \leq u < \infty\}$ and $\theta(c) = \infty$ if $\chi(u) > u - c$ for all $u \geq 0$. If $0 \leq x \leq y$, then*

$$\mathbf{P}\{\chi(u) - u \leq x \text{ for } 0 \leq u \leq \theta(y - x)\} = \frac{W(x)}{W(y)} \tag{1}$$

and

$$\Omega(s) = \int_0^{\infty} e^{-sx}\, dW(x) = \frac{W(0)s}{s - \Phi(s)} \tag{2}$$

for $\text{Re}(s) > \omega$ *where* ω *is the largest nonnegative real root of* $\Phi(s) = s$. *If* $\rho \leq 1$, *then* $\omega = 0$, *whereas if* $\rho > 1$, *then* $\omega > 0$. *Here* $W(0) > 0$ *is chosen arbitrarily.*

Proof. Let

$$Q(x, y) = \mathbf{P}\{\chi(u) - u \leq x \text{ for } 0 \leq u \leq \theta(y - x)\} \tag{3}$$

for $0 \leq x \leq y < \infty$ and $Q(x, y) = 0$ if $x < 0 \leq y < \infty$. If $0 \leq x \leq z \leq y$, then we have

$$Q(x, y) = Q(x, z)Q(z, y). \tag{4}$$

This can be seen as follows: $\chi(u) - u \leq x$ holds for $0 \leq u \leq \theta(y - x)$ if and only if $\chi(u) - u \leq x$ holds for $0 \leq u \leq \theta(z - x)$ and $\chi(u) - u \leq x$ holds for $\theta(z - x) \leq u \leq \theta(y - x)$. Since $\chi(u) - u = x - z$ if $u = \theta(z - x)$, the second event is independent of the first one and has the same probability as $\{\chi(u) - u \leq z \text{ for } 0 \leq u \leq \theta(y - z)\}$. This proves (4). It is easy to see that $Q(x, y)$ is positive for all $0 \leq x \leq y$. By (4) $Q(x, y) \leq Q(x, z)$ if $0 \leq x \leq z \leq y$ and $Q(x, y) \leq Q(z, y)$ if $0 \leq x \leq z \leq y$. Accordingly it follows from (4) that

$$Q(x, y) = \frac{W(x)}{W(y)} \tag{5}$$

where $W(0)$ is an arbitrary positive number and $W(x)$ is a nondecreasing function of x. If $W(x) = 0$ for $x < 0$, then (5) is also valid for $x < 0 \leq y < \infty$.

If $0 < u$ and $0 \leq u + x < y$, then we have

$$Q(x, y) = \int_0^{u+x} Q(u + x - z, y)\, d_z\mathbf{P}\{\chi(u) \leq z\} - Q(0, y)\int_0^u d_z\mathbf{P}\{\chi(z) \leq z + x\}. \tag{6}$$

The first term on the right-hand side of (6) is the probability that $\chi(u) = z$ $(0 \leq z \leq u + x)$ and $\chi(v) - v \leq x$ for $u \leq v \leq \theta(y - x)$. The second term on the right-hand side of (6) is the probability that $\chi(v) - v \leq x$ is violated for some v in the interval $(0, u)$ and $\chi(v) - v \leq x$ for $u \leq v \leq \theta(y - x)$. If $z = \sup\{v : \chi(v) - v > x \text{ and } 0 \leq v \leq u\}$, then $\chi(z) - z = x$ and the event $\{\chi(v) - v \leq x \text{ for } z \leq v \leq \theta(y - x)\}$ has the same probability as $\{\chi(v) \leq v \text{ for } 0 \leq v \leq \theta(y)\}$, that is, $Q(0, y)$. Thus we obtain the second term on the right-hand side of (6). If $-u \leq x < 0$ in (6), then the right-hand side of (6) is 0, because it is the probability of the impossible event.

If we suppose that $y > u + x \geq 0$ and multiply (6) by $W(y)$, then we obtain that

$$W(x) = \int_0^{u+x} W(u+x-z)\,d_z\mathbf{P}\{\chi(u) \leq z\} - W(0)\int_0^u d_z\mathbf{P}\{\chi(z) \leq z + x\} \tag{7}$$

for $0 < u$ and $0 \leq u + x$. If $-u \leq x < 0$, then the right-hand side of (7) is 0.

Let

$$\Omega(s) = \int_0^\infty e^{-sx}\,dW(x) \tag{8}$$

and form the Laplace-Stieltjes transform of (7). Then we get

$$\Omega(s) = e^{u[s-\Phi(s)]}\,\Omega(s) - W(0)s\int_0^u e^{z[s-\Phi(s)]}\,dz \tag{9}$$

for all $u > 0$. In finding (9) we exploited the fact that the right-hand side of (7) is 0 if $-u \leq x < 0$. From(9) it follows that

$$\Omega(s) = \frac{W(0)s}{s - \Phi(s)} \tag{10}$$

and this Laplace-Stieltjes transform is convergent if $\text{Re}(s) > \omega$ where ω is the largest nonnegative real root of $\Phi(s) = s$. If $\rho \leq 1$, then $\omega = 0$, whereas if $\rho > 1$, then $0 < \omega$. This completes the proof of the theorem.

We defined $W(x)$ as a function continuous on the right and thus $W(x)$ is uniquely determined by its Laplace-Stieltjes transform (2).

If ρ is a finite positive number, then $\Phi(s) = \rho s\,\psi^*(s)$ where $\psi^*(s)$ is the Laplace-Stieltjes transform of the distribution function $H^*(x)$ defined by (19) of Section 14. Since $|\rho\psi^*(s)| < 1$ if $\text{Re}(s) > \omega$, we can write

$$\Omega(s) = \frac{W(0)}{1 - \rho\psi^*(s)} = W(0)\sum_{n=0}^\infty \rho^n[\psi^*(s)]^n \tag{11}$$

for $\text{Re}(s) > \omega$, from which by inversion we get

$$W(x) = W(0)\sum_{n=0}^\infty \rho^n H_n^*(x) \tag{12}$$

where $H_n^*(x)$ is the nth iterated convolution of the distribution function $H^*(x)$ with itself; $H_0^*(x) = 1$ if $x \geq 0$ and $H_0^*(x) = 0$ if $x < 0$.

Now $W(x)$ is the unique solution of the following integral equation

$$W(x) = W(0)[H_0^*(x) + \rho H^*(x) * W(x)]. \tag{13}$$

Now we shall give another expression for $W(x)$.

***Theorem* 2.** *If* $\rho \neq 1$, *then*

$$W(x) = W(0)\left[\frac{e^{\omega x}}{1 - \Phi'(\omega)} - \int_{+0}^{\infty} d_y\mathbf{P}\{\chi(y) \leq y + x\}\right] \tag{14}$$

for all x *where* ω *is the largest nonnegative real root of* $\Phi(s) = s$. *If* $\rho < 1$, *then* $\omega = 0$, *whereas if* $\rho > 1$, *then* $\omega > 0$. *If* $x < 0$, *then the right-hand side of* (14) *is* 0.

Proof. In the case of $\rho < 1$ we already proved (14) in Theorem 3 of Section 15. There it was $W(0) = 1 - \rho$. Since $W(0)$ is a factor of proportionality, this does not restrict the generality.

Now we shall prove (14) for $\rho > 1$. Without loss of generality we may suppose that $W(0) = 1$. In this case by (2) we have

$$\int_{0}^{\infty} e^{-sx}W(x)\,dx = \frac{1}{s - \Phi(s)} \tag{15}$$

for $\mathrm{Re}(s) > \omega$ and $W(x) = 0$ if $x < 0$. If we define

$$K(x) = \int_{+0}^{\infty} d_y\mathbf{P}\{\chi(y) \leq y + x\} \tag{16}$$

for all x, then

$$\int_{-\infty}^{\infty} e^{-sx}K(x)\,dx = \frac{1}{\Phi(s) - s} \tag{17}$$

is convergent for $0 < \mathrm{Re}(s) < \omega$.

If we subtract $e^{\omega x}/(1 - \Phi'(\omega))$ from $W(x)$ for $x \geq 0$, then the resulting function has the Laplace transform

$$\frac{1}{s - \Phi(s)} - \frac{1}{(1 - \Phi'(\omega))(s - \omega)} \tag{18}$$

and this transform is convergent for $\mathrm{Re}(s) \geq \omega$. Similarly, if we subtract $e^{\omega x}/(1 - \Phi'(\omega))$ from $K(x)$ for $x < 0$, then the resulting function has the Laplace transform

$$\frac{1}{\Phi(s) - s} + \frac{1}{(1 - \Phi'(\omega))(s - \omega)} \tag{19}$$

and this transform is convergent for $0 < \mathrm{Re}(s) \leq \omega$. If $\mathrm{Re}\,(s) = \omega$, then the sum of the transforms (18) and (19) is 0 and consequently the sum of the original functions is also 0, that is,

$$W(x) + K(x) = \frac{e^{\omega x}}{1 - \Phi'(\omega)} \tag{20}$$

for all x. This proves (14) for $\rho > 1$. If $\rho < 1$, then $\omega = 0$ and both (18) and (19) are convergent Laplace transforms for $\mathrm{Re}(s) = 0$. Thus (20) holds in this case too. This proves (14) for $\rho < 1$ too.

If $x < 0$, then $W(x) = 0$ and by using this fact we can obtain interesting identities by choosing particular processes $\{\chi(u), 0 \leq u < \infty\}$ in (14).

Theorem 3. *If $c \geq 0$, then we have*

$$\mathbf{E}\left\{\sup_{0 \leq u \leq \theta(c)} [\chi(u) - u]\right\} = \int_c^\infty \left(\frac{W(x) - W(x-c)}{W(x)}\right) dx. \tag{21}$$

Proof. Now $\sup_{0 \leq u \leq \theta(c)} [\chi(u) - u]$ is a nonnegative random variable whose expectation is given by

$$\mathbf{E}\left\{\sup_{0 \leq u \leq \theta(c)} [\chi(u) - u]\right\} = \int_0^\infty \mathbf{P}\left\{\sup_{0 \leq u \leq \theta(c)} [\chi(u) - u] > x\right\} dx \tag{22}$$

where the integrand can be obtained by (1).

Finally, we prove a theorem concerning the asymptotic behavior of $W(x)$ as $x \to \infty$.

Theorem 4. *If $\rho < 1$, then*

$$\lim_{x \to \infty} W(x) = \frac{W(0)}{1 - \rho}. \tag{23}$$

If $\rho = 1$, then

$$\lim_{x \to \infty} \frac{W(x)}{x} = \frac{2W(0)}{\sigma^2} \tag{24}$$

where $\sigma^2 = -\Phi''(+0)$. If $\rho > 1$, then

$$\lim_{x \to \infty} W(x) e^{-\omega x} = \frac{W(0)}{1 - \Phi'(\omega)} \tag{25}$$

where ω is the largest nonnegative real root of $\Phi(s) = s$. We have $0 < \omega < \infty$.

Proof. If $W(0)$ is a positive number, then $W(x)$ is nondecreasing for $0 \leq x \leq \infty$ and the limit $\lim_{x \to \infty} W(x)$ exists (possibly ∞). If $\rho < 1$, then by an Abelian theorem for Laplace-Stieltjes transforms (see Appendix) we obtain that

$$\lim_{x \to \infty} W(x) = \lim_{s \to +0} \Omega(s) = \frac{W(0)}{1 - \Phi'(+0)} = \frac{W(0)}{1 - \rho} \tag{26}$$

which proves (23). We note that if $\rho < 1$, then $\lim_{x \to \infty} W(x)$ is finite and we can choose $W(0)$ such that $\lim_{x \to \infty} W(x) = 1$. However, if $\rho \geq 1$

then $\lim_{x\to\infty} W(x) = \infty$ for all $W(0) > 0$, and we cannot choose $W(0)$ such that $\lim_{x\to\infty} W(x) = 1$.

If $\rho = 1$, then by a Tauberian theorem for Laplace-Stieltjes transforms (see Appendix) it follows that

$$\lim_{x\to\infty} \frac{W(x)}{x} = \lim_{s\to+0} s\Omega(s) = \frac{-2W(0)}{\Phi''(+0)} = \frac{2W(0)}{\sigma^2} \tag{27}$$

which proves (24). This result can also be obtained by the theory of recurrent processes. If $\rho = 1$, then $W(x)/W(0)$ can be interpreted as 1 plus the expected number of recurrent events occurring in the interval $(0, x]$ in a recurrent process where the recurrence time has the distribution function $H^*(x)$. Thus by the theory of recurrent processes

$$\lim_{x\to\infty} \frac{W(x)}{x} = \frac{-W(0)}{\psi^{*\prime}(+0)} \tag{28}$$

which is in agreement with (24).

If $\sigma^2 = \infty$, then the right-hand side of (24) is 0. In this case we can use a Tauberian theorem of G. H. Hardy and J. E. Littlewood (see Appendix) to find the asymptotic behavior of $W(x)$ as $x \to \infty$. Accordingly if

$$\Omega(s) \sim \frac{1}{s^\alpha} L\left(\frac{1}{s}\right) \tag{29}$$

as $s \to 0$ $(0 < s < \infty)$ where $\alpha \geq 0$ and $L(cx) \sim L(x)$ for every positive c as $x \to \infty$, then

$$W(x) \sim \frac{x^\alpha L(x)}{\Gamma(\alpha + 1)} \tag{30}$$

as $x \to \infty$.

If $\rho > 1$, then by an Abelian theorem for Laplace-Stieltjes transforms we obtain that

$$\lim_{x\to\infty} e^{-\omega x} W(x) = \lim_{s\to\omega} (s - \omega) \frac{\Omega(s)}{\omega} = \frac{W(0)}{1 - \Phi'(\omega)} \tag{31}$$

provided that $\lim_{x\to\infty} e^{-\omega x} W(x)$ exists. The existence of the limit can be proved by using a Tauberian theorem of S. Ikehara. (See Appendix.)

NOTE. If we use the explicit formula (14) for $W(x)$, then it can be shown that

$$\lim_{x\to\infty} \left[W(x) - \frac{W(0)e^{\omega x}}{1 - \Phi'(\omega)} \right] = -\frac{W(0)}{\rho - 1} \tag{32}$$

if $\rho > 1$.

17. THE DISTRIBUTION OF THE SUPREMUM FOR THE PROCESS $\{u - \chi(u)\}$

First we consider the case when $\{\chi(u), 0 \leq u \leq T\}$ has interchangeable increments, and then we shall show that further results can be obtained if $\{\chi(u), 0 \leq u \leq T\}$ has stationary independent increments.

Theorem 1. *If* $\{\chi(u), 0 \leq u \leq T\}$ *is a separable stochastic process with interchangeable increments almost all of whose sample functions are non-decreasing step functions vanishing at* $u = 0$, *then*

$$\text{(1)} \qquad \mathbf{P}\left\{\sup_{0\leq u\leq t} [u - \chi(u)] \leq x\right\} = 1 - \int_x^t \frac{x}{y}\, d_y\mathbf{P}\{\chi(y) \leq y - x\}$$

for $0 < x \leq t \leq T$.

Proof. We shall find the probability of the complementary event of $\{\sup_{0\leq u\leq t} [u - \chi(u)] \leq x\}$, that is, the probability that $\chi(u) - u > x$ for some $u \in (0, t]$. This latter event can occur in such a way that $\inf \{u : u - \chi(u) > x\} = y$ where $0 \leq y \leq t$. Then $\chi(y) = y - x$ and $u - \chi(u) \leq x$ for $0 \leq u \leq y$, or equivalently, $\chi(y) - \chi(u) \leq y - u$ for $0 \leq u \leq y$. By Theorem 1 of Section 13

$$\text{(2)} \qquad \mathbf{P}\{\chi(y) - \chi(u) \leq y - u \text{ for } 0 \leq u \leq y \mid \chi(y) = y - x\} = \frac{x}{y}$$

for $0 < x \leq y$ where the conditional probability is defined up to an equivalence. If we integrate (2) with respect to $d_y\mathbf{P}\{\chi(y) \leq y - x\} = \mathbf{P}\{y - x < \chi(y) < y - x + dy\}$ from x to t, then we get the probability of the complementary event. This proves (1).

In a similar way as (1) we can also prove the following more general formula

$$\begin{aligned}\text{(3)} \quad \mathbf{P}\{u - \chi(u) \leq x \text{ for } 0 \leq u \leq t \text{ and } t - \chi(t) \leq x - c\} \\ = \mathbf{P}\{\chi(t) \geq t + c - x\} \\ - \int_x^t \frac{x}{y}\, d_y\mathbf{P}\{\chi(y) \leq y - x, \chi(t) \geq t + c - x\}\end{aligned}$$

for $0 < x \leq t \leq T$ and $c > 0$.

Theorem 2. *If* $\{\chi(u), 0 \leq u \leq T\}$ *is a separable stochastic process with interchangeable increments almost all of whose sample functions are non-decreasing step functions vanishing at* $u = 0$, *then*

$$\text{(4)} \qquad \mathbf{E}\left\{\sup_{0\leq u\leq t} [u - \chi(u)]\right\} = \int_0^t \frac{1}{y}\, \mathbf{E}\{[y - \chi(y)]^+\}\, dy.$$

Proof. Now the random variable $\sup_{0 \le u \le t} [u - \chi(u)]$ may take on values in the interval $[0, t]$ and thus

$$\mathbf{E}\left\{\sup_{0 \le u \le t} [u - \chi(u)]\right\} = \int_0^t \mathbf{P}\left\{\sup_{0 \le u \le t} [u - \chi(u)] > x\right\} dx \tag{5}$$

where the integrand can be obtained by (1).

We note that if $T = \infty$ in Theorem 1, then letting $t \to \infty$ in (1) we get

$$\mathbf{P}\left\{\sup_{0 \le u < \infty} [u - \chi(u)] \le x\right\} = 1 - \int_x^\infty \frac{x}{y}\, d_y \mathbf{P}\{\chi(y) \le y - x\} \tag{6}$$

for $x > 0$.

If $\{\chi(u), 0 \le u < \infty\}$ has stationary independent increments then $\sup_{0 \le u < \infty} [u - \chi(u)]$ has an exponential distribution given by the following theorem.

Theorem 3. *If $\{\chi(u), 0 \le u \le \infty\}$ is a separable stochastic process with stationary independent increments for which almost all sample functions are nondecreasing step functions vanishing at $u = 0$, then for $x \ge 0$*

$$\mathbf{P}\left\{\sup_{0 \le u < \infty} [u - \chi(u)] \le x\right\} = 1 - e^{-\omega x} \tag{7}$$

where ω is the largest real root of the equation $\Phi(\omega) = \omega$. If $0 \le \rho \le 1$, then $\omega = 0$ and if $\rho > 1$, then $\omega > 0$.

Proof. Define

$$\theta(x) = \inf\{u : u - \chi(u) > x \text{ and } 0 \le u < \infty\} \tag{8}$$

and $\theta(x) = \infty$ if $u - \chi(u) \le x$ for all $u \ge 0$. Then $\{\theta(x), 0 \le x < \infty\}$ is a stochastic process with nonnegative, stationary independent increments. Thus for $\mathrm{Re}(z) > 0$

$$\mathbf{E}\{e^{-z\theta(x)}\} = e^{-x\omega(z)} \tag{9}$$

with an appropriate $\omega(z)$. Now if we suppose that $\chi(x) = y$, then $\theta(x) = x + \theta^*(y)$ where $\theta^*(y)$ has the same distribution as $\theta(y)$ and $\{\theta^*(y)\}$ is independent of $\{\chi(x)\}$. Thus we get

$$\mathbf{E}\{e^{-z\theta(x)}\} = e^{-xz - x\Phi(\omega(z))} \tag{10}$$

for $\mathrm{Re}(z) > 0$. If we compare (9) and (10), then we get

$$\omega(z) = z + \Phi(\omega(z)) \tag{11}$$

for $\mathrm{Re}(z) > 0$. If z is a positive real number, then

$$s = z + \Phi(s) \tag{12}$$

has one and only one nonnegative real root and thus necessarily $s = \omega(z)$. If $z \to 0$, then $\omega(z) \to \omega$ where ω is the largest nonnegative real root of $\Phi(s) = s$. If $0 \leq \rho \leq 1$, then $\omega = 0$, whereas if $\rho > 1$, then $\omega > 0$.

By the definition of $\theta(x)$ we have

$$\mathbf{P}\left\{\sup_{0 \leq u \leq t} [u - \chi(u)] \leq x\right\} = 1 - \mathbf{P}\{\theta(x) \leq t\} \tag{13}$$

for $x \geq 0$ and $t \geq 0$ and by an Abelian theorem

$$\lim_{t \to \infty} \mathbf{P}\{\theta(x) \leq t\} = \lim_{z \to +0} e^{-x\omega(z)} = e^{-x\omega}. \tag{14}$$

This proves (7).

Accordingly, if $\rho > 1$, then $\sup_{0 \leq u < \infty} [u - \chi(u)]$ is a proper random variable which is finite with probability 1. If $\rho \leq 1$, then

$$\mathbf{P}\left\{\sup_{0 \leq u < \infty} [u - \chi(u)] = \infty\right\} = 1.$$

The random variable $\theta(x)$ is the first passage time of the process $\{u - \chi(u)\}$ through x. The distribution of $\theta(x)$ is given by the following theorem.

Theorem 4. *Let $\{\chi(u), 0 \leq u \leq \infty\}$ be a stochastic process with interchangeable increments almost all of whose sample functions are nondecreasing step functions vanishing at $u = 0$. For $x \geq 0$ define $\theta(x)$ as the smallest u such that $u - \chi(u) = x$. Then*

$$\mathbf{P}\{\theta(x) \leq t\} = \int_x^t \frac{x}{y}\, d_y \mathbf{P}\{\chi(y) \leqq y - x\} \tag{15}$$

for $0 < x \leq t$.

Proof. We have evidently

$$\mathbf{P}\{\theta(x) \leq t\} = 1 - \mathbf{P}\left\{\sup_{0 \leq u \leq t} [u - \chi(u)] \leq x\right\} \tag{16}$$

and the right-hand side can be obtained by (1).

In what follows we suppose that, in particular, $\{\chi(u), 0 \leq u < \infty\}$ has stationary independent increments and almost all sample functions of the process are nondecreasing step functions vanishing at $u = 0$.

If $\rho \leq 1$, then $\lim_{t \to \infty} \mathbf{P}\{\theta(x) \leq t\} = 1$, whereas, if $\rho > 1$, then

$$\mathbf{P}\{\theta(x) = \infty\} = 1 - e^{-\omega x} > 0.$$

If $\rho < 1$, then the expectation of $\theta(x)$ is

$$\mathbf{E}\{\theta(x)\} = x \int_x^\infty d_u \mathbf{P}\{\chi(u) \leq u - x\} = \frac{x}{1 - \rho} \tag{17}$$

which follows from (37) of Section 15. If $\rho = 1$, then $\mathbf{E}\{\theta(x)\} = \infty$. It is interesting to observe that by (17) we can write also that

$$\mathbf{E}\{\theta(x)\} = \int_0^\infty \mathbf{P}\{0 < u - \chi(u) \leq x\}\, du \tag{18}$$

for $\rho < 1$.

If $\operatorname{Re}(z) > 0$, then by (9) and (15) we get

$$\mathbf{E}\{e^{-z\theta(x)}\} = e^{-x\omega(z)} = x\int_x^\infty \frac{e^{-zt}}{t}\, d_t\mathbf{P}\{\chi(t) \leq t - x\} \tag{19}$$

and $s = \omega(z)$ is the only root of $\Phi(s) = s - z$ in the domain $\operatorname{Re}(s) \geq 0$.

The distribution of $\theta(x)$ and its Laplace-Stieltjes transform have been found by D. G. Kendall [5]; however, he did not provide a complete proof of his results.

NOTE. If $\{\chi(u), 0 \leq u < \infty\}$ is a separable stochastic process having stationary independent increments and if almost all sample functions of the process are nondecreasing step functions vanishing at $u = 0$, then by comparing (6) and (7) we obtain the following interesting identity

$$\int_x^\infty \frac{x}{y}\, d_y\mathbf{P}\{\chi(y) \leq y - x\} = e^{-\omega x} \tag{20}$$

for $x > 0$ where ω is the largest real root of $\Phi(\omega) = \omega$.

18. THE DISTRIBUTION OF THE SUPREMUM FOR DUAL PROCESSES

With every real-valued separable stochastic process $\{\chi(u), 0 \leq u < \infty\}$ whose sample functions are nondecreasing step functions for which $\chi(u + 0) = \chi(u)$ and $\chi(0) = 0$, we associate a dual stochastic process $\{\chi^*(u), 0 \leq u < \infty\}$ as follows. Suppose that

$$\chi^*(t) = \sup\{u : \chi(u) \leq t \text{ and } 0 \leq u < \infty\} \tag{1}$$

for all $t \geq 0$.

For all $t \geq 0$ and $x \geq 0$ we have the obvious relation

$$\{\chi^*(t) \leq x\} \equiv \{\chi(x) > t\}. \tag{2}$$

This implies that

$$\{\chi^*(u) - u \leq x \text{ for } 0 \leq u \leq t\} \equiv \{u - \chi(u) < x \text{ for } 0 \leq u \leq t + x\} \tag{3}$$

and

$$\{u - \chi^*(u) < x \text{ for } 0 \leq u \leq t\} \equiv \{\chi(u) - u \leq x \text{ for } 0 \leq u \leq t - x\}. \tag{4}$$

Accordingly, if we know the distribution of the supremum for the stochastic processes $\{\chi(u) - u\}$ and $\{u - \chi(u)\}$, then by using the relations (3) and (4) we can obtain immediately the distribution of the supremum for the dual stochastic processes $\{\chi^*(u) - u\}$ and $\{u - \chi^*(u)\}$, and conversely.

19. EXAMPLES

In this section we consider some particular stochastic processes $\{\chi(u),\ 0 \le u < \infty\}$ and determine all those quantities which make it possible to apply the general theorems proved in this chapter.

First we suppose that $\{\chi(u), 0 \le u < \infty\}$ is a separable stochastic process with stationary independent increments for which almost all sample functions are nondecreasing step functions vanishing at $u = 0$. For such processes

$$\mathbf{E}\{e^{-s\chi(u)}\} = e^{-u\Phi(s)} \tag{1}$$

for $\operatorname{Re}(s) \ge 0$ where

$$\Phi(s) = \int_{+0}^{\infty} (1 - e^{-sx})\, dN(x) \tag{2}$$

and $N(x), 0 < x < \infty$, is a nondecreasing function for which $\lim_{x\to\infty} N(x) = 0$ and

$$\int_{+0}^{1} x\, dN(x) < \infty. \tag{3}$$

By specializing $N(x)$ we obtain different types of processes $\{\chi(u), 0 \le u < \infty\}$.

1. *Compound Poisson Process.* If $\lambda = -N(0)$ is a finite positive number, then we speak about a compound Poisson process. Then $N(x)$ can be expressed as follows:

$$N(x) = -\lambda[1 - H(x)] \tag{4}$$

where $H(x)$ is the distribution function of a positive random variable. If

$$\psi(s) = \int_{0}^{\infty} e^{-sx}\, dH(x) \tag{5}$$

for $\operatorname{Re}(s) \ge 0$, then

$$\Phi(s) = \lambda[1 - \psi(s)] \tag{6}$$

for $\operatorname{Re}(s) \ge 0$. In this case

$$\mathbf{P}\{\chi(t) \le x\} = \sum_{n=0}^{\infty} e^{-\lambda t} \frac{(\lambda t)^n}{n!} H_n(x) \tag{7}$$

where $H_n(x)$ denotes the nth iterated convolution of $H(x)$ with itself; $H_0(x) = 1$ if $x \geq 0$ and $H_0(x) = 0$ if $x < 0$.

If

$$\alpha = \int_0^\infty x\, dH(x), \tag{8}$$

then $\rho = \lambda\alpha$.

If ρ is a finite positive number, then we can define a distribution function $H^*(x)$ by

$$H^*(x) = \frac{1}{\alpha}\int_0^x [1 - H(y)]\, dy \tag{9}$$

for $x \geq 0$ and $H^*(x) = 0$ for $x < 0$. Now

$$\psi^*(s) = \int_0^\infty e^{-sx}\, dH^*(x) = \frac{1 - \psi(s)}{\alpha s} \tag{10}$$

for $\text{Re}(s) > 0$.

If ω is the largest nonnegative real root of $\Phi(s) = s$, then $\omega = 0$ if $\rho = \lambda\alpha \leq 1$ and $\omega > 0$ if $\rho = \lambda\alpha > 1$. If $\rho > 1$, then by Lagrange's expansion (see Appendix) we obtain that

$$\omega = \lambda\left[1 - \sum_{j=1}^\infty \int_0^\infty e^{-\lambda x}\frac{(\lambda x)^{j-1}}{j!}\, dH_j(x)\right]. \tag{11}$$

Now we are going to find $W(x)$. We have

$$\Omega(s) = \int_0^\infty e^{-sx}\, dW(x) = \frac{W(0)s}{s - \Phi(s)} \tag{12}$$

for $\text{Re}(s) > \omega$. By inversion we can get different expressions for $W(x)$. If $\rho = \lambda\alpha$ is a finite positive number, then by (6) and (10) $\Phi(s) = \rho s\, \psi^*(s)$ and in this case by (12) of Section 16

$$W(x) = W(0)\sum_{n=0}^\infty \rho^n H_n^*(x) \tag{13}$$

where $H_n^*(x)$ denotes the nth iterated convolution of $H^*(x)$ with itself; $H_0^*(x) = 1$ if $x \geq 0$ and $H_0^*(x) = 0$ if $x < 0$.

If $\rho \neq 1$, then by (14) of Section 16 we have

$$W(x) = W(0)\left[\frac{e^{\omega x}}{1 - \Phi'(\omega)} - K(x)\right] \tag{14}$$

where

$$K(x) = \sum_{n=0}^\infty \int_{+0}^\infty e^{-\lambda u}\frac{(\lambda u)^n}{n!}\, d_u H_n(u + x). \tag{15}$$

By (6) and (12) we can write also that

$$(16) \qquad \int_0^\infty e^{-sx} W(x)\,dx = \frac{W(0)}{s - \lambda[1 - \psi(s)]} = \frac{W(0)}{\lambda} \sum_{n=0}^{\infty} (-1)^n \left(\frac{\lambda}{s-\lambda}\right)^{n+1} [\psi(s)]^n$$

if Re(s) is sufficiently large. Hence by inversion we get

$$(17) \qquad W(x) = W(0) \sum_{n=0}^{\infty} \frac{(-1)^n \lambda^n e^{\lambda x}}{n!} \int_0^x e^{-\lambda y} (x-y)^n \, dH_n(y)$$

for $x \geq 0$.

Using the above expressions, we can apply the general theorems of this chapter to obtain explicit formulas for the probabilities of interest. It is instructive to consider a few particular processes in more detail.

(i) Suppose that

$$(18) \qquad H(x) = \begin{cases} 1 & \text{if } x \geq \alpha, \\ 0 & \text{if } x < \alpha. \end{cases}$$

Then $\psi(s) = e^{-s\alpha}$, $\Phi(s) = \lambda(1 - e^{-\alpha s})$, $\rho = \lambda\alpha$ and

$$(19) \qquad \mathbf{P}\{\chi(t) \leq x\} = \sum_{n=0}^{[x/\alpha]} e^{-\lambda t} \frac{(\lambda t)^n}{n!}$$

for $x \geq 0$. Now by (17)

$$(20) \qquad W(x) = W(0) \sum_{n=0}^{[x/\alpha]} e^{-\lambda(n\alpha - x)} \frac{[\lambda(n\alpha - x)]^n}{n!}$$

for $x \geq 0$ and $W(x) = 0$ for $x < 0$. By (14) we obtain

$$(21) \qquad W(x) = W(0) \left[\frac{e^{\omega x}}{1 - (\lambda - \omega)\alpha} - K(x)\right]$$

where ω is the largest nonnegative real root of $\lambda(1 - e^{-\alpha\omega}) = \omega$ and

$$(22) \qquad K(x) = \sum_{n > x/\alpha} e^{-\lambda(n\alpha - x)} \frac{[\lambda(n\alpha - x)]^n}{n!}.$$

NOTE. If we want to indicate the dependence of $K(x)$ on λ, then we can write that

$$(23) \qquad K(x) = K_\lambda(x) = e^{\lambda x} \sum_{n > x/\alpha} \frac{(e^{-\lambda\alpha}\lambda\alpha)^n}{n!} \left(n - \frac{x}{\alpha}\right)^n.$$

If we know $K_\lambda(x)$ for $\lambda\alpha < 1$, then we can easily obtain $K_\lambda(x)$ for $\lambda\alpha > 1$. For if $\lambda\alpha > 1$, then there is a λ^* such that $\lambda^*\alpha < 1$ and $e^{-\lambda\alpha}\lambda\alpha = e^{-\lambda^*\alpha}\lambda^*\alpha$.

Actually, $\lambda - \lambda^* = \omega$ defined above. Now by (23) $e^{-\lambda x}K_\lambda(x) = e^{-\lambda^* x}K_{\lambda^*}(x)$, that is,

$$K_\lambda(x) = e^{\omega x}K_{\lambda^*}(x) \tag{24}$$

where $\lambda^*\alpha < 1$ and $e^{-\lambda^*\alpha}\lambda^*\alpha = e^{-\lambda\alpha}\lambda\alpha$.

For example, if $\lambda\alpha < 1$ and $x < 0$, then by (37) of Section 15, $K_\lambda(x) = 1/(1 - \lambda\alpha)$. Hence if $\lambda\alpha > 1$ and $x < 0$, we obtain that

$$K_\lambda(x) = e^{\omega x}K_{\lambda^*}(x) = \frac{e^{\omega x}}{1 - \lambda^*\alpha} = \frac{e^{\omega x}}{1 - (\lambda - \omega)\alpha} \tag{25}$$

which is in agreement with (21).

(ii) Suppose that

$$H(x) = \begin{cases} 1 - e^{-\mu x} & \text{if } x \geq 0, \\ 0 & \text{if } x < 0. \end{cases} \tag{26}$$

Then $\psi(s) = \mu/(\mu + s)$, $\Phi(s) = \lambda s/(\mu + s)$, $\rho = \lambda/\mu$, and for $x \geq 0$

$$H_n(x) = \int_0^x e^{-\mu y}\frac{(\mu y)^{n-1}}{(n-1)!}\mu\, dy = \sum_{j=n}^{\infty} e^{-\mu x}\frac{(\mu x)^j}{j!}. \tag{27}$$

Thus for $x \geq 0$

$$\begin{aligned} \mathbf{P}\{\chi(t) \leq x\} &= e^{-\lambda t} + \sum_{n=1}^{\infty} e^{-\lambda t}\frac{(\lambda t)^n}{n!}\int_0^x e^{-\mu y}\frac{(\mu y)^{n-1}}{(n-1)!}\mu\, dy \\ &= e^{-\lambda t}\left[1 + \sqrt{\lambda\mu t}\int_0^x e^{-\mu y}y^{-1/2}I_1(2\sqrt{\lambda\mu t y})\, dy\right] \end{aligned} \tag{28}$$

where

$$I_r(x) = \sum_{n=0}^{\infty}\frac{(x/2)^{2n+r}}{n!\,(n+r)!} \qquad (r = 0, 1, 2, \ldots) \tag{29}$$

is the modified Bessel function of the first kind.

We can also write for $x \geq 0$

$$\begin{aligned} \mathbf{P}\{\chi(t) \leq x\} &= \sum_{n=0}^{\infty} e^{-\lambda t}\frac{(\lambda t)^n}{n!}\sum_{j=n}^{\infty} e^{-\mu x}\frac{(\mu x)^j}{j!} \\ &= \sum_{j=0}^{\infty} e^{-\mu x}\frac{(\mu x)^j}{j!}\sum_{n=0}^{j} e^{-\lambda t}\frac{(\lambda t)^n}{n!} \\ &= 1 - \sum_{j=0}^{\infty} e^{-\mu x}\frac{(\mu x)^j}{j!}\int_0^t e^{-\lambda u}\frac{(\lambda u)^j}{j!}\lambda\, du \\ &= 1 - \lambda e^{-\mu x}\int_0^t e^{-\lambda u}J(\lambda\mu x u)\, du \end{aligned} \tag{30}$$

where

$$J(x) = I_0(2x^{1/2}) = \sum_{n=0}^{\infty} \frac{x^n}{(n!)^2}. \tag{31}$$

Now $\mathbf{P}\{\chi(t) = 0\} = e^{-\lambda t}$ and for $x > 0$

$$\frac{\partial \mathbf{P}\{\chi(t) \leq x\}}{\partial x} = \lambda\mu t\, e^{-\lambda t-\mu x} J'(\lambda\mu t x) \tag{32}$$

which follows from (28) because $J'(x) = I_0'(2x^{1/2})/x^{1/2} = I_1(2x^{1/2})/x^{1/2}$.

In this case $H^*(x) = H(x)$ and by (13) we have

$$W(x) = W(0)\left[1 + \sum_{n=1}^{\infty} \left(\frac{\lambda}{\mu}\right)^n \int_0^x e^{-\mu y} \frac{(\mu y)^{n-1}}{(n-1)!} \mu\, dy\right] \tag{33}$$

for $x \geq 0$, or equivalently,

$$W(x) = \begin{cases} W(0) \dfrac{\mu - \lambda e^{-(\mu-\lambda)x}}{\mu - \lambda} & \text{if } \mu \neq \lambda, \\ W(0)(1 + \lambda x) & \text{if } \mu = \lambda, \end{cases} \tag{34}$$

for $x \geq 0$.

Now if $\lambda \leq \mu$, then $\omega = 0$ and if $\lambda > \mu$, then $\omega = \lambda - \mu$. By (14) we have for $\lambda \neq \mu$

$$W(x) = W(0)\left[\frac{e^{\omega x}}{1 - \Phi'(\omega)} - K(x)\right] \tag{35}$$

where $\omega = 0$ and $\Phi'(0) = \lambda/\mu$ if $\lambda < \mu$ and $\omega = \lambda - \mu$ and $\Phi'(\lambda - \mu) = \mu/\lambda$ if $\lambda > \mu$. Further

$$K(x) = e^{-\mu x} \int_{\max(0,-x)}^{\infty} e^{-(\lambda+\mu)y} \left(\frac{\lambda\mu y}{y + x}\right)^{1/2} I_1(2\sqrt{\lambda\mu y(x + y)})\, dy + \begin{cases} e^{\lambda x} & \text{if } x < 0, \\ 0 & \text{if } x \geqq 0, \end{cases} \tag{36}$$

for all x.

NOTE. If we consider $K(x) = K_{\lambda,\mu}(x)$ as a function of λ and μ, then by (36) we can write that $e^{\mu x} K_{\lambda,\mu}(x) = e^{\lambda x} K_{\mu,\lambda}(x)$. That is, if we know $K(x)$ for $\rho = \lambda/\mu < 1$, then we can obtain easily $K(x)$ for $\rho = \lambda/\mu > 1$ by the relation

$$K_{\lambda,\mu}(x) = e^{(\lambda-\mu)x} K_{\mu,\lambda}(x). \tag{37}$$

2. *Stable Process.* Suppose that

$$N(x) = -\frac{1}{\Gamma(1 - c)x^c} \tag{38}$$

for $0 < x < \infty$ where $0 < c < 1$. Then $\lambda = \infty$ and $\rho = \infty$. Further

$$\Phi(s) = \frac{c}{\Gamma(1-c)} \int_0^\infty (1 - e^{-sx}) \frac{dx}{x^{c+1}} = s^c \tag{39}$$

for $\mathrm{Re}(s) \geq 0$. Now

$$\mathbf{P}\{\chi(t) \leq x\} = \int_0^{x/t^{1/c}} f_c(y)\, dy \tag{40}$$

for $x \geq 0$ where

$$f_c(x) = \sum_{n=1}^{\infty} \frac{(-1)^{n-1}\Gamma(nc+1) \sin nc\pi}{n!\, x^{nc+1}} \tag{41}$$

for $x > 0$. (Cf. H. Pollard [8], and P. Humbert [3].) In particular,

$$f_{1/2}(x) = \frac{1}{(4\pi x^3)^{1/2}} e^{-1/4x} \tag{42}$$

and

$$f_{\frac{2}{3}}(x) = \frac{\sqrt{3\pi}}{x} \exp\left(-\frac{2}{27x^2}\right) W_{\frac{1}{2},\frac{1}{6}}\left(\frac{4}{27x^2}\right) \tag{43}$$

where

$$W_{k,m}(x) = \frac{e^{-x/2}x^k}{\Gamma(\frac{1}{2} - k + m)} \int_0^\infty u^{-k-\frac{1}{2}+m} \left(1 + \frac{u}{x}\right)^{k-\frac{1}{2}+m} e^{-u}\, du \tag{44}$$

is the Whittaker function defined for $\mathrm{Re}(m - k + \frac{1}{2}) > 0$. (See E. T. Whittaker [21].)

Now $\omega = 1$ and

$$\Omega(s) = \frac{W(0)s}{s - s^c} \tag{45}$$

for $\mathrm{Re}(s) > 1$. By inversion we get

$$W(x) = W(0) \sum_{n=0}^{\infty} \frac{x^{n(1-c)}}{\Gamma(n(1-c)+1)} = W(0)E_{1-c}(x^{1-c}) \tag{46}$$

for $x \geq 0$ where

$$E_\alpha(z) = \sum_{n=0}^{\infty} \frac{z^n}{\Gamma(n\alpha + 1)} \tag{47}$$

is the Mittag-Leffler function. Now

$$\lim_{x\to\infty} e^{-x} W(x) = \frac{W(0)}{1 - \Phi'(1)} = \frac{W(0)}{1-c}. \tag{48}$$

By Theorem 2 of Section 16 we have also

$$W(x) = W(0)\left[\frac{e^x}{1-c} - \int_{\max(0,-x)}^{\infty} f_c\left(\frac{x+y}{y^{1/c}}\right) \frac{dy}{y^{1/c}}\right] \tag{49}$$

for all x.

3. *Generalized Stable Process.* Suppose that

$$N(x) = -\frac{c}{\Gamma(1-c)}\int_x^\infty e^{-\mu y}\frac{dy}{y^{c+1}} \tag{50}$$

for $0 < x < \infty$ where $0 < c < 1$ and $\mu \geq 0$. If $\mu = 0$ in (50), we get (38). Now $\lambda = \infty$ and $\rho = c\mu^{c-1}$. Further

$$\Phi(s) = \frac{c}{\Gamma(1-c)}\int_0^\infty (1 - e^{-sx})e^{-\mu x}\frac{dx}{x^{c+1}} = (s+\mu)^c - \mu^c \tag{51}$$

and

$$\mathbf{P}\{\chi(t) \leq x\} = e^{t\mu^c}\int_0^{x/t^{1/c}} e^{-\mu t^{1/c} y} f_c(y)\, dy \tag{52}$$

for $x \geq 0$ where $f_c(x)$ is defined by (41).

Now ω is the largest nonnegative real root of

$$\left(1 + \frac{\omega}{\mu}\right)^c = 1 + \frac{\omega}{\mu^c}. \tag{53}$$

If $\rho = c\mu^{c-1} \leq 1$, then $\omega = 0$ and $\Phi'(0) = c\mu^{c-1}$. If $\rho = c\mu^{c-1} > 1$, then $\omega > 0$ and $\Phi'(\omega) = c(\mu^c + \omega)^{(c-1)/c}$. If $\rho \neq 1$, then by Theorem 2 of Section 16 we have

$$W(x) = W(0)\left[\frac{e^{\omega x}}{1 - \Phi'(\omega)} - \int_{\max(0,-x)}^\infty e^{\mu^c y - \mu(x+y)} f_c\left(\frac{x+y}{y^{1/c}}\right)\frac{dy}{y^{1/c}}\right] \tag{54}$$

for all x.

4. *Gamma Process.* Suppose that

$$N(x) = -\int_x^\infty \frac{e^{-\mu y}}{y}\, dy \tag{55}$$

for $x > 0$ where μ is a positive constant. Then $\lambda = \infty$ and $\rho = 1/\mu$. Further

$$\Phi(s) = \int_0^\infty (1 - e^{-sx})e^{-\mu x}\frac{dx}{x} = \log\left(1 + \frac{s}{\mu}\right), \tag{56}$$

and

$$\mathbf{P}\{\chi(t) \leq x\} = \frac{1}{\Gamma(t)}\int_0^{\mu x} e^{-y} y^{t-1}\, dy \tag{57}$$

for $x > 0$ and $t > 0$. Now ρ is a finite positive number and by (19) of Section 14

$$H^*(x) = \int_0^x h^*(y)\, dy \tag{58}$$

for $x \geq 0$ where

$$h^*(x) = \mu\int_{\mu x}^\infty \frac{e^{-y}}{y}\, dy \tag{59}$$

for $x > 0$. Then

$$\psi^*(s) = \frac{\mu}{s} \log \left(1 + \frac{s}{\mu}\right). \tag{60}$$

Now by (12) of Section 16

$$W(x) = W(0) \sum_{n=0}^{\infty} \left(\frac{1}{\mu}\right)^n H_n^*(x). \tag{61}$$

If $\mu \neq 1$, then by (14) of Section 16

$$W(x) = W(0)\left[\frac{e^{\omega x}}{1 - \Phi'(\omega)} - K_\mu(x)\right] \tag{62}$$

for all x where ω is the largest nonnegative real root of $\mu e^\omega = \mu + \omega$, $\Phi'(\omega) = 1/(\mu + \omega)$ and

$$K_\mu(x) = e^{-\mu x} \int_{\max(0,-x)}^{\infty} \frac{(e^{-\mu}\mu)^y (x + y)^{y-1}}{\Gamma(y)}\, dy. \tag{63}$$

If $\rho = 1/\mu < 1$, then $\omega = 0$ and if $\rho = 1/\mu > 1$, then $\omega > 0$.

NOTE. If we know $K_\mu(x)$ for $\mu > 1$, then it is easy to find $K_\mu(x)$ for $\mu < 1$. For if $\mu < 1$, then there is a $\mu^* > 1$ such that $e^{-\mu}\mu = e^{-\mu^*}\mu^*$. Actually, $\mu^* - \mu = \omega$. Now by (63) $e^{\mu x}K_\mu(x) = e^{\mu^* x}K_{\mu^*}(x)$, that is,

$$K_\mu(x) = e^{\omega x} K_{\mu^*}(x) \tag{64}$$

where $e^{-\mu^*}\mu^* = e^{-\mu}\mu$ and $\mu^* > 1$.

For example, if $\mu > 1$ and $x < 0$, then by (37) of Section 15, $K_\mu(x) = \mu/(\mu - 1)$. Hence if $\mu < 1$ and $x < 0$, we obtain

$$K_\mu(x) = \frac{e^{\omega x}\mu^*}{\mu^* - 1} = \frac{e^{\omega x}(\mu + \omega)}{\mu + \omega - 1} \tag{65}$$

which is in agreement with (62).

Finally, we consider an example of stochastic processes $\{\chi(u), 0 \leq u < \infty\}$ with interchangeable increments for which almost all sample functions are nondecreasing step functions vanishing at $u = 0$.

5. *Pólya Process.* (O. Lundberg [7].) Suppose that $\{\chi(u), 0 \leq u < \infty\}$ is a Markov process with state space $I = \{0, c, 2c, \ldots\}$ and transition probabilities $\mathbf{P}\{\chi(u + \Delta u) = (n + 1)c \mid \chi(u) = nc\} = \lambda_n(u)\, \Delta u + o(\Delta u)$ and $\mathbf{P}\{\chi(u + \Delta u) = nc \mid \chi(u) = nc\} = 1 - \lambda_n(u)\Delta u + o(\Delta u)$ where $\lambda_n(u) = \lambda(h + n)/(\lambda u + h)$ and c, λ and h are positive constants. Suppose that $\mathbf{P}\{\chi(0) = 0\} = 1$. In this case the process $\{\chi(u), 0 \leq u < \infty\}$ has interchangeable increments. The process $\{\chi(u), 0 \leq u < \infty\}$ can be represented as a randomized Poisson process. Suppose that for every

fixed θ, $\{\nu_\theta(u), 0 \leq u < \infty\}$ is a Poisson process of density θ and θ is a nonnegative random variable with distribution function

$$(66) \qquad \mathbf{P}\{\theta \leq x\} = F(x) = \frac{1}{\Gamma(h)} \int_0^x e^{-hy/\lambda} \left(\frac{hy}{\lambda}\right)^{h-1} \frac{h\,dy}{\lambda}$$

for $x \geq 0$. Then we can use the representation $\chi(u) = c\,\nu_\theta(u)$ for $0 \leq u < \infty$.

Now we obtain easily that

$$(67) \qquad \mathbf{E}\{\chi(t)\} = \lambda ct,$$

$$(68) \qquad \mathbf{P}\{\chi(t) = nc\} = P_n(\lambda t, h)$$

and

$$(69) \quad \mathbf{P}\{\chi(u) = mc, \chi(u + t) = (m + n)c\} = P_m(\lambda u, h) P_n\left(\lambda t \frac{h + m}{\lambda u + h}, m + h\right)$$

where

$$(70) \qquad P_n(\lambda t, h) = \binom{n + h - 1}{n} \left(\frac{\lambda t}{\lambda t + h}\right)^n \left(\frac{h}{\lambda t + h}\right)^h.$$

Suppose that the process $\{\chi(u), 0 \leq u < \infty\}$ is separable. In this case by Theorem 1 of Section 15 we have

$$\begin{aligned}(71) \quad \mathbf{P}\Big\{\sup_{0 \leq u \leq t} [\chi(u) - u] \leq x\Big\} &= \mathbf{P}\{\chi(t) \leq t + x\} \\ &\quad - \sum_{0 < y \leq z \leq t}\sum \left(\frac{t - z}{t - y}\right) \mathbf{P}\{\chi(y) = y + x, \chi(t) = z + x\} \\ &= \mathbf{P}\{\chi(t) \leq t + x\} \\ &\quad - \sum_{x < cj \leq ck \leq t + x}\sum \left(\frac{t + x - ck}{t + x - cj}\right) \mathbf{P}\{\chi(cj - x) = cj, \chi(t) = kc\}\end{aligned}$$

and the probabilities on the right-hand side are given by (68) and (69). In particular, by (3) of Section 15 we have

$$\begin{aligned}(72) \quad \mathbf{P}\Big\{\sup_{0 \leq u \leq t} [\chi(u) - u] = 0\Big\} &= 1 - \sum_{0 \leq y \leq t} \left(1 - \frac{y}{t}\right) \mathbf{P}\{\chi(t) = y\} \\ &= 1 - \sum_{j=0}^{[t/c]} \left(1 - \frac{cj}{t}\right) \mathbf{P}\{\chi(t) = cj\}.\end{aligned}$$

Now $\mathbf{E}\{\chi(t) \mid \theta\} = c\theta t$ with probability 1 and hence

$$(73) \qquad \lim_{t \to \infty} \mathbf{P}\left\{\frac{\chi(t)}{t} \leq x\right\} = \mathbf{P}\{c\theta \leq x\} = F\left(\frac{x}{c}\right).$$

Thus by Theorem 2 of Section 14 we have

$$\mathbf{P}\left\{\sup_{0\le u<\infty}[\chi(u)-u]=0\right\}=\int_0^{1/c}(1-cy)\,dF(y). \tag{74}$$

By applying (20) we can write

$$\mathbf{P}\left\{\sup_{0\le u<\infty}[\chi(u)-u]\le x \mid \theta\right\}=(1-c\theta)\sum_{n=0}^{[x/c]}e^{-\theta(cn-x)}\frac{[\theta(cn-x)]^n}{n!} \tag{75}$$

if $0\le\theta\le 1/c$ and $=0$ if $\theta>1/c$ with probability 1. Hence unconditionally

$$\mathbf{P}\left\{\sup_{0\le u\le\infty}[\chi(u)-u]\le x\right\} \tag{76}$$
$$=\sum_{n=0}^{[x/c]}\frac{(cn-x)^n}{n!}\int_0^{1/c}(1-cy)y^n e^{-y(cn-x)}\,dF(y).$$

If $x>0$, then by (1) of Section 17

$$\mathbf{P}\left\{\sup_{0\le u\le t}[u-\chi(u)]\le x\right\}=1-\sum_{x\le y\le t}\frac{x}{y}\mathbf{P}\{\chi(y)=y-x\} \tag{77}$$
$$=1-\sum_{j=0}^{[(t-x)/c]}\left(\frac{x}{cj+x}\right)\mathbf{P}\{\chi(cj+x)=cj\}$$

for finite t as well as for $t=\infty$.

20. PROBLEMS

1. Let $\{\chi(u), 0\le u<\infty\}$ be a separable Poisson process of density λ. Find $\mathbf{P}\{\sup_{0\le u\le t}[\chi(u)-u]\le x\}$ and $\mathbf{P}\{\sup_{0\le u\le t}[u-\chi(u)]\le x\}$ for finite t values.

2. Let $\{\chi(u), 0\le u<\infty\}$ be a separable Poisson process of density λ. Find $\mathbf{P}\{\chi(u)\le u \text{ for } 0\le u<\infty\}$.

3. Let $\{\chi(u), 0\le u<\infty\}$ be a separable compound Poisson process with nonnegative increments for which $\mathbf{E}\{\chi(u)\}=\lambda\alpha u$. Find $\mathbf{P}\{\chi(u)\le xu$ for $0\le u<\infty\}$. (See G. Letac [6].)

4. Suppose that $\{\chi(u), 0\le u<\infty\}$ is a separable Poisson process of density λ. Write down the identities (37) of Section 15 and (20) of Section 17 in this case. (See J. L. W. V. Jensen [4].)

5. Find the sum

$$F_{\lambda\alpha}\left(\frac{x}{\alpha}\right)=\sum_{j=0}^{\infty}e^{-\lambda(\alpha j+x)}\frac{[\lambda(\alpha j+x)]^j}{j!}$$

for $x>0$. (See G. Pólya and G. Szegö [9], Vol. 1, Ch. III., Problem 214.)

6. Prove Abel's identity, that is, that

$$\sum_{k=0}^{n} x \binom{n}{k} (x+k)^{k-1} (t-x-k)^{n-k} = t^n$$

holds for all t and x. (See N. H. Abel [1].)

7. Prove that

$$\frac{1}{n!} \sum_{k=0}^{n} \binom{n}{k} (x+k)^{k} (t-x-k)^{n-k} = \sum_{k=0}^{n} \frac{t^k}{k!}$$

for all t and x. (See G. Arfwedson [2].)

8. Let $\{\nu(u), 0 \le u < \infty\}$ be a separable Poisson process of density λ, and c be a positive constant. Find

$$\mathbf{P}\{\sup_{0 \le u \le t} [\nu(u) - cu] \le x\} \quad \text{and} \quad \mathbf{P}\{\sup_{0 \le u \le t} [cu - \nu(u)] \le x\}$$

and their limits as $t \to \infty$. (See R. Pyke [10].)

9. Suppose that in an electronic tube the distance between the cathode and the anode is t. Electrons leave the cathode with energy 0 and their energies increase linearly with their distance from the cathode if no collision with gas molecules occurs. By choosing a suitable unit of energy we can assume that the energy of an electron at a distance u from the cathode is u if no collison with gas molecules occurs. Suppose that the density of collisions with gas molecules is λ, that is, the probability that an electron has at least one collision passing through a distance Δu is $\lambda \Delta u + o(\Delta u)$. If an electron has energy $\ge \alpha$ when it collides with a gas molecule, then the electron ionizes the gas molecule and loses energy α. If an electron has energy $< \alpha$ when it collides with a gas molecule, then no ionization occurs and the electron does not lose energy. Find $P_n(t)$, the probability that an electron passing through the cathode-anode distance ionizes at least n gas molecules. (See reference [18].)

10. Let $\{\chi(u), 0 \le u < \infty\}$ be a separable compound Poisson process for which

$$\mathbf{P}\{\chi(u) \le x\} = \sum_{n=0}^{\infty} e^{-\lambda u} \frac{(\lambda u)^n}{n!} H_n(x)$$

where $H(x)$ is the distribution function of a nonnegative random variable. Find $W(x) = \mathbf{P}\{\sup_{0 \le u < \infty} [\chi(u) - u] \le x\}$ by using a direct method.

REFERENCES

[1] Abel, N. H. "Démonstration d'une expression de laquelle la formule binome est un cas particulier," *J. reine und angew. Math.* **1** (1826), 159–160. [*Oeuvres complètes*, **I**, Christiania, Grøndahl, 1881 pp. 102–103.]

[2] Arfwedson, G. "Research in collective risk theory. The case of equal risk sums," *Skand. Aktuarietids.* **36** (1953), 1–15.

[3] Humbert, P. "Nouvelles correspondances symboliques," *Bull. Soc. Math. France* **69** (1945), 121–129.

[4] Jensen, J. L. W. V. "Sur une identité d'Abel et sur d'autres formules analogues," *Acta Math.* **26** (1902), 307–318.

[5] Kendall, D. G. "Some problems in the theory of dams," *J. Roy. Stat. Soc. Ser. B* **19** (1957), 207–212.

[6] Letac, G. "Une propriété de fluctuation des processus de Poisson composés croissants," *C.R. Acad. Sci. Paris* **258** (1964), 1700–1703.

[7] Lundberg, O. *On Random Processes and Their Application to Sickness and Accident Statistics*, Thesis, Almqvist and Wiksell, Stockholm, 1940.

[8] Pollard, H. "The representation of e^{-x^λ} as a Laplace integral," *Bull. Amer. Math. Soc.* **52** (1946), 908–910.

[9] Pólya, G., and G. Szegö, *Aufgaben und Lehrsätze aus der Analysis*, I. Springer, Berlin, 1924.

[10] Pyke, R. "The supremum and infimum on the Poisson process," *Ann. Math. Statist.* **30** (1959), 568–576.

[11] Takács, L. "The time dependence of a single-server queue with Poisson input and general service times," *Ann. Math. Statist.* **33** (1962), 1340–1348.

[12] Takács, L. "The distribution of the content of a dam when the input process has stationary independent increments," *J. Math. Mech.* **15** (1966), 101–112.

[13] Takács, L. "Combinatorial methods in the theory of dams," *J. Appl. Probability* **1** (1964), 69–76.

[14] Takács, L. "From ballot theorems to the theory of queues," *Columbia University Report CU*-41-64-*Nonr*-266 **(59),** MS, March 1964.

[15] Takács, L. "On the distribution of the supremum for stochastic processes with interchangeable increments," *Trans. Amer. Math. Soc.* **119** (1965), 367–379.

[16] Takács, L. "A combinatorial theorem for stochastic processes," *Bull. Amer. Math. Soc.* **71** (1965), 649–650.

[17] Takács, L. "Application of ballot theorems in the theory of queues," *Proceedings of the Symposium on Congestion Theory, Chapel Hill, North Carolina, August* 24–26, 1964, Edited by W. L. Smith and W. E. Wilkinson, University of North Carolina Press, Chapel Hill, North Carolina, 1965, pp. 337–398.

[18] Takács, L. "Applications of a ballot theorem in physics and in order statistics," *J. Roy. Stat. Soc. Ser. B* **27** (1965), 130–137.

[19] Takács, L. "On combinatorial methods in the theory of stochastic processes," *Proc. Fifth Berkeley Symp. on Math. Stat. and Prob.*, Vol. II, Part I. University of California Press, 1967, pp. 431–447.

[20] Takács, L. "The distribution of the content of finite dams," *J. Appl. Probability* **4** (1967) to appear.

[21] Whittaker, E. T. "An expression of certain known functions as generalized hypergeometric functions," *Bull. Amer. Math. Soc.* **10** (1904), 125–134.

CHAPTER 4

Random Walk Processes

21. STOCHASTIC PROCESSES WITH INTERCHANGEABLE INCREMENTS AND STOCHASTIC PROCESSES WITH STATIONARY INDEPENDENT INCREMENTS TAKING ON INTEGRAL VALUES

Suppose that $\nu_1, \nu_2, \ldots, \nu_r, \ldots$ are interchangeable random variables taking on nonnegative integers. Set $N_r = \nu_1 + \cdots + \nu_r$ for $r = 1, 2, \ldots$ and $N_0 = 0$. Let $\{\nu(u), 0 \leq u < \infty\}$ be a separable Poisson process of density λ and suppose that $\{\nu_r\}$ and $\{\nu(u)\}$ are independent. Define $\xi(u) = N_{\nu(u)} - \nu(u)$ and $\xi^*(u) = \nu(u) - N_{\nu(u)}$ for $0 \leq u < \infty$.

Then $\{\xi(u), 0 \leq u < \infty\}$ is a separable stochastic process with interchangeable increments almost all of whose sample functions are step functions which may have jumps of magnitude $1, -1, -2, \ldots$. Similarly, $\{\xi^*(u), 0 \leq u < \infty\}$ is a separable stochastic process with interchangeable increments almost all of whose sample functions are step functions which may have jumps of magnitude $-1, 1, 2, \ldots$. Evidently $\xi^*(u) = -\xi(u)$, but it is convenient to make the above distinction and to use separate notations.

If, in particular, $\nu_1, \nu_2, \ldots, \nu_r, \ldots$ are mutually independent and identically distributed random variables taking on nonnegative integers, the processes $\{\xi(u), 0 \leq u < \infty\}$ and $\{\xi^*(u), 0 \leq u < \infty\}$ have stationary independent increments.

In this chapter we shall determine the distributions of the random variables $\sup_{0 \leq u \leq t} \xi(u)$ and $\sup_{0 \leq u \leq t} \xi^*(u)$ for finite t as well as for $t = \infty$.

Throughout this section we shall use the same notation concerning the random variables $\nu_1, \nu_2, \ldots, \nu_r, \ldots$ as in Chapter 2. In particular, $\gamma = \mathbf{E}\{\nu_r\}$, $\pi(z) = \mathbf{E}\{z^{\nu_r}\}$ and δ is the smallest nonnegative real root of $\pi(z) = z$.

If $\{\xi(u), 0 \leq u < \infty\}$ has either interchangeable increments or stationary independent increments then we have

$$\mathbf{P}\{\xi(u) = k\} = \sum_{n=0}^{\infty} \mathbf{P}\{\nu(u) = n\}\mathbf{P}\{N_n - n = k\} \tag{1}$$

$$= \sum_{n=0}^{\infty} e^{-\lambda u} \frac{(\lambda u)^n}{n!} \mathbf{P}\{N_n - n = k\}$$

for $k = 0, \pm 1, \pm 2, \ldots$ and $u \geq 0$, and

$$\mathbf{E}\{\xi(u)\} = \lambda(\gamma - 1)u. \tag{2}$$

If $\{\xi(u), 0 \leq u < \infty\}$ has stationary independent increments, then

$$\mathbf{E}\{z^{\xi(u)}\} = \exp\left[-\lambda u\left(1 - \frac{\pi(z)}{z}\right)\right] \tag{3}$$

for $0 < |z| \leq 1$ or

$$\mathbf{E}\{e^{-s\xi(u)}\} = e^{u\Psi(s)} \tag{4}$$

for $\operatorname{Re}(s) \geq 0$ where

$$\Psi(s) = \lambda(e^s\pi(e^{-s}) - 1). \tag{5}$$

In what follows we shall always suppose that $\{\xi(u), 0 \leq u < \infty\}$ is a separable stochastic process having either interchangeable increments or, in particular, stationary independent increments and that the distribution of $\xi(u)$ is given by (1). In general, the trivial case $\pi_0 = 0$ is excluded. Further it is supposed that $\xi^*(u) = -\xi(u)$ for all $u \geq 0$.

We shall see that each theorem of Sections 6, 7, 8 has a counterpart for the process $\{\xi(u), 0 \leq u < \infty\}$.

Theorem 1. *If $\{\xi(u), 0 \leq u < \infty\}$ has interchangeable increments, then for $k > 0$*

$$\mathbf{P}\left\{\sup_{0 \leq u \leq t} \xi(u) < k\right\} = \mathbf{P}\{\xi(t) < k\} - \sum_{r=1}^{\infty} r \int_0^t \frac{1}{t - u} \mathbf{P}\{\xi(u) = k, \xi(t) = k - r\}\, du. \tag{6}$$

Proof. We shall prove a slightly more general formula from which (6) follows. If $k = 1, 2, \ldots$ and $i = 1, 2, \ldots$, then

$$\mathbf{P}\left\{\sup_{0 \leq u \leq t} \xi(u) < k \text{ and } \xi(t) \leq k - i\right\} = \mathbf{P}\{\xi(t) \leq k - i\} - \sum_{r=i}^{\infty} r \int_0^t \frac{1}{(t - u)} \mathbf{P}\{\xi(u) = k, \xi(t) - \xi(u) = -r\}. \tag{7}$$

Under the condition $\nu(t) = n$, the probability of the event $\{\sup_{0\le u\le t} \xi(u) < k$ and $\xi(t) \le k - i\}$ is given by (2) of Section 6 for $n = 1, 2, \ldots$ and if $n = 0$, the probability is 1 or 0 according as $k \ge i$ or $k < i$. Thus we get

$$\text{(8)}\quad \mathbf{P}\left\{\sup_{0\le u\le t} \xi(u) < k \text{ and } \xi(t) \le k - i\right\} = \mathbf{P}\{\xi(t) \le k - i\}$$

$$-\sum_{n=1}^{\infty}\sum_{j=1}^{n-i}\sum_{r=i}^{n-j}\frac{r}{(n-j)}\mathbf{P}\{N_j - j = k, N_n - N_j - (n-j) = -r\}\mathbf{P}\{\nu(t) = n\}.$$

Now if we use the identity

$$\text{(9)}\quad \mathbf{P}\{\nu(t) = n\} = (n-j)\int_0^t \frac{1}{(t-u)}\mathbf{P}\{\nu(u) = j\}\mathbf{P}\{\nu(t) - \nu(u) = n - j\}\,du$$

for $j = 0, 1, \ldots, n - 1$ and if we interchange the summation in (8) as follows:

$$\sum_{n=1}^{\infty}\sum_{j=1}^{n-i}\sum_{r=i}^{n-j} = \sum_{r=i}^{\infty}\sum_{j=1}^{\infty}\sum_{n=r+j}^{\infty},$$

then we get (7). If $i = 1$ in (7), we get (6) which was to be proved.

Theorem 2. *If $\{\xi(u), 0 \le u < \infty\}$ has interchangeable increments, then*

$$\text{(10)}\qquad \mathbf{E}\left\{\sup_{0\le u\le t}\xi(u)\right\} = \int_0^t \mathbf{E}\{[\xi(u)]^+\}\frac{du}{u}.$$

Proof. We have

$$\text{(11)}\qquad \mathbf{E}\left\{\sup_{0\le u\le t}\xi(u)\right\} = \sum_{k=1}^{\infty}\mathbf{P}\left\{\sup_{0\le u\le t}\xi(u) \ge k\right\},$$

and the right-hand side can be obtained by (6).

If, in particular, $\{\xi(u), 0 \le u < \infty\}$ has stationary independent increments, then (6) can also be written in the following form

$$\text{(12)}\quad \mathbf{P}\left\{\sup_{0\le u\le t}\xi(u) < k\right\} = \mathbf{P}\{\xi(t) < k\} - \int_0^t \frac{\mathbf{E}\{[\xi^*(t-u)]^+\}}{t-u}\mathbf{P}\{\xi(u) = k\}\,du$$

where $\xi^*(t-u) = -\xi(t-u)$.

Theorem 3. *If $\{\xi(u), 0 \le u < \infty\}$ has stationary independent increments and if $\gamma < 1$, then for $k > 0$*

$$\text{(13)}\qquad \mathbf{P}\left\{\sup_{0\le u<\infty}\xi(u) < k\right\} = 1 - \lambda(1-\gamma)\int_0^{\infty}\mathbf{P}\{\xi(u) = k\}\,du.$$

Proof. We can deduce (13) directly from (12). Also it follows from Theorem 3 of Section 6. Since evidently

$$\text{(14)}\qquad \mathbf{P}\left\{\sup_{0\le u<\infty}\xi(u) < k\right\} = \mathbf{P}\left\{\sup_{0\le r<\infty}(N_r - r) < k\right\}$$

for $k > 0$, it follows from (9) of Section 6 that

$$\mathbf{P}\left\{\sup_{0\le u<\infty} \xi(u) < k\right\} = 1 - (1-\gamma)\sum_{j=1}^{\infty}\mathbf{P}\{N_j = j+k\} \tag{15}$$

for $k = 1, 2, \ldots$. The equivalence of (13) and (15) follows from

$$\int_0^\infty \mathbf{P}\{\xi(u) = k\}\,du = \sum_{j=0}^{\infty}\mathbf{P}\{N_j = j+k\}\int_0^\infty \mathbf{P}\{\nu(u) = j\}\,du \tag{16}$$

and

$$\int_0^\infty \mathbf{P}\{\nu(u) = j\}\,du = \int_0^\infty e^{-\lambda u}\frac{(\lambda u)^j}{j!}\,du = \frac{1}{\lambda}. \tag{17}$$

Theorem 4. *If $\{\xi(u), 0 \le u < \infty\}$ has stationary independent increments and if $\gamma < 1$, then for $k > 0$*

$$\mathbf{P}\left\{\sup_{0\le u<\infty} \xi(u) < k\right\} = Q_k \tag{18}$$

where

$$\sum_{k=1}^{\infty} Q_k e^{-sk} = \frac{\lambda(1-\gamma)}{\Psi(s)} \tag{19}$$

for $\mathrm{Re}(s) > 0$ *and* $\Psi(s)$ *is defined by* (5).

Proof. In virtue of (14) the theorem immediately follows from Theorem 4 of Section 6. We can also provide a direct proof easily. For if $k = 1, 2, \ldots$, we have

$$Q_k = (1 - \lambda\,\Delta u)Q_k + \lambda\,\Delta u \sum_{j=0}^{k}\pi_j Q_{k+1-j} + o(\Delta u), \tag{20}$$

whence

$$Q_k = \sum_{j=0}^{k}\pi_j Q_{k+1-j}. \tag{21}$$

By introducing generating functions we get

$$\sum_{k=1}^{\infty} Q_k z^k = \frac{Cz}{\pi(z) - z} \tag{22}$$

for $|z| < 1$ and the constant C is determined by the requirement $\lim_{k\to\infty} Q_k = 1$. Thus we get $C = 1 - \gamma$. If $z = e^{-s}$ in (22), then we obtain (19).

Now define

$$\theta(k) = \inf\{u : \xi(u) = -k \text{ and } 0 \le u < \infty\} \tag{23}$$

for $k > 0$. If $\xi(u) > -k$ for all $u \ge 0$, then $\theta(k) = \infty$. The random variable $\theta(k)$ is the first passage time of $\{\xi(u), 0 \le u < \infty\}$ through $x = -k$, or the first passage time of $\{\xi^*(u), 0 \le u < \infty\}$ through $x = k$.

Theorem 5. *If $\{\xi(u), 0 \le u < \infty\}$ has stationary independent increments and if $\pi_0 > 0$, then*

$$\mathbf{P}\left\{\sup_{0\le u\le\theta(i)} \xi(u) < k - i\right\} = \frac{Q_{k-i}}{Q_k} \tag{24}$$

for $1 \le i \le k$ where

$$\sum_{k=1}^{\infty} Q_k e^{-sk} = \frac{C}{\Psi(s)} \tag{25}$$

for $\operatorname{Re}(s) > \omega$ and ω is the largest nonnegative real root of $\Psi(s) = 0$. Here C is an arbitrary non-null constant.

Proof. This theorem is an immediate consequence of Theorem 2 of Section 7. Accordingly

$$\sum_{k=1}^{\infty} Q_k z^k = \frac{Cz}{\pi(z) - z} \tag{26}$$

for $|z| < \delta$ where δ is the smallest nonnegative real root of $\pi(z) = z$. If $z = e^{-s}$ in (26), then we get (25), and $\delta = e^{-\omega}$.

Theorem 6. *If $\{\xi(u), 0 \le u < \infty\}$ has interchangeable increments, then for $k > 0$*

$$\mathbf{P}\{\theta(k) \le t\} = k\int_0^t \mathbf{P}\{\xi^*(u) = k\}\,\frac{du}{u}\,. \tag{27}$$

Proof. Now by Theorem 1 of Section 8

$$\begin{aligned} \mathbf{P}\{\theta(k) \le t \mid \nu(t) = n\} &= 1 - \mathbf{P}\{r - N_r < k \text{ for } r = 1, \dots, n\} \\ &= \sum_{j=k}^{n} \frac{k}{j}\,\mathbf{P}\{N_j = j - k\} \end{aligned} \tag{28}$$

if $0 < k \le n$. Thus unconditionally

$$\begin{aligned} \mathbf{P}\{\theta(k) \le t\} &= \sum_{n=k}^{\infty} e^{-\lambda t}\frac{(\lambda t)^n}{n!}\sum_{j=k}^{n}\frac{k}{j}\,\mathbf{P}\{N_j = j - k\} \\ &= \sum_{j=k}^{\infty}\frac{k}{j}\,\mathbf{P}\{N_j = j - k\}\sum_{n=j}^{\infty} e^{-\lambda t}\frac{(\lambda t)^n}{n!} \\ &= \sum_{j=k}^{\infty}\frac{k}{j}\,\mathbf{P}\{N_j = j - k\}\int_0^t e^{-\lambda u}\,\frac{(\lambda u)^{j-1}}{(j-1)!}\,\lambda\, du \\ &= k\int_0^t \mathbf{P}\{\xi(u) = -k\}\,\frac{du}{u} \end{aligned} \tag{29}$$

which proves the theorem.

By (27) it follows that

$$\frac{\partial \mathbf{P}\{\theta(k) \le t\}}{\partial t} = \frac{k}{t}\,\mathbf{P}\{\xi^*(t) = k\} \tag{30}$$

for $k = 1, 2, \ldots$ and $t > 0$. This formula preserves the simplicity of formula (3) of Section 2 which was found by A. De Moivre.

Theorem 7. *If $\{\xi(u), 0 \leq u < \infty\}$ has stationary independent increments, then*

$$\mathbf{P}\{\theta(k) < \infty\} = e^{-\omega k} \tag{31}$$

where ω is the largest nonnegative root of $\Psi(s) = 0$. If $\gamma \leq 1$ and $\pi_1 \neq 1$, then $\omega = 0$, whereas if $\gamma > 1$ or $\pi_1 = 1$, then $\omega > 0$. If $\gamma < 1$, then

$$\mathbf{E}\{\theta(k)\} = k\int_0^\infty \mathbf{P}\{\xi^*(u) = k\}\, du = \frac{k}{\lambda(1-\gamma)}. \tag{32}$$

If $\gamma = 1$ and $\pi_1 \neq 1$, then $\mathbf{E}\{\theta(k)\} = \infty$.

Proof. Since $\theta(k) = \infty$ if and only if $\sup_{1 \leq r < \infty} (N_r - r) = \infty$, (31) follows from Theorem 3 of Section 8. In the above theorem we used the notation $\delta = e^{-\omega}$. We obtain (32) by (27) and by using the fact that

$$\int_0^\infty \mathbf{P}\{\xi^*(u) = k\}\, du = \frac{1}{\lambda} \sum_{j=1}^{\infty} \mathbf{P}\{N_j = j - k\} = \frac{1}{\lambda(1-\gamma)} \tag{33}$$

for $k > 0$. The second equality follows from (26) of Section 6.

Evidently (32) can be written in the following equivalent form

$$\mathbf{E}\{\theta(k)\} = \int_0^\infty \mathbf{P}\{0 < \xi^*(u) \leq k\}\, du. \tag{34}$$

Theorem 8. *If $\{\xi(u), 0 \leq u < \infty\}$ has stationary independent increments, then for* $\mathrm{Re}(s) > 0$ *and for* $k = 1, 2, \ldots$ *we have*

$$\mathbf{E}\{e^{-s\theta(k)}\} = k\int_0^\infty e^{-su}\mathbf{P}\{\xi^*(u) = k\}\frac{du}{u}, \tag{35}$$

or

$$\mathbf{E}\{e^{-s\theta(k)}\} = e^{-\omega(s)k} \tag{36}$$

where $z = \omega(s)$ is the only root of

$$\Psi(z) = s \tag{37}$$

in the domain $\mathrm{Re}(z) > 0$.

Proof. (35) immediately follows from (27). Now we shall prove (36). If we define $\rho(k)$ as the smallest r such that $N_r = r - k$, then by (20) of Section 8 we have

$$\mathbf{E}\{z^{\rho(k)}\} = [\delta(z)]^k \tag{38}$$

for $|z| < 1$ where $w = \delta(z)$ is the only root of $w = z\pi(w)$ in the domain $|w| < 1$. Since $\theta(k)$ can be represented as a sum of $\rho(k)$ mutually independent and identically distributed random variables where each variable has the distribution function $F(x) = 1 - e^{-\lambda x}$ for $x \geq 0$ and where the random variables are independent of $\rho(k)$, we obtain by (38) that

$$\mathbf{E}\{e^{-s\theta(k)}\} = \left[\delta\left(\frac{\lambda}{\lambda + s}\right)\right]^k \tag{39}$$

for $\mathrm{Re}(s) > 0$. If we write

$$\delta\left(\frac{\lambda}{\lambda + s}\right) = e^{-\omega(s)}, \tag{40}$$

then we get (36) and $\omega(s)$ can be characterized as the only root in z of $\Psi(z) = s$ in the domain $\mathrm{Re}(z) > 0$. This completes the proof of Theorem 8.

Theorem 9. *If* $\{\xi^*(u), 0 \leq u < \infty\}$ *has interchangeable increments, then for* $k > 0$

$$\mathbf{P}\left\{\sup_{0 \leq u \leq t} \xi^*(u) < k\right\} = 1 - k\int_0^t \mathbf{P}\{\xi^*(u) = k\}\frac{du}{u}. \tag{41}$$

Proof. Evidently

$$\mathbf{P}\left\{\sup_{0 \leq u \leq t} \xi^*(u) < k\right\} = 1 - \mathbf{P}\{\theta(k) \leq t\} \tag{42}$$

and thus (41) follows from (27). It is easy to see that the following more general formula also holds

$$\mathbf{P}\left\{\sup_{0 \leq u \leq t} \xi^*(u) < k \text{ and } \xi^*(t) < k - i\right\} = \mathbf{P}\{\xi^*(t) < k - i\} - k\int_0^t \frac{1}{u}\mathbf{P}\{\xi^*(u) = k, \xi^*(t) - \xi^*(u) < -i\}\,du \tag{43}$$

if $1 \leq i < k$. This follows from (3) of Section 8.

If $t \to \infty$ in (41), then we get

$$\mathbf{P}\left\{\sup_{0 \leq u < \infty} \xi^*(u) < k\right\} = 1 - k\int_0^\infty \mathbf{P}\{\xi^*(u) = k\}\frac{du}{u}. \tag{44}$$

If, in particular, $\{\xi^*(u), 0 \leq u < \infty\}$ has stationary independent increments, then (44) is equal to $1 - e^{-\omega k}$ where ω has the same meaning as in Theorem 7.

22. A RANDOM WALK PROCESS

Suppose that a particle performs a random walk on the x-axis. Starting at $x = 0$ in each step the particle moves either a unit distance to the right with probability p or a unit distance to the left with probability q ($p + q = 1$, $0 < p < 1$). Suppose that the displacements of the particle occur at random times in the time interval $(0, \infty)$. Denote by $\nu(u)$ the number of steps taken in the interval $(0, u]$. We suppose that $\{\nu(u), 0 \leq u < \infty\}$ is a Poisson process of density λ and that the successive displacements are independent of each other and independent of the process $\{\nu(u), 0 \leq u < \infty\}$. Denote by $\xi(u)$ the position of the particle at time u. In this case $\{\xi(u), 0 \leq u < \infty\}$ is a stochastic process having stationary independent increments. $\mathbf{P}\{\xi(0) = 0\} = 1$ and almost all sample functions are step functions having jumps of magnitude 1 or -1.

The process $\{\xi(u), 0 \leq u < \infty\}$ is of the same type as we considered in Section 21 and we can apply the theorems proved there to this process. Now $\xi(u) = N_{\nu(u)} - \nu(u)$ for $0 \leq u < \infty$ where $\nu_1, \nu_2, \ldots, \nu_r, \ldots$ are mutually independent and identically distributed random variables with distribution

$$\text{(1)} \qquad \mathbf{P}\{\nu_r = 0\} = q \quad \text{and} \quad \mathbf{P}\{\nu_r = 2\} = p$$

where $p + q = 1$ and $0 < p < 1$. In this case

$$\text{(2)} \qquad \mathbf{P}\{N_n = n + k\} = \binom{n}{\frac{1}{2}(n+k)} p^{(n+k)/2} q^{(n-k)/2}$$

for $k = n, n - 2, \ldots, -n + 2, -n$ and $\mathbf{P}\{N_n = n + k\} = 0$ otherwise. Further

$$\text{(3)} \qquad \mathbf{P}\{\xi(u) = k\} = \sum_{n=0}^{\infty} e^{-\lambda u} \frac{(\lambda u)^n}{n!} \mathbf{P}\{N_n = n + k\}$$

$$= e^{-\lambda u} \left(\frac{p}{q}\right)^{k/2} I_k(2\lambda p^{1/2} q^{1/2} u)$$

for $k = 0, \pm 1, \pm 2, \ldots$ where $I_r(x)$ is the modified Bessel function of order r defined by

$$\text{(4)} \qquad I_r(x) = \sum_{j=0}^{\infty} \frac{(x/2)^{2j+r}}{j!\,(j+r)!}$$

for $r \geq 0$ and $I_{-r}(x) = I_r(x)$. We have

$$\text{(5)} \qquad \mathbf{E}\{\xi(u)\} = \lambda(p - q)u$$

and

$$\text{(6)} \qquad \mathbf{Var}\,\{\xi(u)\} = \lambda u.$$

Now we shall find the distribution of the random variable $\sup_{0 \leq u \leq t} \xi(u)$. By (12) of Section 21

$$\text{(7)} \quad \mathbf{P}\left\{\sup_{0 \leq u \leq t} \xi(u) < k\right\} = \mathbf{P}\{\xi(t) < k\} - \int_0^t \frac{\mathbf{E}\{[\xi^*(t-u)]^+\}}{t-u} \mathbf{P}\{\xi(u) = k\}\, du$$

for $k > 0$ where $\xi^*(t - u) = -\xi(t - u)$.

Since now the process $\{\xi(u),\ 0 \le u < \infty\}$ is of the same type as $\{\xi^*(u), 0 \le u < \infty\}$ we can also apply Theorem 9 of Section 21 to find the distribution of $\sup_{0\le u\le t} \xi(u)$. By (41) of Section 21 we get

$$\mathbf{P}\left\{\sup_{0\le u\le t} \xi(u) < k\right\} = 1 - k\int_0^t \mathbf{P}\{\xi(u) = k\}\,\frac{du}{u} \tag{8}$$

for $k > 0$.

Now we shall prove directly that

$$\mathbf{P}\left\{\sup_{0\le u\le t} \xi(u) < k\right\} = \mathbf{P}\{\xi(t) < k\} - \left(\frac{p}{q}\right)^k \mathbf{P}\{\xi(t) < -k\} \tag{9}$$

for $k > 0$ also holds. If $k > 0$ and $j < k$, then

$$\begin{aligned} \text{(10)}\quad \mathbf{P}&\left\{\sup_{0\le u\le t} \xi(u) < k \text{ and } \xi(t) = j \mid \nu(t) = n\right\} \\ &= \mathbf{P}\{N_r - r < k \text{ for } r = 0, 1, \ldots, n \text{ and } N_n - n = j\} \\ &= \left[\binom{n}{\frac{1}{2}(n+j)} - \binom{n}{\frac{1}{2}(n+j) - k}\right] p^{(n+j)/2} q^{(n-j)/2}. \end{aligned}$$

(10) can be seen if we take into consideration that the sequence $\{N_r - r, r = 0, 1, \ldots, n\}$ describes the path of the considered random walk during the first n steps. Then (10) can be interpreted as the probability that after n steps the position of the particle is $x = j$ and during these n steps the particle never touches the point $x = k$. Now each path has probability $p^{(n+j)/2}q^{(n-j)/2}$ and the number of favorable paths is

$$\binom{n}{\frac{1}{2}(n+j)} - \binom{n}{\frac{1}{2}(n+j) - k} \tag{11}$$

which can be seen by using the reflection principle. This proves (10). Formula (10) can also be written in the following form

$$\begin{aligned} \text{(12)}\quad \mathbf{P}\left\{\sup_{0\le u\le t} \xi(u) < k \text{ and } \xi(t) = j \mid \nu(t) = n\right\} &= \mathbf{P}\{\xi(t) = j \mid \nu(t) = n\} \\ &\quad - \left(\frac{p}{q}\right)^k \mathbf{P}\{\xi(t) = j - 2k \mid \nu(t) = n\}. \end{aligned}$$

Thus unconditionally we get

$$\begin{aligned} \text{(13)}\quad \mathbf{P}&\left\{\sup_{0\le u\le t} \xi(u) < k \text{ and } \xi(t) = j\right\} \\ &= \mathbf{P}\{\xi(t) = j\} - \left(\frac{p}{q}\right)^k \mathbf{P}\{\xi(t) = j - 2k\}. \end{aligned}$$

If we add (13) for $j < k$, then we get (9) which was to be proved.

We note that since in this case the process $\{\xi^*(u), 0 \le u < \infty\}$ is of exactly the same type as $\{\xi(u), 0 \le u < \infty\}$ formulas (7), (8), and (9) are also valid for $\{\xi^*(u), 0 \le u < \infty\}$.

If $\theta(k)$ denotes the first passage time of the process $\{\xi(u), 0 \le u < \infty\}$ through $x = -k$ where $k > 0$, then for $k > 0$

$$\mathbf{P}\{\theta(k) \le t\} = 1 - \mathbf{P}\left\{\sup_{0 \le u \le t} \xi^*(u) < k\right\} \tag{14}$$

where $\xi^*(u) = -\xi(u)$ and the right-hand side can be obtained either by (7) or (8) or (9).

By Theorem 4 of Section 21 we have

$$\mathbf{P}\left\{\sup_{0 \le u < \infty} \xi(u) < k\right\} = 1 - \left(\frac{p}{q}\right)^k \tag{15}$$

if $p < q$ and $k > 0$, and by Theorem 7 of Section 21

$$\mathbf{P}\{\theta(k) < \infty\} = \left(\frac{q}{p}\right)^k \tag{16}$$

if $q < p$ and $k > 0$.

If $1 \le i \le k$, then by Theorem 5 of Section 21 we obtain that

$$\mathbf{P}\left\{\sup_{0 \le u \le \theta(i)} \xi(u) < k - i\right\} = \frac{Q_{k-i}}{Q_k} \tag{17}$$

where

$$Q_k = \frac{C}{q}\left(\frac{1 - (p/q)^k}{1 - (p/q)}\right) \tag{18}$$

if $p \ne q$ and $k > 0$ and

$$Q_k = 2Ck \tag{19}$$

if $p = q$ and $k > 0$. C is an arbitrary non-null constant.

23. THE BROWNIAN MOTION PROCESS

Suppose that $\{\zeta(u), 0 \le u < \infty\}$ is a real-valued, separable stochastic process with stationary independent increments for which $\mathbf{P}\{\zeta(0) = 0\} = 1$ and

$$\mathbf{P}\{\zeta(u) \le x\} = \Phi\left(\frac{x - au}{\sigma u^{1/2}}\right) \tag{1}$$

for all x where a is a real constant, σ is a positive constant and

$$\Phi(x) = \frac{1}{\sqrt{2\pi}} \int_{-\infty}^{x} e^{-y^2/2}\, dy \tag{2}$$

is the normal distribution function. In this case the process $\{\zeta(u), 0 \leq u < \infty\}$ is said to be a Brownian motion or a Wiener process. We have $\mathbf{E}\{\zeta(u)\} = au$ and $\mathbf{Var}\,\{\zeta(u)\} = \sigma^2 u$ for $u \geq 0$, and

(3) $$\mathbf{E}\{e^{-s\zeta(u)}\} = e^{u\Psi(s)}$$

where

(4) $$\Psi(s) = -as + \tfrac{1}{2}\sigma^2 s^2$$

for $u \geq 0$ and all s.

Define $\theta(x)$ as the first passage time of the process $\{\zeta(u), 0 \leq u < \infty\}$ through $-x$. We have

(5) $$\theta(x) = \inf\{u : \zeta(u) < -x \text{ and } 0 \leq u < \infty\}$$

for $x > 0$.

Now we shall find the distributions of the random variables $\sup\limits_{0 \leq u \leq t} \zeta(u)$, $\sup\limits_{0 \leq u < \infty} \zeta(u)$, $\theta(x)$ and $\sup\limits_{0 \leq u \leq \theta(c)} \zeta(u)$. To find these distributions we shall approximate $\{\zeta(u), 0 \leq u < \infty\}$ by a family of suitable normalized random walk processes (as defined in Section 22) and then the distributions in question can be obtained as the limits of the corresponding probabilities in Section 22.

Define a family of stochastic processes $\{\xi_\lambda(u), 0 \leq u < \infty\}$ as follows. For each λ, $\{\xi_\lambda(u)\}$ is a separable random walk process with stationary independent increments as is defined in Section 22 where now the underlying Poisson process has density λ and

(6) $$p = \frac{1}{2} + \frac{a}{2\sigma\lambda^{1/2}}, \qquad q = \frac{1}{2} - \frac{a}{2\sigma\lambda^{1/2}}$$

for $\lambda > \sigma^2/a^2$ if $a \neq 0$. For this process let

(7) $$\mathbf{E}\{e^{-s\xi_\lambda(u)}\} = e^{u\Psi_\lambda(s)}.$$

If $\lambda \to \infty$, then the finite dimensional distributions of the process $\{\sigma\xi_\lambda(u)/\lambda^{1/2}\}$ converge to the corresponding finite dimensional distributions of the process $\{\zeta(u)\}$. In order to prove this, it is sufficient to show that

(8) $$\lim_{\lambda\to\infty} \Psi_\lambda\left(\frac{\sigma s}{\lambda^{1/2}}\right) = \Psi(s)$$

where $\Psi(s)$ is defined by (4). Since

(9) $$\Psi_\lambda(s) = \lambda(qe^s + pe^{-s} - 1),$$

(8) follows easily.

Accordingly we can conclude that for $x > 0$

$$\mathbf{P}\left\{\sup_{0 \le u \le t} \zeta(u) \le x\right\} = \lim_{\lambda \to \infty} \mathbf{P}\left\{\sup_{0 \le u \le t} \xi_\lambda(u) < k\right\} \tag{10}$$

where $k = [\lambda^{1/2}x/\sigma]$ and the right-hand side of (10) can be obtained either by (7) or (8) or (9) of Section 22. By (8) of Section 22 we obtain that

$$\begin{aligned} \mathbf{P}\left\{\sup_{0 \le u \le t} \zeta(u) \le x\right\} &= 1 - x\int_0^t \frac{\partial \mathbf{P}\{\zeta(u) \le x\}}{\partial x} \frac{du}{u} \\ &= 1 - \frac{x}{\sigma}\int_0^t \Phi'\left(\frac{x - au}{\sigma u^{1/2}}\right)\frac{du}{u^{3/2}} \end{aligned} \tag{11}$$

for $x > 0$ and by (9) of Section 22 we obtain that

$$\begin{aligned} \mathbf{P}\left\{\sup_{0 \le u \le t} \zeta(u) \le x\right\} &= \mathbf{P}\{\zeta(t) \le x\} - e^{2ax/\sigma^2}\mathbf{P}\{\zeta(t) \le -x\} \\ &= \Phi\left(\frac{x - at}{\sigma t^{1/2}}\right) - e^{2ax/\sigma^2}\Phi\left(\frac{-x - at}{\sigma t^{1/2}}\right) \end{aligned} \tag{12}$$

for $x > 0$ where we used that

$$\lim_{\lambda \to \infty}\left(\frac{p}{q}\right)^k = \lim_{\lambda \to \infty}\left(\frac{1 + \dfrac{a}{\sigma\lambda^{1/2}}}{1 - \dfrac{a}{\sigma\lambda^{1/2}}}\right)^{x\lambda^{1/2}/\sigma} = e^{2ax/\sigma^2}. \tag{13}$$

The distribution of $\sup_{0 \le u \le t} \zeta(u)$ has also been obtained by G. Baxter and M. Donsker [1] by using analytical methods.

If we suppose that $a < 0$ and let $t \to \infty$ in (11) then we get

$$\mathbf{P}\left\{\sup_{0 \le u < \infty} \zeta(u) \le x\right\} = 1 - \frac{x}{\sigma}\int_0^\infty \Phi'\left(\frac{x - au}{\sigma u^{1/2}}\right)\frac{du}{u^{3/2}} = 1 - e^{2ax/\sigma^2} \tag{14}$$

for $x > 0$. If we let $t \to \infty$ in (12), then we get immediately the same result. For a direct proof of (14) we refer to J. L. Doob [4]. If $a \ge 0$, then $\mathbf{P}\{\sup_{0 \le u < \infty} \zeta(u) \le x\} = 0$ for all x.

If $\theta(x)$ denotes the time when $\xi(u) = -x$ for the first time, then by (8) and (14) of Section 22 we have

$$\mathbf{P}\{\theta(x) \le t\} = x\int_0^t \frac{\partial \mathbf{P}\{\zeta^*(u) \le x\}}{\partial x}\frac{du}{u} \tag{15}$$

for $x > 0$ and $t > 0$ where $\zeta^*(u) = -\zeta(u)$ for $u \ge 0$. Hence

$$\frac{\partial \mathbf{P}\{\theta(x) \le t\}}{\partial t} = \frac{x}{t}\frac{\partial \mathbf{P}\{\zeta^*(t) \le x\}}{\partial x} = \frac{x}{\sigma t^{3/2}}\Phi'\left(\frac{x + at}{\sigma t^{1/2}}\right) \tag{16}$$

for $x > 0$ and $t > 0$.

Finally, by (17) of Section 22 we obtain that

$$\mathbf{P}\left\{\sup_{0\le u\le\theta(c)} \zeta(u) \le x - c\right\} = \frac{W(x-c)}{W(x)} \tag{17}$$

for $0 < c < x$ where

$$W(x) = \frac{C}{a}(e^{2ax/\sigma^2} - 1) \qquad \text{if} \quad a \ne 0, \tag{18}$$

and

$$W(x) = 2Cx/\sigma^2 \qquad \text{if} \quad a = 0, \tag{19}$$

with a non-null C. This follows immediately from (17), (18), and (19) of Section 22 if we suppose that $k = [\lambda^{1/2}x/\sigma]$, and $i = [\lambda^{1/2}c/\sigma]$ and let $\lambda \to \infty$.

If $Q_k^{(\lambda)}$, $k = 1, 2, \ldots$, is defined by (18) and (19) of Section 22 where p and q are given by (6), then we can also obtain that

$$\int_0^\infty e^{-sx}W(x)\,dx = \lim_{\lambda\to\infty} \frac{\sigma}{\lambda^{1/2}} \sum_{k=1}^{\infty} Q_k^{(\lambda)} \exp\left[-\frac{sk\sigma}{\lambda^{1/2}}\right] \tag{20}$$

$$= \lim_{\lambda\to\infty} \frac{C_\lambda}{\lambda^{1/2}} \frac{\sigma}{\Psi_\lambda\left(\dfrac{s\sigma}{\lambda^{1/2}}\right)} = \frac{C}{\Psi(s)}$$

for $\operatorname{Re}(s) > \omega$ where $\omega = 0$ if $a \le 0$ and $\omega = 2a/\sigma^2$ if $a > 0$. Here we had chosen $C_\lambda = C\lambda^{1/2}/\sigma$ with $C \ne 0$, and $\Psi(s)$ is given by (4). Thus

$$\int_0^\infty e^{-sx}W(x)\,dx = \frac{2C}{s(\sigma^2 s - 2a)} = \frac{C}{a}\left[\frac{\sigma^2}{\sigma^2 s - 2a} - \frac{1}{s}\right] \tag{21}$$

for $\operatorname{Re}(s) > \omega$ and (18) and (19) can be obtained by inversion.

24. STOCHASTIC PROCESSES WITH STATIONARY INDEPENDENT INCREMENTS HAVING NO NEGATIVE JUMPS

Let $\{\zeta(u), 0 \le u < \infty\}$ be a real-valued stochastic process with stationary independent increments for which the sample functions have no negative jumps and vanish at $u = 0$ with probability 1. Then

$$\mathbf{E}\{e^{-s\zeta(u)}\} = e^{u\Psi(s)} \tag{1}$$

exists for $\operatorname{Re}(s) \ge 0$ and the most general form of $\Psi(s)$ is given by

$$\Psi(s) = as + \tfrac{1}{2}\sigma^2 s^2 - \int_{+0}^{\infty}\left(1 - e^{-sx} - \frac{sx}{1+x^2}\right) dN(x) \tag{2}$$

where a is a real constant, σ^2 is a nonnegative constant, $N(x)$, $0 < x < \infty$, is a nondecreasing function of x satisfying the conditions $\lim_{x\to\infty} N(x) = 0$ and

$$\int_{+0}^{1} x^2\, dN(x) < \infty. \tag{3}$$

We note that if

$$\int_{+0}^{1} x\, dN(x) < \infty, \tag{4}$$

then (2) can be reduced to the following form

$$\Psi(s) = as + \tfrac{1}{2}\sigma^2 s^2 - \int_{+0}^{\infty} (1 - e^{-sx})\, dN(x) \tag{5}$$

where, in general, the constant a is not the same as in (2). If

$$\int_{1}^{\infty} x\, dN(x) < \infty, \tag{6}$$

then (2) can be written in the following equivalent form

$$\Psi(s) = as + \tfrac{1}{2}\sigma^2 s^2 - \int_{+0}^{\infty} (1 - e^{-sx} - sx)\, dN(x) \tag{7}$$

where, in general, the constant a is not the same as in (2).

The expectation of $\zeta(u)$ is of the form $\mathbf{E}\{\zeta(u)\} = -\rho u$ where

$$\rho = a - \int_{+0}^{\infty} \frac{x^3}{1 + x^2}\, dN(x). \tag{8}$$

Possibly $\rho = -\infty$, however, $\rho = \infty$ is impossible. If $\rho \neq -\infty$, then both (4) and (6) are satisfied and $\Psi(s)$ can be expressed in the form (5).

In what follows we suppose that $\{\zeta(u), 0 \leq u < \infty\}$ is a real-valued separable stochastic process with stationary independent increments for which $\mathbf{P}\{\zeta(0) = 0\} = 1$ and (1) holds for $\mathrm{Re}(s) \geq 0$ where, in general, $\Psi(s)$ is defined by (2). The trivial cases $\mathbf{P}\{\zeta(u) \geq 0\} = 1$ for all $u \geq 0$ and $\mathbf{P}\{\zeta(u) \leq 0\} = 1$ for all $u \geq 0$ are excluded. We also use the notation $\zeta^*(u) = -\zeta(u)$ for $u \geq 0$. We define ρ by $\mathbf{E}\{\zeta(u)\} = -\rho u$, that is, $\rho = \Psi'(+0)$.

In this section we shall show that all the theorems of Section 21 have a counterpart for the process $\{\zeta(u), 0 \leq u < \infty\}$. To find these analogous theorems we shall approximate $\{\zeta(u), 0 \leq u < \infty\}$ by a family of processes of the type defined in Section 21 and then the distributions in question will be obtained as the limits of the corresponding probabilities in Section 21.

Consider the process $\xi(u) = N_{\nu(u)} - \nu(u)$, $0 \leq u \leq \infty$, defined in Section 21 where now $\{\nu(u), 0 \leq u < \infty\}$ is a Poisson process of density

λ and $\nu_1, \nu_2, \ldots, \nu_r, \ldots$ are mutually independent and identically distributed random variables with distribution $\mathbf{P}\{\nu_r = j\} = \pi_j^{(\lambda)}$, $j = 0, 1, 2, \ldots$, and $\{\nu_r\}$ and $\{\nu(u)\}$ are independent. That is, now we suppose that the distribution of ν_r, $r = 1, 2, \ldots$, also depends on λ. For a fixed λ we shall use the notation $\{\xi_\lambda(u), 0 \leq u < \infty\}$ for the corresponding process. For each λ the process $\{\xi_\lambda(u), 0 \leq u < \infty\}$ has stationary independent increments, $\mathbf{P}\{\xi_\lambda(0) = 0\} = 1$ and

$$\mathbf{E}\{e^{-s\xi_\lambda(u)}\} = e^{u\Psi_\lambda(s)} \tag{9}$$

exists for $\mathrm{Re}(s) \geq 0$.

It is easy to see that we can choose the distributions $\pi_j^{(\lambda)}, j = 0, 1, 2, \ldots$, and a normalizing factor $g(\lambda) = c\lambda^{-1/2}$, such that as $\lambda \to \infty$, the finite dimensional distributions of the process $\{g(\lambda)\xi_\lambda(u), 0 \leq u < \infty\}$ converge to the corresponding finite dimensional distributions of the process $\{\zeta(u), 0 \leq u < \infty\}$ defined at the beginning of this section. In order to prove this it is sufficient to show that we can choose $\pi_j^{(\lambda)}, j = 0, 1, 2, \ldots$, and $g(\lambda)$ such that

$$\lim_{\lambda\to\infty} \Psi_\lambda(g(\lambda)s) = \Psi(s) \tag{10}$$

for $\mathrm{Re}(s) \geq 0$. In the previous section we considered a Brownian motion process and we expressed $g(\lambda)$ and $\pi_j^{(\lambda)}$ explicitly. In the present case we can apply similar procedure to find a $g(\lambda)$ and suitable distributions $\{\pi_j^{(\lambda)}\}$.

Now if we consider a family of separable stochastic processes $\{\xi_\lambda(u), 0 \leq u < \infty\}$, as defined above, then it is valid that

$$\mathbf{P}\left\{\sup_{0\leq u\leq t} \zeta(u) \leq x\right\} = \lim_{\lambda\to\infty} \mathbf{P}\left\{g(\lambda) \sup_{0\leq u\leq t} \xi_\lambda(u) \leq x\right\} \tag{11}$$

for all x.

For the process $\{\xi_\lambda(u), 0 \leq u < \infty\}$ we use similar notation as for the process $\{\xi(u), 0 \leq u < \infty\}$ defined in Section 21 except that a λ is added. Thus we use the symbols $\gamma_\lambda = \mathbf{E}\{\nu_r\}$, $r = 1, 2, \ldots$, $\rho_\lambda = \lambda(1 - \gamma_\lambda)$ and $Q_k^{(\lambda)}$, $k = 0, 1, 2, \ldots$, defined by (25) of Section 21 where now $\Psi(s)$ is replaced by $\Psi_\lambda(s)$.

Now we are going to formulate the analogous theorems of Section 21.

Theorem 1. *We have*

$$\mathbf{P}\left\{\sup_{0\leq u\leq t} \zeta(u) \leq x\right\} = \mathbf{P}\{\zeta(t) \leq x\} - \int_0^t \frac{\mathbf{E}\{[\zeta^*(t-u)]^+\}}{t-u} \mathbf{P}\{x < \zeta(u) < x + du\} \tag{12}$$

for $x > 0$ where $\zeta^*(u) = -\zeta(u)$ for $u \geq 0$.

Proof. If we apply (12) of Section 21 to the process $\{\xi_\lambda(u), 0 \leq u < \infty\}$ and suppose that $k = [x/g(\lambda)]$, then we obtain (12) by letting $\lambda \to \infty$.

Theorem 2. *We have*

$$\mathbf{E}\left\{\sup_{0\leq u\leq t} \zeta(u)\right\} = \int_0^t \mathbf{E}\{[\zeta(u)]^+\}\frac{du}{u}. \tag{13}$$

Proof. If we apply (10) of Section 21 to the process $\{\xi_\lambda(u), 0 \leq u < \infty\}$ and let $\lambda \to \infty$, then we get (13).

Theorem 3. *If $\rho > 0$, then for $x > 0$*

$$\mathbf{P}\{\sup_{0\leq u<\infty} \zeta(u) \leq x\} = 1 - \rho\int_0^\infty \mathbf{P}\{x < \zeta(u) < x + du\}. \tag{14}$$

Proof. Apply (13) of Section 21 to the process $\{\xi_\lambda(u), 0 \leq u < \infty\}$ and suppose that $k = [x/g(\lambda)]$. Since $\lim_{\lambda\to\infty} g(\lambda)\,\lambda(1 - \gamma_\lambda) = \rho$, we get (14). We can also deduce (14) directly from (12). We note that if $\rho \leq 0$, then $\mathbf{P}\{\sup_{0\leq u<\infty} \zeta(u) \leq x\} = 0$ for all x.

Theorem 4. *If $\rho > 0$, then for $x > 0$*

$$\mathbf{P}\left\{\sup_{0\leq u<\infty} \zeta(u) \leq x\right\} = W(x) \tag{15}$$

where

$$\int_0^\infty e^{-sx}W(x)\,dx = \frac{\rho}{\Psi(s)} \tag{16}$$

for $\mathrm{Re}(s) > 0$.

Proof. By Theorem 4 of Section 21 we have

$$W(x) = \lim_{\lambda\to\infty} Q^{(\lambda)}_{[x/g(\lambda)]} \tag{17}$$

and by (19) of Section 21

$$\int_0^\infty e^{-sx}W(x)\,dx = \lim_{\lambda\to\infty} g(\lambda)\sum_{k=1}^{\infty} Q_k^{(\lambda)}e^{-g(\lambda)sk} \tag{18}$$

$$= \lim_{\lambda\to\infty}\frac{g(\lambda)\rho_\lambda}{\Psi_\lambda(g(\lambda)s)} = \frac{\rho}{\Psi(s)}$$

for $\mathrm{Re}(s) > 0$. This proves (16)

Now define $\theta(x)$ as the first passage time of the process $\{\zeta(u), 0 \leq u < \infty\}$ through $-x$. For $x > 0$

$$\theta(x) = \inf\{\zeta(u) \leq -x \text{ and } 0 \leq u < \infty\} \tag{19}$$

and $\theta(x) = \infty$ if $\zeta(u) > -x$ for all $u \geq 0$.

Theorem 5. *We have*

$$\mathbf{P}\left\{\sup_{0\le u\le\theta(c)}\zeta(u)\le x-c\right\}=\frac{W(x-c)}{W(x)} \tag{20}$$

for $0<c\le x$ *where*

$$\int_0^\infty e^{-sx}W(x)\,dx=\frac{C}{\Psi(s)} \tag{21}$$

for $\mathrm{Re}(s)>\omega$ *where* ω *is the largest nonnegative real root of* $\Psi(s)=0$ *and* C *is a non-null constant. If* $\rho\ge 0$, *then* $\omega=0$; *whereas if* $\rho<0$, *then* $\omega>0$.

Proof. If we apply Theorem 5 of Section 21 to the process $\{\xi_\lambda(u), 0\le u<\infty\}$ and suppose that $k=[x/g(\lambda)]$ and $i=[c/g(\lambda)]$, then we get (20) by letting $\lambda\to\infty$. In (20)

$$W(x)=\lim_{\lambda\to\infty}Q^{(\lambda)}_{[x/g(\lambda)]} \tag{22}$$

for $x\ge 0$. By (25) of Section 21

$$\begin{aligned}\int_0^\infty e^{-sx}W(x)\,dx&=\lim_{\lambda\to\infty}g(\lambda)\sum_{k=1}^{\infty}Q_k^{(\lambda)}e^{-g(\lambda)sk}\\&=\lim_{\lambda\to\infty}\frac{g(\lambda)C_\lambda}{\Psi_\lambda(g(\lambda)s)}=\frac{C}{\Psi(s)},\end{aligned} \tag{23}$$

where we obtained the extreme right expression by choosing $C_\lambda=C/g(\lambda)$ with $C\ne 0$. The Laplace transform is convergent if $\mathrm{Re}(s)>\omega$ where ω is the largest nonnegative real root of $\Psi(s)=0$.

Theorem 6. *If* $x>0$, *then*

$$\mathbf{P}\{\theta(x)\le t\}=\int_0^t\frac{x}{u}\mathbf{P}\{x<\zeta^*(u)<x+du\} \tag{24}$$

where $\zeta^*(u)=-\zeta(u)$ *for all* $u\ge 0$.

Proof. This theorem follows directly from Theorem 6 of Section 21 if we apply it to the process $\{\xi_\lambda(u), 0\le u<\infty\}$, put $k=[x/g(\lambda)]$ in it and let $\lambda\to\infty$.

Theorem 7. *If* $x>0$, *then*

$$\mathbf{P}\{\theta(x)<\infty\}=e^{-\omega x} \tag{25}$$

where ω *is the largest nonnegative real root of* $\Psi(s)=0$. *If* $\rho\ge 0$, *then* $\omega=0$ *and if* $\rho<0$, *then* $\omega>0$. *If* $\rho>0$, *then*

$$\mathbf{E}\{\theta(x)\}=\frac{x}{\rho} \tag{26}$$

and if $\rho=0$, *then* $\mathbf{E}\{\theta(x)\}=\infty$.

Proof. Denote by ω_λ the largest nonnegative real root of $\Psi_\lambda(s) = 0$. Then by Theorem 7 of Section 21 we can conclude that (25) holds with $\omega = \lim_{\lambda\to\infty} g(\lambda)\omega_\lambda$. Then $\Psi(\omega) = 0$ and ω can be characterized as the largest nonnegative real root of $\Psi(\omega) = 0$. By (32) of Section 21 it follows that

$$\mathbf{E}\{\theta(x)\} = x\int_0^\infty \frac{1}{u}\mathbf{P}\{x < \zeta^*(u) < x + du\} = \frac{x}{\rho} \tag{27}$$

if $x > 0$ and $\rho > 0$. Equivalently we can write

$$\mathbf{E}\{\theta(x)\} = \int_0^\infty \mathbf{P}\{0 < \zeta^*(u) \leq x\}\, du. \tag{28}$$

Theorem 8. *If $x > 0$, then*

$$\mathbf{E}\{e^{-s\theta(x)}\} = e^{-x\omega(s)} \tag{29}$$

for $\mathrm{Re}(s) > 0$ *where $z = \omega(s)$ is the only root of*

$$\Psi(z) = s \tag{30}$$

in the domain $\mathrm{Re}(z) > 0$.

Proof. For $\mathrm{Re}(s) > 0$ denote by $\omega_\lambda(s)$ the only root of $\Psi_\lambda(z) = s$ in the domain $\mathrm{Re}(z) > 0$. Then by Theorem 8 of Section 21 we have (29) where $\omega(s) = \lim_{\lambda\to\infty} g(\lambda)\omega_\lambda(s)$. Then $z = \omega(s)$ satisfies $\Psi(z) = s$ and $\omega(s)$ can be characterized as the only root of $\Psi(z) = s$ in the domain $\mathrm{Re}(z) > 0$. This proves Theorem 8.

Now consider the process $\{\zeta^*(u), 0 \leq u < \infty\}$ where $\zeta^*(u) = -\zeta(u)$ for $u \geq 0$.

Theorem 9. *If $x > 0$, then*

$$\mathbf{P}\left\{\sup_{0\leq u\leq t} \zeta^*(u) \leq x\right\} = 1 - \int_0^t \frac{x}{u}\mathbf{P}\{x < \zeta^*(u) < x + du\}. \tag{31}$$

Proof. Since

$$\mathbf{P}\left\{\sup_{0\leq u\leq t} \zeta^*(u) \leq x\right\} = 1 - \mathbf{P}\{\theta(x) \leq t\}, \tag{32}$$

(31) follows from (24).

If $t \to \infty$ in (31), then we get

(33)

$$\mathbf{P}\left\{\sup_{0\leq u<\infty} \zeta^*(u) \leq x\right\} = 1 - \int_0^\infty \frac{x}{u}\mathbf{P}\{x < \zeta^*(u) < x + du\} = 1 - e^{-\omega x}$$

for $x > 0$ where ω is the largest nonnegative real root of $\Psi(s) = 0$.

Theorems 4, 6, 7, 8 of this section have also been proved by V. M. Zolotarev [10] by using analytical methods.

25. STOCHASTIC PROCESSES WITH STATIONARY INDEPENDENT INCREMENTS

If $\{\zeta(u), 0 \leq u < \infty\}$ is a real-valued stochastic process with stationary independent increments for which $\mathbf{P}\{\zeta(0) = 0\} = 1$, then

$$\mathbf{E}\{e^{-s\zeta(u)}\} = e^{u\Psi(s)} \tag{1}$$

exists for $\text{Re}(s) = 0$ and

$$\Psi(s) = as + \tfrac{1}{2}\sigma^2 s^2 - \int_{+0}^{\infty}\left(1 - e^{-sx} - \frac{sx}{1+x^2}\right) dN(x) - \int_{-\infty}^{-0}\left(1 - e^{-sx} - \frac{sx}{1+x^2}\right) dM(x) \tag{2}$$

where a is a real constant, σ^2 is a nonnegative constant, $N(x)$, $0 \leq x < \infty$, is a nondecreasing function of x satisfying the conditions $\lim_{x\to\infty} N(x) = 0$ and

$$\int_{+0}^{1} x^2\, dN(x) < \infty, \tag{3}$$

and $M(x)$, $0 \leq x < \infty$, is a nondecreasing function of x satisfying the conditions $\lim_{x\to-\infty} M(x) = 0$ and

$$\int_{-1}^{-0} x^2\, dM(x) < \infty. \tag{4}$$

In this general case, for a separable process $\{\zeta(u), 0 \leq u < \infty\}$, G. Baxter and M. D. Donsker [1] gave a method of finding the distribution function of the random variable $\eta(t) = \sup_{0\leq u\leq t} \zeta(u)$. Their result can be presented in the following way. If $\text{Re}(s) \geq 0$ and $0 < w < \infty$, then

$$w\int_0^{\infty} e^{-wt}\mathbf{E}\{e^{-s\eta(t)}\}\, dt = \exp\left[-\mathbf{A}\left\{\log\left(1 - \frac{\Psi(s)}{w}\right)\right\}\right] \tag{5}$$

where the operator $\mathbf{A}$ is defined in the same way as in Section 11.

Actually, by extending Spitzer's result (formula (9) of Section 11) Baxter and Donsker showed that if $s > 0$ and $w > 0$, then

$$w\int_0^{\infty} e^{-wt}\mathbf{E}\{e^{-s\eta(t)}\}\, dt = \exp\left\{-\int_w^{\infty}\int_0^{\infty} e^{-ut}[1 - \mathbf{A}e^{t\Psi(s)}]\, dt\, du\right\}. \tag{6}$$

If we interchange the integration and the forming of the operation $\mathbf{A}$, then we get (5). By choosing a special form for the operator $\mathbf{A}$ (formula (17) of Section 11) and making some restrictions on $\Psi(s)$, Baxter and Donsker reduced (6) to simpler forms. It seems to be true that no restriction is needed for the validity of (5). We need to impose restrictions on $\Psi(s)$ only if we specialize the operator **A**.

In many cases the double Laplace-Stieltjes transform (5) can be expressed explicitly by using the method of factorization. Suppose that for $\text{Re}(w) > 0$

$$(7) \qquad 1 - \frac{\Psi(z)}{w} = [\Psi^{+}(z, w)]^{\alpha}[\Psi^{-}(z, w)]^{\beta}$$

if $\text{Re}(z) = 0$ where $\alpha = \pm 1$, $\beta = \pm 1$, $\Psi^{+}(z, w)$ is regular and free from zeros in the domain $\text{Re}(z) > 0$ and continuous for $\text{Re}(z) \geq 0$, $\Psi^{-}(z, w)$ is regular and free from zeros in the domain $\text{Re}(z) < 0$ and continuous for $\text{Re}(z) \leq 0$, furthermore $\lim_{|z|\to\infty} \dfrac{\log \Psi^{+}(z, w)}{z} = 0$ $(\text{Re}(z) > 0)$ and $\lim_{|z|\to\infty} \dfrac{\log \Psi^{-}(z, w)}{z} = 0$ $(\text{Re}(z) < 0)$. Then

$$(8) \qquad \mathbf{A}\left\{\log\left(1 - \frac{\Psi(s)}{w}\right)\right\} = \alpha \log \Psi^{+}(s, w) + \beta \log \Psi^{-}(0, w)$$

and

$$(9) \qquad w\int_0^\infty e^{-wt}\mathbf{E}\{e^{-s\eta(t)}\}\, dt = \left[\frac{\Psi^{+}(0, w)}{\Psi^{+}(s, w)}\right]^{\alpha}$$

for $\text{Re}(w) > 0$ and $\text{Re}(s) \geq 0$.

If $\eta = \sup_{0 \leq u < \infty} \zeta(u)$ is a proper random variable, then

$$(10) \qquad \mathbf{E}\{e^{-s\eta}\} = \lim_{w\to 0} w\int_0^\infty e^{-wt}\mathbf{E}\{e^{-s\eta(t)}\}\, dt$$

for $\text{Re}(s) \geq 0$. (10) can also be obtained by factorizing $\Psi(z)$.

26. PROBLEMS

1. Suppose that in the time interval $(0, \infty)$ customers arrive at a counter in accordance with a Poisson process of density λ and are served by a single server. The service times are mutually independent and identically distributed random variables with distribution function $H(x) = 1 - e^{-\mu x}$ $(x \geq 0)$ and independent of the arrival times. Suppose that the server is idle if and only if there is no customer in the system. Denote by $\zeta(t)$ the queue size at time t. Find the probability $P_{ik}(t) = \mathbf{P}\{\zeta(t) \leq k \mid \zeta(0) = i\}$.

2. In the previous problem denote by $\theta(i)$ the time when $\zeta(u) = 0$ for the first time in the interval $(0, \infty)$ given that $\zeta(0) = i$, that is, $\theta(i)$ is the length of the initial busy period. Find the probability $\mathbf{P}\{\theta(i) \leq t\}$.

3. Let $\{\zeta(u), 0 \le u < \infty\}$ be a separable Brownian motion process for which $\mathbf{E}\{\zeta(u)\} = \alpha u$ and $\mathbf{Var}\,\{\zeta(u)\} = \sigma^2 u$. Find the probability $\mathbf{P}\{-y \le \zeta(u) \le x \text{ for } 0 \le u \le t\}$ where x and y are positive numbers.

4. Let $\{\zeta(u), 0 \le u < \infty\}$ be a separable Brownian motion process for which $\mathbf{E}\{\zeta(u)\} = au$ and $\mathbf{Var}\{\zeta(u)\} = \sigma^2 u$. Find $\mathbf{P}\{\sup_{0 \le u \le t} \zeta(u) \le x\}$ by the method of factorization. (See G. Baxter and M. D. Donsker [1] and H. Dinges [3].)

5. Let $\{\xi(u), 0 \le u < \infty\}$ be a separable stochastic process with stationary independent increments and with distribution

$$\mathbf{P}\{\xi(u) = k\} = e^{-\lambda u}\left(\frac{p}{q}\right)^{k/2} I_k(2\lambda p^{1/2} q^{1/2} u)$$

for $k = 0, \pm 1, \pm 2, \ldots.$ (See Section 22.) Prove that

$$1 - k\int_0^t \mathbf{P}\{\xi(u) = k\}\frac{du}{u} = \mathbf{P}\{\xi(t) < k\} - \left(\frac{p}{q}\right)^k \mathbf{P}\{\xi(t) < -k\}$$

if $k > 0$.

6. Let $\{\zeta(u), 0 \le u < \infty\}$ be a separable stochastic process with stationary independent increments for which $\mathbf{E}\{e^{-s\zeta(u)}\} = e^{u\Psi(s)}$ for $\text{Re}(s) \ge 0$ where

$$\Psi(s) = as - \int_0^\infty \left(1 - e^{-sx} - \frac{sx}{1 + x^2}\right) dN(x)$$

and $N(x) = -1/x$ for $x > 0$. Denote by $\theta(c)$ the first passage time of the process $\{\zeta(u), 0 \le u < \infty\}$ through $x = -c$. Find

$$\mathbf{P}\{\sup_{0 \le u \le \theta(c)} \zeta(u) \le x - c\}$$

for $0 < c < x$.

7. Let $\{\zeta(u), 0 \le u < \infty\}$ be a separable stochastic process with stationary independent increments for which $\mathbf{E}\{e^{-s\zeta(u)}\} = e^{-u|s|}$ if $\text{Re}(s) = 0$ or $\mathbf{P}\{\zeta(u) \le x\} = \frac{1}{2} + \frac{1}{\pi}\,\text{arctg}\, x/u$. The process $\{\zeta(u), 0 \le u < \infty\}$ is a stable process with index $c = 1$, the so-called Cauchy process. Find

$$\mathbf{P}\{\sup_{0 \le u \le t} \zeta(u) \le x\}.$$

(See D. A. Darling [2].)

8. Prove formula (5) of Section 25.

REFERENCES

[1] Baxter, G. and M. D. Donsker, "On the distribution of the supremum functional for processes with stationary independent increments," *Trans. Amer. Math. Soc.* **85** (1957), 73–87.

[2] Darling, D. A. "The maximum of sums of stable random variables," *Trans. Amer. Math. Soc.* **83** (1956), 164–169.

[3] Dinges, H. "Ein verallgemeinertes Spiegelungsprinzip für den Prozess der Brownschen Bewegung," *Zeitschr. Wahrscheinlichkeitstheorie* **1** (1962), 177–196.

[4] Doob, J. L. "Heuristic approach to the Kolmogorov-Smirnov theorems," *Ann. Math. Statist.* **20** (1949), 393–403.

[5] Kac, M. "Some remarks on stable processes with independent increments," *Probability and Statistics*, The Harald Cramér Volume, Edited by U. Grenander, Almqvist and Wiksell, Stockholm and John Wiley and Sons, New York, 1959, pp. 130–138.

[6] Keilson, J. "The first passage time density for homogeneous skip-free walks on the continuum," *Ann. Math. Statist.* **34** (1963), 1003–1011.

[7] Reich, E. "Some combinatorial theorems for continuous parameter processes," *Math. Scand.* **9** (1961), 243–257.

[8] Takács, L. "On combinatorial methods in the theory of stochastic processes," *Proc. Fifth Berkeley Symp. on Math. Statist. and Prob.* Vol. **II.** Part **I,** University of California Press, 1967, pp. 431–447.

[9] Zolotarev, V. M. "A duality law in the class of infinitely divisible laws," (Russian) *Trudy Mat. Inst. Steklov* **64** (1961), 52–60. [English translation: *Selected Translations in Mathematical Statistics and Probability, IMS and AMS,* **5** (1965), 201–209.]

[10] Zolotarev, V. M. "The first passage time of a level and the behavior at infinity for a class of processes with independent increments," *Theory of Probability and its Applications* **9** (1964), 653–662.

CHAPTER 5

Queuing Processes

27. SINGLE SERVER QUEUES

The theory of queues developed in the twentieth century with the investigation of telephone traffic problems. The pioneer work has been done by A. K. Erlang [20, 21, 22] who studied the stochastic law of the delay of calls in a telephone exchange. The mathematical theory of queues made considerable progress in the 1930's through the work of F. Pollaczek [53, 54], A. N. Kolmogorov [45], A. Y. Khintchine [42, 43], and others. At present there is a huge literature on the theory of queues and on its applications. (See A. Doig [19], T. L. Saaty [66], and H. O. A. Wold [90].) The theory of queues is mainly applied in engineering (telephone traffic, communications networks, electronic computers), in industry (servicing automatic machines, production lines, storage), in transportation (airports, harbors, railway stations, bus stations, road traffic, postal service), in business (supermarkets, banks, ticket offices), and in everyday life (elevators, restaurants, barber shops).

We shall use the terminology of service systems, customers, servers, and service times. Every conceivable process can always be described in this terminology. For instance, in the case of telephone traffic, the telephone exchange, calls, lines and holding times correspond to the service system, customers, servers, and service times respectively.

The mechanism of a queuing process is very simple. Customers arrive at a counter and are attended by one or more servers. After being served, each customer departs. The time spent in the system by a customer consists of the waiting time (possibly 0) and the service time. The time of a server includes alternating busy periods and idle periods.

The most important problems in the theory of queues are connected with the random fluctuations of the queue size (waiting line) and with the random fluctuations of the waiting time (delay). Knowing the stochastic laws governing these fluctuations, we can design adequate service systems (a sufficiently large waiting room, sufficient number of servers, and so on).

In this chapter we shall consider the following mathematical model of queues: In the time interval $[0, \infty)$ customers arrive at a counter in accordance with a random process. The customers are served by a single server and the service times are random variables. The order of serving is not specified, but it is supposed that the server is busy if there is at least one customer in the system.

We shall study problems which are connected with the fluctuations of the queue size and with the fluctuations of the waiting time.

The *queue size* at time t, denoted by $\xi(t)$, is defined as the total number of customers in the system at time t including the one who is being served (if any). We shall denote by ξ_n the queue size immediately before the nth arrival and by ζ_n the queue size immediately after the nth departure.

The *waiting time* at time t, denoted by $\eta(t)$, is defined as the time needed to complete the serving of all those customers who are present in the system at time t. If, in particular, service is in order of arrival, then $\eta(t)$ is the time that a customer would have to wait if he arrived at time t. In this case $\eta(t)$ can be interpreted as the virtual waiting time at time t, which is defined for all $t \geq 0$. If a customer arrives at time t, then his actual waiting time is equal to $\eta(t - 0)$. We can imagine that the virtual waiting time has real physical meaning. For instance, if we consider reading of messages in a telegraph office, then the virtual waiting time at time t is equal to the length of messages to be read at time t. Or we can even imagine that we use a reading-timer (chemical clock) which has a clock mechanism and each time a customer arrives we set the hand forward by the length of the time of his future service. Since this clock runs as long as there are customers in the system, it will at any given time show the appropriate virtual waiting time. Thus an arriving customer can see immediately his actual waiting time on this clock. In general, $\eta(t)$ can be interpreted as the occupation time (total load) of the server at time t. We shall denote by η_n the waiting time immediately before the nth arrival. If service is in order of arrival, then η_n is the actual waiting time of the nth arriving customer.

We can characterize the queuing process from two different points of view according to whether we are interested in the fluctuations of the queue size or in the fluctuations of the waiting time.

The Process Q. Suppose that the server starts working at time $t = 0$ and at that time ζ_0 customers are already waiting for service. The initial queue size, ζ_0, is a random variable taking on nonnegative integral values. Denote by $\nu_1, \nu_2, \dots, \nu_r, \dots$ the number of customers joining the queue during the 1st, 2nd, ..., rth, ... service respectively, and write $N_0 = 0$ and

$N_r = \nu_1 + \cdots + \nu_r$ for $r = 1, 2, \ldots$. In this case we speak about a queuing process of type

$$Q = \{\zeta_0; N_r, r = 0, 1, 2, \ldots\}.$$

We shall be interested in finding the distributions of the following random variables:

ξ_n, $n = 1, 2, \ldots$, the queue size immediately before the nth arrival;

ζ_n, $n = 1, 2, \ldots$, the queue size immediately after the nth departure; ζ_0 is the initial queue size;

ρ_n, $n = 0, 1, 2, \ldots$, the number of customers served in the nth busy period;

α_n, the number of zeros among $\zeta_0, \zeta_1, \ldots, \zeta_{n-1}$; and

β_n, the number of positive quantities among $\zeta_0, \zeta_1, \ldots, \zeta_{n-1}$. Obviously $\alpha_n + \beta_n = n$.

The random variables α_n and β_n can also be interpreted as follows: α_n is the number of services among the first n services that are preceded by an idle period and β_n is the number of services among the first n services that are not preceded by an idle period. If $\zeta_0 = i$, then the number of customers among the first n arriving customers who at their arrival find the server busy is $\beta_{n+i} - i$.

All these random variables are completely determined by ζ_0 and N_r, $r = 0, 1, 2, \ldots$.

In what follows we shall always make the following assumptions: ζ_0 and $\{N_r, r = 0, 1, 2, \ldots\}$ are independent. The random variables ν_1, $\nu_2, \ldots, \nu_r, \ldots$ are either interchangeable random variables taking on nonnegative integral values, or, in particular, mutually independent and identically distributed random variables taking on nonnegative integral values.

The Process W. Suppose that the server starts working at time $u = 0$ and at that time he has an initial occupation time $\eta(0)$ where $\eta(0)$ is a nonnegative random variable. Denote by $\chi(u)$ the total (accumulated) service time of all those customers who arrive in the interval $[0, t]$. In this case we speak about a queuing process of type

$$W = \{\eta(0); \chi(u), 0 \leq u < \infty\}.$$

We shall be interested in finding the distributions of the following random variables:

$\eta(t)$, the waiting time at time t;

θ_r, $r = 0, 1, 2, \ldots$, the length of the rth busy period;

$\alpha(t)$, the total (accumulated) idle time of the server in the time interval $(0, t)$; and

$\beta(t)$, the total (accumulated) occupation time of the server in the time interval $(0, t)$. Obviously $\alpha(t) + \beta(t) = t$.

All these random variables are completely determined by $\eta(0)$ and $\{\chi(u), 0 \le u < \infty\}$.

In what follows we shall always suppose that the random variable $\eta(0)$ and the stochastic process $\{\chi(u), 0 \le u < \infty\}$ are independent. The stochastic process $\{\chi(u), 0 \le u < \infty\}$ is supposed to have either interchangeable increments or stationary independent increments for which almost all sample functions are nondecreasing step functions vanishing at $u = 0$.

Dual Processes

It is convenient to associate with the queuing processes Q and W closely related processes Q^* and W^* in the following way.

The Process Q^*. Consider the queuing process $Q = \{\zeta_0; N_r, r = 0, 1, 2, \ldots\}$ defined previously. Instead of $\nu_1, \nu_2, \ldots, \nu_r, \ldots$, suppose that the number of customers arriving during the 1st, 2nd, . . . , rth, . . . service is $\nu_1^*, \nu_2^*, \ldots, \nu_r^*, \ldots$ respectively where $\{\nu_r^*\}$ is the dual sequence of $\{\nu_r\}$ defined in Section 9. Let $N_0^* = 0$ and $N_r^* = \nu_1^* + \cdots + \nu_r^*$ for $r = 1, 2, \ldots$. In this case the queuing process

$$Q^* = \{\zeta_0; N_r^*, r = 0, 1, 2, \ldots\}$$

is called the dual process of $Q = \{\zeta_0; N_r, r = 0, 1, 2, \ldots\}$. Conversely Q is the dual process of Q^*. In the dual process Q^*, the queue size immediately before $u = 0$ is ζ_0. For the dual process Q^* we use the same notation as for Q except that an asterisk is added. Thus we shall use the notations $\xi_n^*, \zeta_n^*, \rho_n^*, \alpha_n^*, \beta_n^*$ for Q^* with the same meanings that $\xi_n, \zeta_n, \rho_n, \alpha_n, \beta_n$ have for Q.

The Process W^*. Consider the queuing process $W = \{\eta(0); \chi(u), 0 \le u < \infty\}$ defined before. Instead of $\chi(u)$ suppose that the total service time of all those customers who arrive in the time interval $[0, u]$ is $\chi^*(u)$ where $\{\chi^*(u), 0 \le u < \infty\}$ is the dual process of $\{\chi(u), 0 \le u < \infty\}$ defined in Section 18. The queuing process

$$W^* = \{\eta(0); \chi^*(u), 0 \le u < \infty\}$$

is called the dual process of $W = \{\eta(0); \chi(u), 0 \le u < \infty\}$. Conversely W is the dual process of W^*. In the dual process W^*, the occupation time of the server immediately before $u = 0$ is $\eta(0)$. For the dual process W^* we use the same notation as for W except that an asterisk is added. Thus we shall use the notations $\eta^*(t), \theta_r^*, \alpha^*(t), \beta^*(t)$ for W^* with the same meanings that $\eta(t), \theta_r, \alpha(t), \beta(t)$ have for W.

Several results can be carried over from processes Q and W to processes Q^* and W^* and conversely.

Inverse Processes

Consider the processes Q and W, previously introduced, in the following case. In the time interval $(0, \infty)$ customers arrive at a counter at times τ_r, $r = 1, 2, \ldots$. Let $\tau_0 = 0$; however, there is no arrival at time $u = 0$. Denote by χ_r, $r = 1, 2, \ldots$, the length of the rth service. In the case of the process Q, the initial state is given by ζ_0, the initial queue size at time $u = 0$, and in the case of the process W, the initial state is given by $\eta(0)$, the initial occupation time of the server at $u = 0$.

Now define the processes Q' and W' in the following way. In the time interval $(0, \infty)$ customers arrive at a counter at times τ_r', $r = 1, 2, \ldots$, and let $\tau_0' = 0$. In the case of the process Q' there is no arrival at time $\tau_0' = 0$, whereas, in the case of the process W' there is an arrival at time $\tau_0' = 0$. Denote by χ_r', $r = 1, 2, \ldots$, the length of the rth service. In the case of the process Q' the initial state is given by ζ_0, the initial queue size immediately before $u = 0$, and in the case of the process W', the initial state is given by $\eta(0)$, the initial occupation time of the server immediately before $u = 0$. (The service time of the customer arriving at time $u = 0$ is not included in $\eta(0)$.)

If we suppose that

$$\tau_r' = \chi_1 + \chi_2 + \cdots + \chi_r \qquad \text{for} \quad r = 1, 2, \ldots$$

and

$$\chi_r' = \tau_r - \tau_{r-1} \qquad \text{for} \quad r = 1\ 2, \ldots,$$

then Q' is called the inverse process of Q and W' is called the inverse process of W. That is, if in the original process we interchange the interarrival times and service times leaving the initial state unchanged, then we obtain the inverse process.

For a given queuing process the inverse processes Q' and W' and the dual processes Q^* and W^* are strongly related. Many probabilities for the inverse processes are identical with the corresponding probabilities for the dual processes.

28. FLUCTUATIONS OF THE QUEUE SIZE

Consider the queuing process $Q = \{\zeta_0; N_r, r = 0, 1, 2, \ldots\}$ introduced in Section 27. It is supposed that $N_r = \nu_1 + \cdots + \nu_r$, $r = 1, 2, \ldots$, where $\{\nu_r\}$ are random variables taking on nonnegative integral values. We are interested in finding the distributions of ξ_n, ζ_n, α_n, β_n, and ρ_n for every n. These random variables are completely determined by the process Q. It can easily be seen that the following relations hold.

The queue size immediately after the nth departure is given by

$$(1) \quad \zeta_n = \max \{N_n - N_r - n + r + 1 \text{ for } r = 0, 1, \ldots, n-1 \text{ and } \zeta_0 + N_n - n\}.$$

For

$$(2) \qquad \zeta_n = [\zeta_{n-1} - 1]^+ + \nu_n, \qquad n = 1\ 2, \ldots,$$

and (1) follows if we take into consideration that if r is the greatest index for which $\zeta_r = 0$ and $0 \leq r \leq n-1$, then $\zeta_n = \nu_{r+1} + \cdots + \nu_n - n + r + 1$, and if there is no such r among $0, 1, \ldots, n-1$, then $\zeta_n = \zeta_0 + \nu_1 + \cdots + \nu_n - n$. In each case (1) holds.

If we know the distribution of ζ_n for every n, then the distribution of ξ_n can be obtained immediately because we have

$$(3) \qquad \mathbf{P}\{\xi_{n+k+1} \leq k \mid \zeta_0 = i\} = \mathbf{P}\{\zeta_{n+i} \leq k \mid \zeta_0 = i\}.$$

For if $\zeta_0 = i$, then each of the events $\{\xi_{n+k+1} \leq k\}$ and $\{\zeta_{n+i} \leq k\}$ occurs if and only if the $n + i$th departure precedes the $n + k + 1$st arrival.

The number of services among the first n services that are preceded by an idle period is given by

$$(4) \quad \alpha_n = \max \{0 \text{ and } r - N_r + 1 - \zeta_0 \text{ for } r = 0, 1, \ldots, n-1\}$$

and $\beta_n = n - \alpha_n$. Also we have the obvious relation

$$(5) \qquad \beta_n = \zeta_0 + N_n - \zeta_n.$$

The number of services in the initial busy period is given by

$$(6) \qquad \rho_0 = \min \{r : \zeta_0 + N_r = r \text{ and } r = 0, 1, \ldots\}.$$

If there is no such r, then $\rho_0 = \infty$.

There is an interesting relation between the distributions of α_n and ρ_0. For $0 \leq k < n$ we have

$$(7) \qquad \mathbf{P}\{\alpha_n > k \mid \zeta_0 = i\} = \mathbf{P}\{\rho_0 < n \mid \zeta_0 = i + k\}$$

and

$$(8) \qquad \mathbf{P}\{\alpha_n = 0 \mid \zeta_0 = i\} = \mathbf{P}\{\rho_0 \geq n \mid \zeta_0 = i\}.$$

The relation (8) is evident. To prove (7) we note that by (4)

$$(9) \quad \mathbf{P}\{\alpha_n > k\} = \mathbf{P}\{\zeta_0 + N_r + k \leq r \text{ for some } r = 0, 1, \ldots, n-1\}$$

and by (6)

$$(10) \quad \mathbf{P}\{\rho_0 < n\} = \mathbf{P}\{\zeta_0 + N_r \leq r \text{ for some } r = 0, 1, \ldots, n-1\}.$$

If we compare (9) and (10), then we can conclude that the probability that $\alpha_n > k$ in a process with initial queue size $\zeta_0 = i$ is the same as the probability that $\rho_0 < n$ in a process with initial queue size $\zeta_0 = i + k$. This proves (7).

The Process Q

In what follows we shall suppose that either $\{\nu_r\}$ are interchangeable random variables taking on nonnegative integers, or, in particular, $\{\nu_r\}$ are mutually independent and identically distributed random variables taking on nonnegative integers. Concerning the random variables $\{\nu_r\}$ we use the same notations as in Chapter 2, namely, $\mathbf{P}\{\nu_r = j\} = \pi_j$, $j = 0, 1, 2, \ldots$, $\mathbf{E}\{z^{\nu_r}\} = \pi(z)$, $\mathbf{E}\{\nu_r\} = \gamma$, $\mathbf{E}\{\nu_r(\nu_r - 1)\} = \gamma_2$, $\mathbf{Var}\,\{\nu_r\} = \sigma^2$ and $z = \delta$ is the smallest nonnegative real root of $\pi(z) = z$. If $\gamma \leq 1$ and $\pi_1 \neq 1$, then $\delta = 1$. If $\gamma > 1$ or $\pi_1 = 1$, then $0 \leq \delta < 1$.

Theorem 1. *If $\nu_1, \nu_2, \ldots, \nu_n$ are interchangeable random variables, then for $i \geq 1$*

$$(11)\quad \mathbf{P}\{\zeta_n \leq k \mid \zeta_0 = i\} = \mathbf{P}\{N_n \leq n + k - i\} - \sum_{j=1}^{n-i} \sum_{l=0}^{n-i-j} \left(1 - \frac{l}{n-j}\right) \mathbf{P}\{N_j = j + k, N_n = j + k + l\},$$

$$\mathbf{P}\{\zeta_n \leq k \mid \zeta_0 = 0\} = \mathbf{P}\{\zeta_n \leq k \mid \zeta_0 = 1\}$$

and, in particular,

$$(12)\qquad \mathbf{P}\{\zeta_n = 0 \mid \zeta_n = i\} = \sum_{j=0}^{n-i} \left(1 - \frac{j}{n}\right) \mathbf{P}\{N_n = j\}$$

for $i \geq 0$.

Proof. Now ζ_n is given by (1). If we replace $\nu_1, \nu_2, \ldots, \nu_n$ by $\nu_n, \nu_{n-1}, \ldots, \nu_1$ respectively in (1), then we obtain a new random variable

$$(13)\quad \tilde{\zeta}_n = \max\,\{N_r - r + 1 \text{ for } r = 1, \ldots, n \text{ and } N_n - n + \zeta_0\}$$

which has exactly the same distribution as ζ_n. Thus

$$(14)\quad \mathbf{P}\{\zeta_n \leq k \mid \zeta_0 = i\} = \mathbf{P}\{N_r < r + k \text{ for } r = 1, \ldots, n \text{ and } N_n \leq n + k - i\},$$

and for $i \geq 1$ the right-hand side of (14) is given by (2) of Section 6. If $i = 0$, then (14) is the same as for $i = 1$. If $k = 0$, then (14) is given by (4) of Section 6. This completes the proof of the theorem.

If $\nu_1, \nu_2, \ldots, \nu_n$ are mutually independent and identically distributed random variables, then in (11) we can write $\mathbf{P}\{N_j = j + k, N_n = j + k + l\} = \mathbf{P}\{N_j = j + k\}\mathbf{P}\{N_{n-j} = l\}$. In this case by (11) and (12) we have also

$$(15)\quad \mathbf{P}\{\zeta_n \leq k \mid \zeta_0 = i\} = \mathbf{P}\{N_n \leq n + k - i\} - \sum_{j=1}^{n-i} \mathbf{P}\{\zeta_{n-j} = 0 \mid \zeta_0 = i\}\mathbf{P}\{N_j = j + k\}$$

for $i \geq 0$. If we remove the condition $\zeta_0 = i$, we get

$$(16)\quad \mathbf{P}\{\zeta_n \leq k\} = \mathbf{P}\{\zeta_0 + N_n \leq n + k\} - \sum_{j=1}^{n} \mathbf{P}\{\zeta_{n-j} = 0\}\mathbf{P}\{N_j = j + k\}.$$

Theorem 2. *If $\{\nu_r\}$ are mutually independent and identically distributed random variables and if $\gamma < 1$, then the limiting distribution* $\lim_{n\to\infty} \mathbf{P}\{\xi_n = k\} =$ *P_k, $k = 0, 1, 2, \ldots$, exists and is independent of the distribution of the initial queue size. For $|z| < 1$ we have*

$$(17)\qquad P(z) = \sum_{k=0}^{\infty} P_k z^k = \frac{(1-\gamma)(1-z)\pi(z)}{\pi(z) - z}.$$

Here $P_0 = 1 - \gamma$ and P_k, $k = 1, 2, \ldots$, is explicitly given by (15) *and* (16) *of Section* 7. *The probabilities $Q_k = P_0 + \cdots + P_k$, $k = 0, 1, 2, \ldots$, are explicitly given by* (10) *and* (11) *of Section* 7. *We have also*

$$(18)\qquad Q_k = 1 - (1-\gamma)\sum_{j=1}^{\infty} \mathbf{P}\{N_j = j + k\}$$

for $k = 0, 1, 2, \ldots$.

If $\gamma \geq 1$ and $\pi_1 \neq 1$, then $\lim_{n\to\infty} \mathbf{P}\{\xi_n = k\} = 0$ *for every k irrespective of the distribution of the initial queue size.*

Proof. The limiting distribution of $\{\xi_n\}$ is exactly the same as that of $\{\zeta_n\}$ because by (3)

$$(19)\qquad \lim_{n\to\infty} \mathbf{P}\{\xi_n \leq k \mid \zeta_0 = i\} = \lim_{n\to\infty} \mathbf{P}\{\zeta_n \leq k \mid \zeta_0 = i\}$$

for every i. Now by (14)

$$(20)\quad \mathbf{P}\{N_r < r + k \text{ for } r = 1, \ldots, n\} - \mathbf{P}\{\zeta_0 + N_n > n + k\} \leq \mathbf{P}\{\zeta_n \leq k\} \leq \mathbf{P}\{N_r < r + k \text{ for } r = 1, \ldots, n\}.$$

By the weak law of large numbers $\lim_{n\to\infty} N_n/n = \gamma$ in probability. If $\gamma < 1$, then this implies that $\lim_{n\to\infty} \mathbf{P}\{\zeta_0 + N_n > n + k\} = 0$ for any random variable ζ_0 and for any k. If $\gamma < 1$ and let $n \to \infty$ in (20), then by the continuity theorem for probabilities we get

$$(21)\qquad \lim_{n\to\infty} \mathbf{P}\{\zeta_n \leq k\} = \mathbf{P}\{N_r < r + k \text{ for } r = 1, 2, \ldots\} = Q_k$$

independently of the distribution of the initial queue size. The probabilities $\{Q_k\}$ are given by Theorem 3 or by Theorem 4 of Section 6. Explicit formulas for Q_k, $k = 0, 1, 2, \ldots$, and for $P_k = Q_k - Q_{k-1}$, $k = 1, 2, \ldots$, are given in Section 7.

If $\gamma \geq 1$ and $\pi_1 \neq 1$, then by Theorem 3 of Section 6 the extreme right member of (20) tends to 0 as $n \to \infty$ which implies that $\lim_{n\to\infty} \mathbf{P}\{\zeta_n \leq k\} = 0$ for all k. This completes the proof of the theorem.

NOTE. If we suppose that $\pi_0 > 0$ and $\pi_0 + \pi_1 < 1$, then Theorem 2 can also be proved by using the theory of Markov chains. In this case $\{\zeta_n, n = 0, 1, 2, \ldots\}$ is an irreducible and aperiodic Markov chain with state space $I = \{0, 1, 2, \ldots\}$. Consequently the limits $\lim_{n\to\infty} \mathbf{P}\{\zeta_n = k\} = P_k$, $k = 0, 1, 2, \ldots$, exist and are independent of the distribution of the initial queue size. There are two possibilities: (i) either $P_k > 0$ for $k = 0, 1, 2, \ldots$ and $\{P_k\}$ is a probability distribution, that is, $\sum_{k=0}^{\infty} P_k = 1$, or (ii) $P_k = 0$ for $k = 0, 1, 2, \ldots$. In the case (i), $\{\zeta_n\}$ has a unique stationary distribution which agrees with $\{P_k\}$. In the case (ii), $\{\zeta_n\}$ has no stationary distribution.

If we suppose that $\{P_k\}$ is a stationary distribution of $\{\zeta_n\}$ and

$$(22) \qquad P(z) = \sum_{k=0}^{\infty} P_k z^k$$

for $|z| \leq 1$, then by (2)

$$(23) \qquad P(z) = \left[P_0 + \frac{P(z) - P_0}{z}\right]\pi(z)$$

whence

$$(24) \qquad P(z) = P_0 \frac{(1 - z)\pi(z)}{\pi(z) - z}.$$

The requirement $P(1) = 1$ yields that $P_0 = 1 - \pi'(1) = 1 - \gamma$. Consequently, if $\gamma < 1$, then there is a stationary distribution $\{P_k\}$ whose generating function $P(z)$ is given by (24) with $P_0 = 1 - \gamma$, and $\{\zeta_n, n = 0, 1, \ldots\}$ belongs to (i). If $\gamma \geq 1$, then the assumption that a stationary distribution exists leads to a contradiction, that is, $\{\zeta_n, n = 0, 1, 2, \ldots\}$ has no stationary distribution and $\{\zeta_n, n = 0, 1, 2, \ldots\}$ belongs to (ii).

The probability $\mathbf{P}\{\beta_n < k\} = \mathbf{P}\{\alpha_n > n - k\}$ for $0 < k \leq n$ is given by the following theorem.

Theorem 3. *If $\nu_1, \nu_2, \ldots, \nu_n$ are interchangeable random variables, then*

$$(25) \qquad \mathbf{P}\{\alpha_n > k - i \mid \zeta_0 = i\} = \sum_{j=k}^{n-1} \frac{k}{j} \mathbf{P}\{N_j = j - k\}$$

for $i \leq k < n$ and $k > 0$. If $k = i = 0$, then $\mathbf{P}\{\alpha_n > 0 \mid \zeta_0 = 0\} = 1$.

Proof. By (4)

$$(26) \qquad \mathbf{P}\{\alpha_n > k - i \mid \zeta_0 = i\} = 1 - \mathbf{P}\{r - N_r < k \text{ for } r = 0, 1, \ldots, n - 1\}.$$

If $k > 0$, then the right-hand side is given by (1) of Section 8. The case $k = 0$ is trivial.

Theorem 4. *If ν_r, $r = 1, 2, \ldots$, are mutually independent and identically distributed random variables, if* $\mathbf{E}\{\nu_r\} = \gamma < 1$ *and if* $\mathbf{Var}\{\nu_r\} = \sigma^2$ *is a finite positive number, then*

$$\lim_{n\to\infty} \mathbf{P}\left\{\frac{\beta_n - n\gamma}{\sigma n^{1/2}} \leq x\right\} = \Phi(x) \tag{27}$$

independently of the distribution of ζ_0. Here $\Phi(x)$ is the normal distribution function with mean 0 *and variance* 1.

Proof. By (5)

$$\beta_n = \zeta_0 + N_n - \zeta_n. \tag{28}$$

Now by the central limit theorem

$$\lim_{n\to\infty} \mathbf{P}\left\{\frac{N_n - n\gamma}{\sigma n^{1/2}} \leq x\right\} = \Phi(x). \tag{29}$$

For any ζ_0 we have $\lim_{n\to\infty} \zeta_0/n^{1/2} = 0$ in probability. If $\gamma < 1$, then $\lim_{n\to\infty} N_n/n = \gamma < 1$ in probability and this implies that $\lim_{n\to\infty} \dfrac{\zeta_n}{n^{1/2}} = 0$ in probability. Accordingly, if $\gamma < 1$, then β_n and N_n have the same asymptotic distribution for $n \to \infty$. This proves the theorem.

NOTE. If the limiting distribution

$$\lim_{n\to\infty} \mathbf{P}\left\{\frac{N_n - n\gamma}{g_n} \leq x\right\} = G(x) \tag{30}$$

exists and $\lim_{n\to\infty} g_n = \infty$, then by (28) it follows that β_n has the same asymptotic distribution as N_n provided that $\gamma < 1$.

For example, if $\mathbf{P}\{\nu_r > x\} = h(x)/x^\alpha$ where $1 < \alpha < 2$ and $\lim_{x\to\infty} \dfrac{h(cx)}{h(x)} = 1$ for every positive c and if g_n is such that $\mathbf{P}\{\nu_r > g_n\} \sim 1/n$, then in (30) $G(x) = G_\alpha(x)$ where $G_\alpha(x)$ is the stable distribution function whose characteristic function is given by

$$\int_{-\infty}^{\infty} e^{izx}\, dG_\alpha(x) = \exp\left\{-\,|z|^\alpha\left(\cos\frac{\pi\alpha}{2} - i\sin\frac{\pi\alpha}{2}\operatorname{sgn} z\right)\Gamma(1-\alpha)\right\} \tag{31}$$

for real z values.

Theorem 5. *If $\nu_1, \nu_2, \ldots, \nu_n$ are interchangeable random variables, and if the initial queue size $\zeta_0 = i \geq 1$, then the probability that the initial busy period consists of n services is given by*

$$\mathbf{P}\{\rho_0 = n \mid \zeta_0 = i\} = \frac{i}{n}\mathbf{P}\{N_n = n - i\}. \tag{32}$$

Proof. By (6) and by Theorem 1 of Section 4 we have

$$(33)\quad \mathbf{P}\{\rho_0 = n \mid \zeta_0 = i\}$$
$$= \mathbf{P}\{N_r > r - i \text{ for } r = 1, \ldots, n-1 \text{ and } N_n = n - i\}$$
$$= \mathbf{P}\{N_r < r \text{ for } r = 1, \ldots, n \text{ and } N_n = n - i\}$$
$$= \frac{i}{n}\mathbf{P}\{N_n = n - i\}.$$

This proves (32).

If, in particular, $\nu_1, \nu_2, \ldots, \nu_r, \ldots$ are mutually independent and identically distributed random variables, then ρ_r, $r = 0, 1, 2, \ldots$, are mutually independent random variables and

$$\mathbf{P}\{\rho_r = n\} = \mathbf{P}\{\rho_0 = n \mid \zeta_0 = 1\} \tag{34}$$

for $r = 1, 2, \ldots$ and $n = 1, 2, \ldots$.

Theorem 6. *If $\nu_1, \nu_2, \ldots, \nu_r, \ldots$ are mutually independent and identically distributed random variables, then*

$$\mathbf{P}\{\rho_0 < \infty \mid \zeta_0 = i\} = \delta^i \tag{35}$$

for $i \geq 1$, where δ is the smallest nonnegative real root of the equation $\pi(z) = z$. If $\gamma \leq 1$ and $\pi_1 \neq 1$, then $\delta = 1$, whereas if $\gamma > 1$ or $\pi_1 = 1$, then $\delta < 1$.

Proof. By (6)

$$\mathbf{P}\{\rho_0 < \infty \mid \zeta_0 = i\} = 1 - \mathbf{P}\left\{\sup_{1 \leq r < \infty} (r - N_r) < i\right\} \tag{36}$$

and the right-hand side is given by (7) of Section 8.

Theorem 7. *If $\nu_1, \nu_2, \ldots, \nu_r, \ldots$ are mutually independent and identically distributed random variables and the initial queue size is $\zeta_0 = i \geq 1$, then the probability that the maximal queue length during the initial busy period is $\leq k$ is given by*

$$\mathbf{P}\{\zeta_r \leq k \text{ for } r = 1, \ldots, \rho_0 \mid \zeta_0 = i\} = \frac{Q_{k-i}}{Q_k} \tag{37}$$

for $k \geq i$ where Q_k is defined by the generating function

$$Q(z) = \sum_{k=0}^{\infty} Q_k z^k = \frac{Q_0 \pi(z)}{\pi(z) - z} \tag{38}$$

for $|z| < \delta$ where δ is the smallest nonnegative real root of $\pi(z) = z$ and Q_0 is an arbitrary non-null constant.

Proof. Let $\rho(i)$ be the smallest r for which $N_r = r - i$. If $\zeta_0 = i$, then the probability that the maximal queue length in the initial busy period is $\leq k$ is given by

$$\mathbf{P}\{N_r < r + k - i \text{ for } r = 1, \ldots, \rho(i)\} = \frac{Q_{k-i}}{Q_k} \tag{39}$$

where Q_k, $k = 0, 1, \ldots$, is given by Theorem 2 of Section 7.

If, in particular, $i = 1$ in (37), then we get the probability that the maximal queue length in the rth busy period ($r = 1, 2, \ldots$) is $\leq k$.

EXAMPLES. (i) Suppose that in the time interval $(0, \infty)$ customers arrive at a counter in accordance with a Poisson process of density λ. The initial queue size at time $u = 0$ is ζ_0. The customers are served by a single server who starts working at time $u = 0$. The server is busy if there is at least one customer in the system. The service times, $\chi_1, \chi_2, \ldots, \chi_r, \ldots$ are mutually independent and identically distributed positive random variables with distribution function $\mathbf{P}\{\chi_r \leq x\} = H(x)$ and independent of the arrival times. Let

$$\psi(s) = \int_0^\infty e^{-sx}\, dH(x) \tag{40}$$

for $\text{Re}(s) \geq 0$,

$$a = \int_0^\infty x\, dH(x) \tag{41}$$

and

$$\sigma_a^2 = \int_0^\infty (x - a)^2\, dH(x), \tag{42}$$

if they exist.

Denote by ν_r, $r = 1, 2, \ldots$, the number of arrivals during the rth service time. Then $\{\nu_r\}$ is a sequence of mutually independent and identically distributed random variables with distribution

$$\mathbf{P}\{\nu_r = j\} = \int_0^\infty e^{-\lambda x} \frac{(\lambda x)^j}{j!}\, dH(x) \qquad (j = 0, 1, 2, \ldots). \tag{43}$$

The distribution of N_r, $r = 0, 1, 2, \ldots$, is given by

$$\mathbf{P}\{N_r = j\} = \int_0^\infty e^{-\lambda x} \frac{(\lambda x)^j}{j!}\, dH_r(x) \qquad (j = 0, 1, 2, \ldots) \tag{44}$$

where $H_r(x)$ denotes the rth iterated convolution of $H(x)$ with itself; $H_0(x) = 1$ if $x \geq 0$ and $H_0(x) = 0$ if $x < 0$.

In this case $\pi(z) = \psi(\lambda(1 - z))$, $\gamma = \lambda a$ and $\sigma^2 = \lambda(a^2 + \sigma_a^2)$. The theorems of this section can be applied to find the distributions of ξ_n, ζ_n, α_n, β_n, ρ_n and their asymptotic distributions.

(ii) Consider the previous example with the modification that in the time interval $(0, \infty)$ customers arrive at the counter in batches of random size in accordance with a Poisson process of density λ. Suppose that the batch sizes are mutually independent and identically distributed random variables and independent of the arrival times. Denote by $p_j, j = 1, 2, \ldots,$ the probability that a batch consists of j customers and let

$$p(z) = \sum_{j=1}^{\infty} p_j z^j. \tag{45}$$

If ν_r, $r = 1, 2, \ldots,$ denotes the number of customers joining the queue during the rth service time, then $\nu_1, \nu_2, \ldots, \nu_r, \ldots$ are mutually independent and identically distributed random variables whose common generating function is given by

$$\pi(z) = \psi[\lambda(1 - p(z))]. \tag{46}$$

Knowing the distribution of ν_r, $r = 1, 2, \ldots,$ we can apply the theorems of this section to find the distributions of ξ_n, ζ_n, α_n, β_n, ρ_n and their asymptotic distributions.

The Process Q^*

Consider the queuing process $Q^* = \{\zeta_0; N_r^*, r = 0, 1, 2, \ldots\}$ introduced in Section 27. It is supposed that $N_r^* = \nu_1^* + \cdots + \nu_r^*$ for $r = 1, 2, \ldots$ where $\{\nu_r^*\}$ is the dual sequence of $\{\nu_r\}$ and $\{\nu_r\}$ are either interchangeable random variables taking on nonnegative integral values, or, in particular, mutually independent and identically distributed random variables taking on nonnegative integral values. Write $N_r = \nu_1 + \cdots + \nu_r$ for $r = 1, 2, \ldots.$

We are interested in finding the distributions of ξ_n^*, ζ_n^*, α_n^*, β_n^*, ρ_n^* for every n. These random variables are completely determined by the process Q^*, or equivalently by the process Q. For the process Q the distributions of the random variables ξ_n, ζ_n, α_n, β_n, ρ_n have been determined in this section. Now we shall reduce the problem of finding the distributions of α_n^*, β_n^* and ρ_n^* to that of ζ_n.

The probability $\mathbf{P}\{\beta_n^* < k\} = \mathbf{P}\{\alpha_n^* > n - k\}$ for $0 < k \le n$ is given by the following theorem.

Theorem 8. *If $\{\nu_r\}$ are interchangeable random variables, then*

$$\mathbf{P}\{\beta_n^* < k + i \mid \zeta_0 = i\} = \mathbf{P}\{N_k \ge n - 1\} + \sum_{j=1}^{k-1} \sum_{l=0}^{k-j} \left(1 - \frac{l}{k - j}\right) \mathbf{P}\{N_j = j + n - k - 1, N_k - N_j = l\} \tag{47}$$

provided that $0 < k \le n - i$, and $0 < k < n$. If $k = n - 1$, then (47) *reduces to*

$$\mathbf{P}\{\beta_n^* < n - 1 + i \mid \zeta_0 = i\} = \sum_{j=1}^{n-1} \left(1 - \frac{j}{n - 1}\right) \mathbf{P}\{N_{n-1} = j\}. \tag{48}$$

Proof. If $k \leq n - i$, then by (4) we have

$$(49)\quad \mathbf{P}\{\beta_n^* < k + i \mid \zeta_0 = i\} = \mathbf{P}\{N_r^* \leq r - n + k \text{ for some } r = 0, 1, \ldots, n - 1\}.$$

Hence if $k \leq n - 1$, then by (2) of Section 9

$$(50)\quad \begin{aligned} \mathbf{P}\{\beta_n^* < k + i \mid \zeta_0 = i\} &= \mathbf{P}\{N_r \geq r - n - k - 1 \text{ for some } r = 1, 2, \ldots, k\} \\ &= 1 - \mathbf{P}\{N_r - r < n - k - 1 \text{ for } r = 1, 2, \ldots, k\} \end{aligned}$$

and the extreme right member is given by (1) of Section 6. This proves (47). If, in particular, $k = n - 1$ in (50), then by (4) of Section 6 we get (48). In this case $i = 0$ or $i = 1$.

It is interesting to mention the following relation

$$(51)\quad \mathbf{P}\{\beta_n^* < k + i \mid \zeta_0 = i\} = 1 - \mathbf{P}\{\zeta_k \leq n - k - 1 \mid \zeta_0 = 0\}$$

which follows from (14) and (50).

Theorem 9. *If $\{\nu_r\}$ are mutually independent and identically distributed random variables, if $\mathbf{E}\{\nu_r\} = \gamma > 1$, and if $\mathbf{Var}\,\{\nu_r\} = \sigma^2$ is a finite positive number, then*

$$(52)\quad \lim_{n\to\infty} \mathbf{P}\left\{\frac{\beta_n^* - \dfrac{n}{\gamma}}{\sqrt{n\sigma^2/\gamma^3}} \leq x\right\} = \Phi(x)$$

independently of the distribution of ζ_0.

Proof. Now we have

$$(53)\quad \beta_n^* = \zeta_0 + N_n^* - \zeta_n^*$$

where ζ_n^* is given by (1) except that N_r is replaced by N_r^*. By (2) of Section 9 we have

$$(54)\quad \mathbf{P}\{N_n^* < k\} = \mathbf{P}\{N_k \geq n\}$$

for $n + k > 0$. Thus by using (29) we can prove easily that

$$(55)\quad \lim_{n\to\infty} \mathbf{P}\left\{\frac{N_n^* - \dfrac{n}{\gamma}}{\sqrt{n\sigma^2/\gamma^3}} \leq x\right\} = \Phi(x).$$

Since $\lim_{n\to\infty} N_n/n = \gamma$ in probability, it follows that

$$(56)\quad \lim_{n\to\infty} \frac{N_n^*}{n} = \frac{1}{\gamma}$$

in probability. This implies that if $\gamma > 1$, then

$$\lim_{n\to\infty} \frac{\zeta_n^*}{n^{1/2}} = 0$$

in probability. Evidently

$$\lim_{n\to\infty} \frac{\zeta_0}{n^{1/2}} = 0$$

in probability. Accordingly if $\gamma > 1$, then β_n^* has the same asymptotic distribution as N_n^* when $n \to \infty$. This completes the proof of the theorem.

NOTE. If $\mathbf{P}\{\nu_r > x\} = h(x)/x^\alpha$ where $1 < \alpha < 2$ and $\lim_{x\to\infty} h(cx)/h(x) = 1$ for every positive c and g_n is such that $\mathbf{P}\{\nu_r > g_n\} \sim 1/n$, then

$$\lim_{n\to\infty} \mathbf{P}\left\{\frac{N_n - n\gamma}{g_n} \leq x\right\} = G_\alpha(x) \tag{57}$$

where $G_\alpha(x)$ is the stable distribution function defined by (31). Now by using (54) we can prove that

$$\lim_{n\to\infty} \mathbf{P}\left\{\frac{N_n^* - \dfrac{n}{\gamma}}{g_n/\gamma^{(1+\alpha)/\alpha}} \leq x\right\} = 1 - G_\alpha(-x) \tag{58}$$

and if $\gamma > 1$, then β_n^* has the same asymptotic distribution as N_n^* when $n \to \infty$.

Theorem 10. *If $\nu_1, \nu_2, \ldots, \nu_n$ are interchangeable random variables, then*

$$\mathbf{P}\{\rho_0^* < n + k \mid \zeta_0 = k\} = \mathbf{P}\{N_n \geq n + k - 1\} + \sum_{j=1}^{n-1} \sum_{l=0}^{n-j} \left(1 - \frac{l}{n-j}\right) \mathbf{P}\{N_j = j + k - 1, N_n - N_j = l\} \tag{59}$$

for $n \geq 0$ and $k \geq 1$. If $k = 1$, then (59) reduces to

$$\mathbf{P}\{\rho_0^* \leq n \mid \zeta_0 = 1\} = 1 - \sum_{j=0}^{n} \left(1 - \frac{j}{n}\right) \mathbf{P}\{N_n = j\}. \tag{60}$$

Proof. By (6) we have

$$\mathbf{P}\{\rho_0^* < n + k \mid \zeta_0 = k\} = \mathbf{P}\{N_r^* \leq r - k \text{ for some } r = 0, 1, \ldots, n + k - 1\}. \tag{61}$$

Hence by (2) of Section 9 we obtain for $k \geq 1$ that

$$\begin{aligned} \mathbf{P}\{\rho_0^* < n + k \mid \zeta_0 = k\} &= \mathbf{P}\{N_r \geq r + k - 1 \text{ for some } r = 1, 2, \ldots, n\} \\ &= 1 - \mathbf{P}\{N_r - r < k - 1 \text{ for } r = 1, 2, \ldots, n\} \end{aligned} \tag{62}$$

and the extreme right member is given by (1) of Section 6 for $k \geq 1$ and by (4) of Section 6 for $k = 1$.

By (7) we have

$$\mathbf{P}\{\rho_0^* < n + k \mid \zeta_0 = k\} = \mathbf{P}\{\beta_{n+k}^* < n \mid \zeta_0 = 0\} \tag{63}$$

and the right-hand side can be obtained by (47).

It is interesting to mention the following relation

$$\mathbf{P}\{\rho_0^* < n + k \mid \zeta_0 = k\} = 1 - \mathbf{P}\{\zeta_n < k \mid \zeta_0 = 0\} \tag{64}$$

which follows from (1) and (62).

Theorem 11. *If $\{\nu_r\}$ are mutually independent and identically distributed random variables, then*

$$\mathbf{P}\{\rho_0^* < \infty \mid \zeta_0 = k\} = 1 - Q_{k-1} \tag{65}$$

for $k \geq 1$ where Q_k, $k = 0, 1, 2, \ldots$, is defined in Theorem 2.

Proof. By (62)

$$\mathbf{P}\{\rho_0^* < \infty \mid \zeta_0 = k\} = 1 - \mathbf{P}\left\{\sup_{1 \leq r < \infty} (N_r - r) < k - 1\right\} \tag{66}$$

and the right-hand side is given by Theorem 3 and Theorem 4 of Section 6. If $\gamma \geq 1$ and $\pi_1 \neq 1$, then $Q_k = 0$ for every k. If $\gamma < 1$, then $Q_k > 0$ for $k \geq 0$.

EXAMPLE. Suppose that in the time interval $(0, \infty)$ customers arrive at a counter at times $\tau_1', \tau_2', \ldots, \tau_r', \ldots$ where $\tau_r' - \tau_{r-1}'$, $r = 1, 2, \ldots$, $(\tau_0' = 0)$ are mutually independent, identically distributed, positive random variables with distribution function $F(x)$. The customers are attended by a single server who starts working at time $u = 0$. Suppose that the service times are mutually independent and identically distributed random variables with distribution function $H(x) = 1 - e^{-\mu x}$ $(x \geq 0)$ and independent of the arrival times. Denote by ζ_0 the initial queue size. This queuing process, which we shall denote by Q', is the inverse process of a queuing process Q defined in the following way.

In the time interval $(0, \infty)$ customers arrive at a counter in accordance with a Poisson process of density μ. The customers are attended by a single server who starts working at time $u = 0$. The service times are mutually independent and identically distributed random variables with distribution function $F(x)$ and independent of the arrival times. The initial queue size is ζ_0. That is, Q' is the inverse process of $Q = \{\zeta_0; N_r, r = 0, 1, 2, \ldots\}$ where $\nu_1, \nu_2, \ldots, \nu_r, \ldots$ are mutually independent and identically distributed random variables with distribution

$$\mathbf{P}\{\nu_r = j\} = \int_0^\infty e^{-\mu x} \frac{(\mu x)^j}{j!}\, dF(x) \qquad (j = 0, 1, 2, \ldots). \tag{67}$$

The distribution of $N_r = \nu_1 + \cdots + \nu_r$, $r = 0, 1, 2, \ldots$, is given by

$$(68) \qquad \mathbf{P}\{N_r = j\} = \int_0^\infty e^{-\mu x} \frac{(\mu x)^j}{j!} \, dF_r(x) \qquad (j = 0, 1, 2, \ldots)$$

where $F_r(x)$ denotes the rth iterated convolution of $F(x)$ with itself; $F_0(x) = 1$ if $x \geq 0$ and $F_0(x) = 0$ if $x < 0$.

For the inverse process Q' denote by ξ_n', ζ_n', α_n', β_n', ρ_n' the same random variables that ξ_n, ζ_n, α_n, β_n, ρ_n denote for the process Q. If Q^* denotes the dual process of Q and we shall denote by ξ_n^*, ζ_n^*, α_n^*, β_n^*, ρ_n^* the corresponding random variables for Q^*, then it is easy to see that $\alpha_n' = \alpha_n^*$, $\beta_n' = \beta_n^*$ and $\rho_0' = \rho_0^*$. The distributions of the random variables α_n^*, β_n^* and ρ_n^* are given in this section. To apply the general theorems we introduce the following notation:

$$(69) \qquad \phi(s) = \int_0^\infty e^{-sx} \, dF(x)$$

for $\mathrm{Re}(s) \geq 0$,

$$(70) \qquad b = \int_0^\infty x \, dF(x)$$

and

$$(71) \qquad \sigma_b^2 = \int_0^\infty (x - b)^2 \, dF(x)$$

if they exist.

Only the distributions of ξ_n' and ζ_n' need to be determined. By (3) we have

$$(72) \qquad \mathbf{P}\{\zeta'_{n+i} \leq k \mid \zeta_0 = i\} = \mathbf{P}\{\xi'_{n+k+1} \leq k \mid \zeta_0 = i\}$$

and thus it is sufficient to determine the distribution of ξ_n' for $n = 1, 2, \ldots$. In what follows we shall use the notation $\xi_0' = \zeta_0 - 1$ and determine the distribution of ξ_n'.

Theorem 12. *We have*

$$(73) \quad \mathbf{P}\{\xi_n' < k \mid \xi_0' = i\} = \mathbf{P}\{N_n > n + i - k\} - \sum_{j=k}^{n} \frac{k}{j} \mathbf{P}\{N_j = j - k\}\mathbf{P}\{N_{n-j} > n + i - j\}$$

if $k = 1, 2, \ldots$ *and* $i = 0, 1, \ldots$. *In particular,*

$$(74) \qquad \mathbf{P}\{\xi_n' < k \mid \xi_0' = 0\} = \sum_{j=k}^{n} \frac{k}{j} \mathbf{P}\{N_j = j - k\}$$

if $k = 1, 2, \ldots$. *The distribution of* N_r, $r = 0, 1, 2, \ldots$, *is given by* (68).

Proof. It can easily be seen that

$$(75) \qquad \xi_n' = [\xi'_{n-1} + 1 - \nu_n]^+$$

for $n = 1, 2, \ldots,$ whence

$$(76) \quad \xi_n' = \max \{(n - r) - (N_n - N_r) \text{ for } r = 0, 1, \ldots, n \text{ and } \xi_0' + n - N_n\}.$$

If in (76) we replace $\nu_1, \nu_2, \ldots, \nu_n$ by $\nu_n, \nu_{n-1}, \ldots, \nu_1$ respectively then we obtain a new random variable

$$(77) \quad \xi_n' = \max \{r - N_r \text{ for } r = 0, 1, \ldots, n \text{ and } \xi_0' + n - N_n\}$$

which has exactly the same distribution as (76). Thus

$$(78) \quad \mathbf{P}\{\xi_n' < k \mid \xi_0' = i\} = \mathbf{P}\{r - N_r < k \text{ for } r = 0, 1, \ldots, n \text{ and } n - N_n < k - i\}$$

and the right-hand side is given by (3) of Section 8. In the particular case $i = 0$, (78) is given by (1) of Section 8. This proves the theorem.

Theorem 13. *If $k \geq 1$, then*

$$(79) \qquad \lim_{n\to\infty} \mathbf{P}\{\xi_n' < k\} = 1 - \delta^k$$

independently of the distribution of ξ_0'. In (79) δ is the smallest nonnegative real root of

$$(80) \qquad \phi(\mu(1 - \delta)) = \delta.$$

If $\mu b \leq 1$, then $\delta = 1$, and if $\mu b > 1$, then $\delta < 1$.

Proof. By (78) we obtain that

$$(81) \qquad \lim_{n\to\infty} \mathbf{P}\{\xi_n' < k\} = \mathbf{P}\left\{\sup_{1\leq r<\infty} (r - N_r) < k\right\}$$

independently of the distribution of ξ_0'. The right-hand side of (81) is given by Theorem 3 of Section 8.

29. FLUCTUATIONS OF THE WAITING TIME

Consider the queuing process $W = \{\eta(0); \chi(u), 0 \leq u < \infty\}$ introduced in Section 27. It is supposed that $\{\chi(u), 0 \leq u < \infty\}$ is a real-valued separable stochastic process almost all of whose sample functions are non-decreasing step functions vanishing at $u = 0$. We are interested in finding the distributions of $\eta(t)$, $\alpha(t)$, $\beta(t)$ and θ_r, $r = 0, 1, 2, \ldots.$ These random variables are completely determined by the process W.

The waiting time at time t is given by

$$(1) \quad \eta(t) = \sup \{\chi(t) - \chi(u) - (t - u) \text{ for } 0 \leq u \leq t \text{ and } \eta(0) + \chi(t) - t\}.$$

For if in the interval $[0, t]$, u is the greatest u such that $\eta(u) = 0$, then $\eta(t) = \chi(t) - \chi(u) - (t - u)$ and if there is no such u in $[0, t]$, then $\eta(t) = \eta(0) + \chi(t) - t$, and in each case (1) holds.

The total idle time of the server in the interval $[0, t]$ is given by

$$\alpha(t) = \sup \{u - \chi(u) - \eta(0) \text{ for } 0 \leq u \leq t \text{ and } 0\}, \tag{2}$$

and $\beta(t) = t - \alpha(t)$. Also we have the obvious relation

$$\beta(t) = \eta(0) + \chi(t) - \eta(t). \tag{3}$$

The length of the initial busy period is given by

$$\theta_0 = \inf \{u : \eta(0) + \chi(u) \leq u \text{ and } 0 \leq u < \infty\}. \tag{4}$$

If there is no such u, then $\theta_0 = \infty$.

There is an interesting relation between the distributions of $\alpha(t)$ and θ_0. If $0 < x \leq t$ and $c \geq 0$, then we have

$$\mathbf{P}\{\alpha(t) \geq x \mid \eta(0) = c\} = \mathbf{P}\{\theta_0 \leq t \mid \eta(0) = c + x\} \tag{5}$$

and

$$\mathbf{P}\{\alpha(t) = 0 \mid \eta(0) = c\} = \mathbf{P}\{\theta_0 \geq t \mid \eta(0) = c\}. \tag{6}$$

The relation (6) is evident. To prove (5) we note that by (2)

$$\mathbf{P}\{\alpha(t) \geq x\} = \mathbf{P}\{\eta(0) + \chi(u) + x \leq u \text{ for some } u \in [0, t]\} \tag{7}$$

and by (4)

$$\mathbf{P}\{\theta_0 \leq t\} = \mathbf{P}\{\eta(0) + \chi(u) \leq u \text{ for some } u \in [0, t]\}. \tag{8}$$

If we compare (7) and (8), then we can conclude that the probability that $\alpha(t) \geq x$ in a process with initial occupation time $\eta(0) = c$ is the same as the probability that $\theta_0 \leq t$ in a process with initial occupation time $\eta(0) = c + x$. This proves (5).

The Process W

In what follows we shall suppose that $\{\chi(u), 0 \leq u < \infty\}$ is a separable stochastic process either with interchangeable increments or, in particular, with stationary independent increments and that in both cases almost all sample functions of the process are nondecreasing step functions vanishing at $u = 0$. In both cases we have $\mathbf{E}\{\chi(u)\} = \rho u$ for $u \geq 0$ where ρ is a nonnegative number (possibly ∞). In what follows we shall exclude the trivial case $\mathbf{P}\{\chi(u) = 0\} = 1$ for all $u \geq 0$.

If $\{\chi(u), 0 \leq u < \infty\}$ has stationary independent increments, then

$$\mathbf{E}\{e^{-s\chi(u)}\} = e^{-u\Phi(s)} \tag{9}$$

for $\text{Re}(s) \geq 0$ with an appropriate $\Phi(s)$. We have $\rho = \Phi'(+0)$. If $\lambda = \Phi(\infty)$ is a finite positive number, then we can define a distribution function $H(x)$ such that

$$\psi(s) = \int_0^\infty e^{-sx}\, dH(x) = 1 - \frac{\Phi(s)}{\lambda} \tag{10}$$

for $\text{Re}(s) \geq 0$ and $H(x) = 0$ if $x < 0$. If ρ is a finite positive number, then we can define a distribution function $H^*(x)$ such that

$$\psi^*(s) = \int_0^\infty e^{-sx}\, dH^*(x) = \frac{\Phi(s)}{\rho s} \tag{11}$$

for $\text{Re}(s) > 0$ and $H^*(x) = 0$ if $x < 0$. We shall write $H_n^*(x)$, $n = 0, 1, 2, \ldots$, for the nth iterated convolution of $H^*(x)$ with itself; $H_0^*(x) = 1$ if $x \geq 0$ and $H_0^*(x) = 0$ if $x < 0$. We shall denote by ω the largest non-negative real root of $\Phi(s) = s$. If $\rho \leq 1$, then $\omega = 0$, and if $\rho > 1$, then $\omega > 0$. Further we write $\sigma^2 = -\Phi''(+0)$. Then $\mathbf{Var}\,\{\chi(u)\} = \sigma^2 u$ for $u \geq 0$.

Theorem 1. *If $\{\chi(u), 0 \leq u \leq \infty\}$ has interchangeable increments, then*

$$\mathbf{P}\{\eta(t) \leq x \mid \eta(0) = c\} = \mathbf{P}\{\chi(t) \leq t + x - c\} - \iint\limits_{0<y\leq z\leq t-c} \left(\frac{t-z}{t-y}\right) d_y\, d_z \mathbf{P}\{\chi(y) \leq y + x, \chi(t) \leq z + x\} \tag{12}$$

for all x, $c \geq 0$ and $t > 0$. In particular,

$$\mathbf{P}\{\eta(t) = 0 \mid \eta(0) = c\} = \int_0^{t-c} \left(1 - \frac{y}{t}\right) d_y \mathbf{P}\{\chi(t) \leq y\} \tag{13}$$

if $0 \leq c \leq t$ and $\mathbf{P}\{\eta(t) = 0 \mid \eta(0) = c\} = 0$ if $t < c$.

Proof. Now $\eta(t)$ is defined by (1). If we replace $\chi(t) - \chi(u)$ by $\chi(t - u)$ in (1), then we obtain a new random variable

$$\tilde{\eta}(t) = \sup\,\{\chi(u) - u \text{ for } 0 \leq u \leq t \text{ and } \eta(0) + \chi(t) - t\} \tag{14}$$

which has exactly the same distribution as $\eta(t)$. Thus

$$\mathbf{P}\{\eta(t) \leq x \mid \eta(0) = c\} = \mathbf{P}\{\chi(u) \leq u + x \text{ for } 0 \leq u \leq t \text{ and } \chi(t) \leq t + x - c\} \tag{15}$$

and the right-hand side is given by (2) of Section 15. If $x = 0$, then (15) is also given by (3) of Section 15. This completes the proof of the theorem.

We note that if we consider a process $\{\chi(u), 0 \leq u \leq T\}$ with interchangeable increments where T is a finite positive number, then (12) and (13) are valid for all $t \in (0, T]$.

If the process $\{\chi(u), 0 \le u < \infty\}$ has stationary independent increments, then in (12)

$$\mathbf{P}\{\chi(y) \le y + x, \chi(t) \le z + x\} = \mathbf{P}\{\chi(y) \le y + x\}\mathbf{P}\{\chi(t - y) \le z - y\}.$$

In this case by (13) we can write

$$(16)\quad \mathbf{P}\{\eta(t) \le x \mid \eta(0) = c\} = \mathbf{P}\{\chi(t) \le t + x - c\} - \int_{+0}^{t-c} \mathbf{P}\{\eta(t - y) = 0 \mid \eta(0) = c\}\, d_y\mathbf{P}\{\chi(y) \le y + x\},$$

and if we remove the condition $\eta(0) = c$, we get

$$(17)\quad \mathbf{P}\{\eta(t) \le x\} = \mathbf{P}\{\eta(0) + \chi(t) \le t + x\} - \int_{+0}^{t} \mathbf{P}\{\eta(t - y) = 0\}\, d_y\mathbf{P}\{\chi(y) \le y + x\}$$

for all x. If $x < 0$, then both sides of (17) are 0.

Theorem 2. *If $\{\chi(u), 0 \le u \le \infty\}$ has stationary independent increments and if $\rho < 1$, then the limiting distribution $\lim_{t\to\infty} \mathbf{P}\{\eta(t) \le x\} = W(x)$ exists and is independent of the distribution of the initial occupation time of the server. We have*

$$(18)\qquad W(x) = 1 - (1 - \rho)\int_{+0}^{\infty} d_y\mathbf{P}\{\chi(y) \le y + x\}$$

or

$$(19)\qquad W(x) = (1 - \rho)\sum_{n=0}^{\infty} \rho^n H_n{}^*(x)$$

for all x. If $\rho \ge 1$, then $\lim_{t\to\infty} \mathbf{P}\{\eta(t) \le x\} = 0$ for every x irrespective of the distribution of $\eta(0)$.

Proof. By (15) we have

$$(20)\quad \mathbf{P}\Big\{\sup_{0\le u\le t} [\chi(u) - u] \le x\Big\} - \mathbf{P}\{\eta(0) + \chi(t) > t + x\} \le \mathbf{P}\{\eta(t) \le x\} \le \mathbf{P}\Big\{\sup_{0\le u\le t} [\chi(u) - u] \le x\Big\}.$$

If $\rho < 1$, then by the weak law of large numbers $\lim_{t\to\infty} \mathbf{P}\{\eta(0) + \chi(t) > t + x\} = 0$ for any $\eta(0)$ and x. By the continuity theorem for probabilities we get that

$$(21)\qquad \lim_{t\to\infty} \mathbf{P}\{\eta(t) \le x\} = \mathbf{P}\Big\{\sup_{0\le u<\infty} [\chi(u) - u] \le x\Big\}$$

independently of the distribution of $\eta(0)$. The right-hand side of (21) is given by (15) or by (34) of Section 15. If $\rho \ge 1$, then by (16) of Section 15 the extreme right member of (20) tends to 0 as $t \to \infty$. Hence if $\rho \geq 1$, $\lim_{t\to\infty} \mathbf{P}\{\eta(t) \leq x\} = 0$ for all x independently of the distribution of $\eta(0)$. This completes the proof of the theorem.

By Theorem 4 of Section 15 we can also write

$$\Omega(s) = \int_0^\infty e^{-sx}\, dW(x) = \frac{1-\rho}{1-\rho\psi^*(s)} \tag{22}$$

for $\text{Re}(s) \geq 0$ where $\psi^*(s)$ is defined by (11).

NOTE. If $\rho < 1$, then $\Omega(s)$ can also be found in the following way. Since $\{\eta(t), 0 \leq t < \infty\}$ is a Markov process we can conclude that if $\eta(t)$ has a limiting distribution independent of the distribution of $\eta(0)$, then $\{\eta(t), 0 \leq t < \infty\}$ has a unique stationary distribution which is identical with the limiting distribution.

If $\{\eta(t), 0 \leq t < \infty\}$ is a stationary process, then $\mathbf{P}\{\eta(t) \leq x\} = W(x)$ for all $t \geq 0$. If

$$\Omega(s) = \int_0^\infty e^{-sx}\, dW(x) \tag{23}$$

for $\text{Re}(s) \geq 0$, then by forming the Laplace-Stieltjes transform of (17) we get

$$\Omega(s) = e^{t[s-\Phi(s)]}\Omega(s) - sW(0)\int_0^t e^{y[s-\Phi(s)]}\, dy \tag{24}$$

for all $t \geq 0$ and $\text{Re}(s) \geq 0$. Hence

$$\Omega(s) = \frac{W(0)s}{s - \Phi(s)} \tag{25}$$

for $\text{Re}(s) > 0$. The requirement $\Omega(0) = 1$ yields $W(0) = 1 - \rho$. Accordingly if $\rho < 1$, then $\{\eta(t), 0 \leq t < \infty\}$ has exactly one stationary distribution $W(x)$ whose Laplace-Stieltjes transform is given by (25) with $W(0) = 1 - \rho$. If $\rho < 1$, then $\lim_{t\to\infty} \mathbf{P}\{\eta(t) \leq x\}$ exists and is independent of the initial distribution and thus it is necessarily equal to $W(x)$, the stationary distribution of the process. If $\rho \geq 1$, then the assumption that $\{\eta(t), 0 \leq t < \infty\}$ has a stationary distribution leads to a contradiction.

Since $\alpha(t) + \beta(t) = t$ for all $t \geq 0$, therefore it is sufficient to determine the distribution of $\alpha(t)$ or $\beta(t)$. We have $\mathbf{P}\{\beta(t) < x\} = \mathbf{P}\{\alpha(t) > t - x\}$ for $0 < x \leq t$.

Theorem 3. *If $\{\chi(u), 0 \leq u < \infty\}$ has interchangeable increments, then*

$$\mathbf{P}\{\alpha(t) > x - c \mid \eta(0) = c\} = \int_x^t \frac{x}{y}\, d_y\mathbf{P}\{\chi(y) \leq y - x\} \tag{26}$$

for $0 \leq c < x \leq t$.

Proof. By (2)

$$\mathbf{P}\{\alpha(t) > x - c \mid \eta(0) = c\} = 1 - \mathbf{P}\{u - \chi(u) \leq x \text{ for } 0 \leq u \leq t\} \tag{27}$$

for $0 \leq c < x$ and the right-hand side is given by Theorem 1 of Section 17.

We note that if we consider a process $\{\chi(u), 0 \leq u \leq T\}$ with interchangeable increments where T is a finite positive number, then (26) is valid for all $t \in (0, T]$.

Theorem 4. *If $\{\chi(u), 0 \leq u < \infty\}$ has stationary independent increments, if $\rho < 1$ and if σ^2 is a finite positive number, then*

$$\lim_{t\to\infty} \mathbf{P}\left\{\frac{\beta(t) - \rho t}{\sqrt{\sigma^2 t}} \leq x\right\} = \Phi(x) \tag{28}$$

independently of the distribution of $\eta(0)$. Here $\Phi(x)$ is the normal distribution function with mean 0 and variance 1.

Proof. We have seen that

$$\beta(t) = \eta(0) + \chi(t) - \eta(t). \tag{29}$$

By the central limit theorem

$$\lim_{t\to\infty} \mathbf{P}\left\{\frac{\chi(t) - \rho t}{\sqrt{\sigma^2 t}} \leq x\right\} = \Phi(x). \tag{30}$$

If $\rho < 1$, then by the weak law of large numbers $\lim_{t\to\infty} \frac{\eta(t)}{\sqrt{t}} = 0$ in probability and obviously $\lim_{t\to\infty} \frac{\eta(0)}{\sqrt{t}} = 0$ in probability for any random variable $\eta(0)$. Accordingly if $\rho < 1$, then $\beta(t)$ and $\chi(t)$ have the same asymptotic distribution for $t \to \infty$. This proves the theorem.

NOTE. If the limiting distribution

$$\lim_{t\to\infty} \mathbf{P}\left\{\frac{\chi(t) - \rho t}{g(t)} \leq x\right\} = G(x) \tag{31}$$

exists where $g(t)$ is such that $\lim_{t\to\infty} g(t) = \infty$, then by (29) it follows that in the case of $\rho < 1$ both $\beta(t)$ and $\chi(t)$ have the same asymptotic distribution for $t \to \infty$.

For example, if $\{\chi(u), 0 \leq u < \infty\}$ is a compound Poisson process for which

$$\chi(u) = \sum_{r=1}^{\nu(u)} \chi_r \tag{32}$$

where $\{\nu(u), 0 \leq u < \infty\}$ is a Poisson process of density λ and $\chi_1, \chi_2, \ldots, \chi_r, \ldots$ are mutually independent and identically distributed positive random variables which are independent of $\{\nu(u)\}$ and which satisfy the following conditions: $\mathbf{E}\{\chi_r\} = a$, and $\mathbf{P}\{\chi_r > x\} = h(x)/x^\alpha$ where $1 < \alpha < 2$ and

$$\lim_{x \to \infty} \frac{h(cx)}{h(x)} = 1$$

for every positive c, then

$$\lim_{t \to \infty} \mathbf{P}\left\{\frac{\chi(t) - \rho t}{\lambda^{1/\alpha} g(t)} \leq x\right\} = G_\alpha(x) \tag{33}$$

where $G_\alpha(x)$ is the stable distribution function defined by (31) of Section 28, $\rho = \lambda a$ and $g(t)$ is chosen such that $\mathbf{P}\{\chi_r > g(t)\} \sim 1/t$.

Theorem 5. *If $\{\chi(u), 0 \leq u < \infty\}$ has interchangeable increments, and the initial occupation time of the server is $\eta(0) = c > 0$, then the probability that the length of the initial busy period is $\leq t$ is given by*

$$\mathbf{P}\{\theta_0 \leq t \mid \eta(0) = c\} = \int_c^t \frac{c}{y}\, d_y \mathbf{P}\{\chi(y) \leq y - c\} \tag{34}$$

for $t \geq c$. If $t < c$, then $\mathbf{P}\{\theta_0 \leq t \mid \eta(0) = c\} = 0$.

Proof. By (4)

$$\mathbf{P}\{\theta_0 \leq t \mid \eta(0) = c\} = 1 - \mathbf{P}\{u - \chi(u) \leq c \text{ for } 0 \leq u \leq t\} \tag{35}$$

and the probability on the right-hand side is given by Theorem 1 of Section 17. This proves (34).

If we suppose that $\{\chi(u), 0 \leq u < \infty\}$ has stationary independent increments and $\lambda = \Phi(\infty) < \infty$, then $\{\chi(u), 0 \leq u < \infty\}$ is a compound Poisson process and $\theta_0, \theta_1, \theta_2, \ldots$ are mutually independent random variables, and $\theta_1, \theta_2, \ldots$ have a common distribution. For $r = 1, 2, \ldots$ we have $\mathbf{P}\{\theta_r \leq t\} = \mathbf{P}\{\theta_0 \leq t\}$ provided that $\eta(0)$ is a random variable which has the same distribution as the magnitude of a positive jump of the process $\{\chi(u), 0 \leq u < \infty\}$. Thus we obtain that

$$\mathbf{P}\{\theta_r \leq t\} = \frac{1}{\lambda} \int_0^t \frac{1}{y}\, d_y \mathbf{P}\{0 < \chi(y) \leq y\} \tag{36}$$

for $t \geq 0$ and $r = 1, 2, \ldots$.

Theorem 6. *If $\{\chi(u), 0 \leq u < \infty\}$ has stationary independent increments, then*

$$\mathbf{P}\{\theta_0 < \infty \mid \eta(0) = c\} = e^{-\omega c} \tag{37}$$

where ω is the largest real root of the equation

$$\Phi(\omega) = \omega. \tag{38}$$

If $0 \le \rho \le 1$, *then* $\omega = 0$, *whereas if* $\rho > 1$, *then* $\omega = 0$.

Proof. Evidently

$$\mathbf{P}\{\theta_0 < \infty \mid \eta(0) = c\} = 1 - \mathbf{P}\left\{\sup_{0 \le u < \infty} [u - \chi(u)] \le c\right\} \tag{39}$$

and the probability on the right-hand side is given by Theorem 3 of Section 17.

***Theorem** 7. If* $\{\chi(u), 0 \le u < \infty\}$ *has stationary independent increments, and if the initial occupation time of the server is* $\eta(0) = c > 0$, *then the probability that the maximal waiting time during the initial busy period is* $\le x$ *is given by*

$$\mathbf{P}\left\{\sup_{0 \le u \le \theta_0} \eta(u) \le x \mid \eta(0) = c\right\} = \frac{W(x - c)}{W(x)} \tag{40}$$

for $x \ge c$ *where* $W(x)$ *is defined by*

$$\int_0^\infty e^{-sx}\, dW(x) = \frac{W(0)s}{s - \Phi(s)} \tag{41}$$

for $\mathrm{Re}(s) > \omega$ *with an arbitrary non-null* $W(0)$. $W(x)$ *is given explicitly by* (12) *or* (14) *of Section* 16.

Proof. Let $\theta(c) = \inf\{u : \chi(u) - u \le -c \text{ and } 0 \le u < \infty\}$ and $\theta(c) = \infty$ if $\chi(u) - u > -c$ for all $u \ge 0$. If $\eta(0) = c$, then the probability that the maximal waiting time during the initial busy period is $\le x$ equals

$$\mathbf{P}\{\chi(u) \le u + x - c \text{ for } 0 \le u \le \theta(c)\} = \frac{W(x - c)}{W(x)} \tag{42}$$

for $x \ge c$ where $W(x)$ is defined by Theorem 1 of Section 16. This proves the theorem.

EXAMPLES. (i) Suppose that in the time interval $(0, \infty)$ customers arrive at a counter in accordance with a Poisson process of density λ. The customers are attended by a single server who starts working at time $u = 0$. The initial occupation time of the server is $\eta(0)$ where $\eta(0)$ is a nonnegative random variable. The service times $\chi_1, \chi_2, \ldots, \chi_r, \ldots$ are mutually independent and identically distributed positive random variables with distribution function $\mathbf{P}\{\chi_r \le x\} = H(x)$ and independent of the arrival times. It is supposed that the server is busy if there is at least one customer in the system.

Let

$$\psi(s) = \int_0^\infty e^{-sx}\, dH(x) \tag{43}$$

for $\text{Re}(s) \geq 0$,

$$a = \int_0^\infty x\, dH(x) \tag{44}$$

and

$$\sigma_a^{\,2} = \int_0^\infty (x - a)^2\, dH(x) \tag{45}$$

if they exist.

Denote by $\chi(u)$ the sum of the service times of all those customers who arrive in the interval $(0, u]$. Then $\{\chi(u), 0 \leq u < \infty\}$ is a stochastic process with stationary independent increments. The process $\{\chi(u), 0 \leq u < \infty\}$ is a compound Poisson process.

We have

$$\mathbf{P}\{\chi(u) \leq x\} = \sum_{n=0}^{\infty} e^{-\lambda u} \frac{(\lambda u)^n}{n!} H_n(x) \tag{46}$$

where $H_n(x)$ denotes the nth iterated convolution of $H(x)$ with itself; $H_0(x) = 1$ if $x \geq 0$ and $H_0(x) = 0$ if $x < 0$. Furthermore,

$$\mathbf{E}\{e^{-s\chi(u)}\} = e^{-u\Phi(s)} \tag{47}$$

for $\text{Re}(s) \geq 0$ where

$$\Phi(s) = \lambda[1 - \psi(s)]. \tag{48}$$

Now $\rho = \Phi'(+0) = \lambda a$ and $\sigma^2 = -\Phi''(+0) = \lambda(a^2 + \sigma_a^{\,2})$.

The theorems of this section can be applied to find the distributions of $\eta(t)$, $\alpha(t)$, $\beta(t)$, θ_r $(r = 0, 1, 2, \ldots)$ and their asymptotic distributions.

In particular, for $\lambda a < 1$ the limiting distribution of the virtual waiting time,

$$\lim_{t\to\infty} \mathbf{P}\{\eta(t) \leq x\} = \mathbf{P}\left\{\sup_{0\leq u<\infty} [\chi(u) - u] \leq x\right\} = W(x), \tag{49}$$

is given by

$$\Omega(s) = \int_0^\infty e^{-sx}\, dW(x) = \frac{1 - \lambda a}{1 - \lambda \dfrac{1 - \psi(s)}{s}} \tag{50}$$

for $\text{Re}(s) > 0$. If $\lambda a \geq 1$, then $W(x) = 0$ for all x.

Pollaczek-Khintchine Formula. Consider the above example and suppose that customers are served in the order of the arrivals. Denote by η_n, $n = 1, 2, \ldots$, the waiting time of the nth arriving customer and let

$\eta_0 = \eta(0)$. In 1932 A. Y. Khintchine [42] proved that for $\lambda a < 1$, $\lim_{n\to\infty} \mathbf{P}\{\eta_n \leq x\} = W(x)$ where $W(x)$ has the Laplace-Stieltjes transform (50). In 1930 F. Pollaczek [53] considered the queuing process where n customers arrive in the interval $(0, t)$ such that the arrival times are mutually independent and uniformly distributed random variables. He determined the distribution of the waiting time of a customer chosen at random in the case when the customers are served by a single server in order of arrival and the service times are mutually independent and identically distributed random variables with distribution function $H(x)$ and independent of the arrival times. Pollaczek found that if $\lambda a < 1$ and $n \to \infty$ and $t \to \infty$ in such a way that $n/t \to \lambda$, then the distribution function of the waiting time of a customer chosen at random tends to $W(x)$ where $W(x)$ has the Laplace-Steiltjes transform (50).

In what follows we shall show that

$$\lim_{n\to\infty} \mathbf{P}\{\eta_n \leq x\} = \mathbf{P}\left\{\sup_{0\leq u<\infty} [\chi(u) - u] \leq x\right\} \tag{51}$$

independently of the distribution of $\eta(0)$. Thus we shall provide a new proof for the result of Pollaczek and Khintchine. It is interesting to mention that (50) was also found in 1930 by H. Cramér [16] in connection with a problem of insurance risk.

Now we are going to prove (51). Denote by $\tau_1, \tau_2, \ldots, \tau_r, \ldots$ the arrival times of the customers. Then $\tau_r - \tau_{r-1}$ ($r = 1, 2, \ldots$; $\tau_0 = 0$) are mutually independent and identically distributed random variables with distribution function $F(x) = 1 - e^{-\lambda x}$ for $x \geq 0$. Now evidently we have

$$\begin{aligned} \sup_{0\leq u<\infty} [\chi(u) - u] &= \sup_{0\leq r<\infty} [\chi(\tau_r + 0) - \tau_r] \\ &= \sup_{0\leq r<\infty} (\chi_1 + \cdots + \chi_r - \tau_r) \end{aligned} \tag{52}$$

and we shall show that

$$\lim_{n\to\infty} \mathbf{P}\{\eta_n \leq x\} = \mathbf{P}\left\{\sup_{0\leq r<\infty} (\chi_1 + \cdots + \chi_r - \tau_r) \leq x\right\} \tag{53}$$

which implies (51).

The random variables $\eta_0, \eta_1, \ldots, \eta_n, \ldots$ satisfy the following recurrence relation

$$\eta_{n+1} = [\eta_n + \chi_n - (\tau_n - \tau_{n-1})]^+ \tag{54}$$

for $n = 0, 1, 2, \ldots$. Hence

$$\begin{aligned} \eta_{n+1} = \max [0, \chi_n - (\tau_n - \tau_{n-1}), \chi_{n-1} + \chi_n - (\tau_n - \tau_{n-2}), \ldots, \\ \chi_2 + \cdots + \chi_n - (\tau_n - \tau_1), \chi_1 + \cdots + \chi_n - (\tau_n - \tau_0) + \eta_0]. \end{aligned} \tag{55}$$

If in (55) we replace $\chi_n, \chi_{n-1}, \ldots, \chi_1$ by $\chi_1, \chi_2, \ldots, \chi_n$ respectively and $(\tau_n - \tau_{n-1}), (\tau_n - \tau_{n-2}), \ldots, (\tau_n - \tau_0)$ by $\tau_1, \tau_2, \ldots, \tau_n$ respectively, then we obtain a new random variable which has exactly the same distribution as (55). Accordingly

$$(56)\quad \mathbf{P}\{\eta_{n+1} \le x\} = \mathbf{P}\{\max(0, \chi_1 - \tau_1, \chi_1 + \chi_2 - \tau_2, \ldots, \chi_1 + \cdots + \chi_{n-1} - \tau_{n-1}, \chi_1 + \cdots + \chi_n - \tau_n + \eta_0) \le x\}.$$

If we let $n \to \infty$ in (56), then we get (53) regardless of the distribution of η_0. This completes the proof of the statement.

(ii) Consider the previous example with the modification that in the time interval $(0, \infty)$ customers arrive at the counter in batches of random size in accordance with a Poisson process of density λ. Suppose that the batch sizes are mutually independent and identically distributed random variables and independent of the arrival times. Denote by $p_j, j = 1, 2, \ldots$, the probability that a batch consists of j customers and let

$$(57)\qquad p(z) = \sum_{j=1}^{\infty} p_j z^j.$$

If $\chi(u)$ denotes the sum of the service times of all those customers who arrive in the interval $(0, u]$, then $\{\chi(u), 0 \le u < \infty\}$ is a stochastic process with stationary independent increments. The process $\{\chi(u), 0 \le u < \infty\}$ is a compound Poisson process. For $\mathrm{Re}(s) \ge 0$ we have

$$(58)\qquad \mathbf{E}\{e^{-s\chi(u)}\} = e^{-u\Phi(s)}$$

where

$$(59)\qquad \Phi(s) = \lambda[1 - p(\psi(s))].$$

Now

$$(60)\qquad \rho = \lambda a \sum_{j=1}^{\infty} j p_j$$

and

$$(61)\qquad \sigma^2 = \lambda \sigma_a^{\ 2} \sum_{j=1}^{\infty} j p_j + \lambda a^2 \sum_{j=1}^{\infty} j^2 p_j.$$

Knowing the distribution of $\chi(u), 0 \le u < \infty$, we can apply the theorems of this section to find the distributions of $\eta(t), \alpha(t), \beta(t), \theta_r$ $(r = 0, 1, 2, \ldots)$ and their asymptotic distributions.

The Process W^*

Consider the queuing process $W^* = \{\eta(0); \chi^*(u), 0 \le u < \infty\}$ introduced in Section 27. It is supposed that $\{\chi^*(u), 0 \le u < \infty\}$ is the dual process of $\{\chi(u), 0 \leq u < \infty\}$ where $\{\chi(u), 0 \leq u < \infty\}$ is a separable stochastic process either with interchangeable increments or with stationary independent increments for which almost all sample functions are non-decreasing step functions vanishing at $u = 0$.

We are interested in finding the distributions of $\eta^*(t)$, $\alpha^*(t)$, $\beta^*(t)$ for $t > 0$ and θ_r^* for $r = 0, 1, 2, \ldots$, and their asymptotic distributions. These random variables are completely determined by the process W^* or equivalently by the process W. For the process W the distributions of the random variables $\eta(t)$, $\alpha(t)$, $\beta(t)$, θ_r have already been determined in this section. Now we shall reduce the problem of finding the distributions of $\alpha^*(t)$, $\beta^*(t)$ and θ_r^* to that of $\eta(t)$.

The probability $\mathbf{P}\{\beta^*(t) \leq x\} = \mathbf{P}\{\alpha^*(t) \geq t - x\}$ for $0 \leq x < t$ is given by the following theorem.

Theorem 8. *If $\{\chi(u), 0 \leq u < \infty\}$ has interchangeable increments, then*

$$(62)\quad \mathbf{P}\{\beta^*(t) \leq x + c \mid \eta(0) = c\} = \mathbf{P}\{\chi(x) > t\} + \iint\limits_{0<y\leq z\leq x} \left(\frac{x-z}{x-y}\right) d_y\, d_z \mathbf{P}\{\chi(y) \leq y + t - x, \chi(x) \leq z + t - x\}$$

for $0 \leq x < t - c$.

Proof. By (2) we have

$$(63)\quad \mathbf{P}\{\beta^*(t) \leq x + c \mid \eta(0) = c\} = \mathbf{P}\{\chi^*(u) \leq u + x - t \text{ for some } u \in [0, t]\}.$$

Hence by (2) of Section 18

$$(64)\quad \begin{aligned} \mathbf{P}\{\beta^*(t) \leq x + c \mid \eta(0) = c\} &= \mathbf{P}\{\chi(u) > u + t - x \text{ for some } u \in [0, x]\} \\ &= 1 - \mathbf{P}\{\chi(u) - u \leq t - x \text{ for } 0 \leq u \leq x\} \end{aligned}$$

and the extreme right member is given by (1) of Section 15. This proves (62).

It is interesting to mention the following relation

$$(65)\quad \mathbf{P}\{\beta^*(t) \leq x + c \mid \eta(0) = c\} = 1 - \mathbf{P}\{\eta(x) \leq t - x \mid \eta(0) = 0\}$$

which follows from (15) and (64).

Theorem 9. *If $\{\chi(u), 0 \leq u < \infty\}$ has stationary independent increments, if $\rho > 1$ and σ^2 is a finite positive number, then*

$$(66)\quad \lim_{t\to\infty} \mathbf{P}\left\{\frac{\beta^*(t) - \dfrac{t}{\rho}}{\sqrt{\sigma^2 t/\rho^3}} \leq x\right\} = \Phi(x)$$

independently of the distribution of $\eta(0)$.

Proof. Now we have

$$\beta^*(t) = \eta(0) + \chi^*(t) - \eta^*(t) \tag{67}$$

where $\eta^*(t)$ is defined by (1) except that $\chi(u)$ is replaced by $\chi^*(u)$. By (2) of Section 18 we have

$$\mathbf{P}\{\chi^*(t) \leq x\} = \mathbf{P}\{\chi(x) > t\} \tag{68}$$

for all $t \geq 0$ and $x \geq 0$. Thus by using (30) we can prove easily that

$$\lim_{t\to\infty} \mathbf{P}\left\{\frac{\chi^*(t) - \dfrac{t}{\rho}}{\sqrt{\sigma^2 t/\rho^3}} \leq x\right\} = \Phi(x). \tag{69}$$

Since $\lim_{t\to\infty} \dfrac{\chi(t)}{t} = \rho$ in probability, it follows that

$$\lim_{t\to\infty} \frac{\chi^*(t)}{t} = \frac{1}{\rho} \tag{70}$$

in probability. This implies that if $\rho > 1$, then $\lim_{t\to\infty} \dfrac{\eta^*(t)}{\sqrt{t}} = 0$ in probability. Evidently $\lim_{t\to\infty} \dfrac{\eta(0)}{\sqrt{t}} = 0$ in probability. Accordingly if $\rho > 1$, then $\beta^*(t)$ and $\chi^*(t)$ have the same asymptotic distribution for $t \to \infty$. This completes the proof of the theorem.

NOTE. If we suppose that $\{\chi(u), 0 \leq u < \infty\}$ is the compound Poisson process defined by (32) for which (33) holds, then by using (68) we can prove that

$$\lim_{t\to\infty} \mathbf{P}\left\{\frac{\chi^*(t) - \dfrac{t}{\rho}}{g(t)\lambda^{1/\alpha}/\rho^{(1+\alpha)/\alpha}} \leq x\right\} = 1 - G_\alpha(-x) \tag{71}$$

and if $\rho > 1$, then $\beta^*(t)$ has the same asymptotic distribution as $\chi^*(t)$ when $t \to \infty$.

Theorem 10. *If $\{\chi(u), 0 \leq u < \infty\}$ has interchangeable increments, then*

$$\mathbf{P}\{\theta_0^* \leq t + c \mid \eta(0) = c\} = \mathbf{P}\{\chi(t) > t + c\} + \iint\limits_{0<y\leq z\leq t} \left(\frac{t-z}{t-y}\right) d_y\, d_z \mathbf{P}\{\chi(y) \leq y + c, \chi(t) \leq z + c\} \tag{72}$$

for $t \geq 0$ and $c \geq 0$. If $c = 0$ in (72), then

$$\mathbf{P}\{\theta_0^* \leq t \mid \eta(0) = 0\} = 1 - \int_0^t \left(1 - \frac{y}{t}\right) d_y \mathbf{P}\{\chi(t) \leq y\}. \tag{73}$$

Proof. By (4) we have

$$(74)\quad \mathbf{P}\{\theta_0^* \leq t + c \mid \eta(0) = c\} = \mathbf{P}\{\chi^*(u) \leq u - c \text{ for some } u \in [0, t + c]\}.$$

Hence, by (2) of Section 18

$$(75)\quad \mathbf{P}\{\theta_0^* \leq t + c \mid \eta(0) = c\} = \mathbf{P}\{\chi(u) > u + c \text{ for some } u \in [0, t]\} = 1 - \mathbf{P}\{\chi(u) - u \leq c \text{ for } 0 \leq u \leq t\},$$

and the probability on the extreme right is given by (1) of Section 15. If $c = 0$, then (75) can be obtained by (3) of Section 15.

If we compare (64) and (75), then we obtain that

$$(76)\quad \mathbf{P}\{\theta_0^* \leq t + c \mid \eta(0) = c\} = \mathbf{P}\{\beta^*(t + c) \leq t \mid \eta(0) = 0\}$$

for $c > 0$ and the right-hand side is given by (62). This also proves (72).

It is interesting to mention the following relation

$$(77)\quad \mathbf{P}\{\theta_0^* \leq t + c \mid \eta(0) = c\} = 1 - \mathbf{P}\{\eta(t) \leq c \mid \eta(0) = 0\}$$

for $c \geq 0$ which follows from (1) and (75).

Theorem 11. *If $\{\chi(u), 0 \leq u < \infty\}$ has stationary independent increments, then for $c \geq 0$*

$$(78)\quad \mathbf{P}\{\theta_0^* < \infty \mid \eta(0) = c\} = 1 - W(c)$$

where $W(x)$ is defined by Theorem 2 for $\rho < 1$ and $W(x) = 0$ for $\rho \geq 1$.

Proof. By (75)

$$(79)\quad \mathbf{P}\{\theta_0^* < \infty \mid \eta(0) = c\} = 1 - \mathbf{P}\left\{\sup_{0 \leq u < \infty} [\chi(u) - u] \leq c\right\}$$

and the right-hand side can be obtained by Theorem 2. If $\rho < 1$, then $W(c) > 0$ for $c \geq 0$ and if $\rho \geq 1$, then $W(c) = 0$ for $c \geq 0$.

EXAMPLE. Suppose that in the time interval $[0, \infty)$ customers arrive at a counter at times $\tau_0', \tau_1', \ldots, \tau_r', \ldots$ where $\tau_0' = 0$ and $\tau_r' - \tau_{r-1}'$, $r = 1, 2, \ldots$, are mutually independent, identically distributed, positive random variables with distribution function $\mathbf{P}\{\tau_r' - \tau_{r-1}' \leq x\} = F(x)$. The customers are attended by a single server who starts working at time $u = 0$. The initial occupation time of the server is $\eta(0)$. The service times χ_1', $\chi_2', \ldots, \chi_r', \ldots$ are mutually independent and identically distributed random variables with distribution function $H(x) = 1 - e^{-\mu x}$ $(x \geq 0)$ and independent of the arrival times. It is supposed that the server is busy if there is at least one customer in the system.

If $\chi'(u)$ denotes the total service time of all those customers who arrive in the interval $[0, u]$, then the process $W' = \{\eta(0); \chi'(u), 0 \leq u < \infty\}$ is the inverse process of a queuing process $W = \{\eta(0); \chi(u), 0 \le u < \infty\}$ defined in the following way. In the time interval $(0, \infty)$ customers arrive at a counter in accordance with a Poisson process of density μ. The customers are attended by a single server who starts working at time $u = 0$. The initial occupation time of the server is $\eta(0)$. The service times are mutually independent and identically distributed random variables with distribution function $F(x)$, and independent of the arrival times. That is W' is the inverse process of $W = \{\eta(0); \chi(u), 0 \le u < \infty\}$ where $\{\chi(u), 0 \le u < \infty\}$ is a compound Poisson process for which

$$\mathbf{P}\{\chi(u) \le x\} = \sum_{n=0}^{\infty} e^{-\mu u} \frac{(\mu u)^n}{n!} F_n(x) \tag{80}$$

and here $F_n(x)$ denotes the nth iterated convolution of $F(x)$ with itself; $F_0(x) = 1$ if $x \ge 0$ and $F_0(x) = 0$ if $x < 0$.

For the inverse process W' denote by $\eta'(t)$, $\alpha'(t)$, $\beta'(t)$, θ_r' the same random variables that $\eta(t)$, $\alpha(t)$, $\beta(t)$, θ_r denote for the process W. If W^* denotes the dual process of W and we shall denote by $\eta^*(t)$, $\alpha^*(t)$, $\beta^*(t)$, θ_r^* the corresponding random variables for W^*, then it is easy to see that $\alpha'(t) = \alpha^*(t)$, $\beta'(t) = \beta^*(t)$ and $\theta_0' = \theta_0^*$. The distributions of the random variables $\alpha^*(t)$, $\beta^*(t)$ and θ_0^* are given in this section. To apply the general theorems we introduce the following notation

$$\phi(s) = \int_0^\infty e^{-sx}\, dF(x) \tag{81}$$

for $\text{Re}(s) \ge 0$,

$$b = \int_0^\infty x\, dF(x) \tag{82}$$

and

$$\sigma_b^2 = \int_0^\infty (x - b)^2\, dF(x) \tag{83}$$

if they exist. In this case

$$\Phi(s) = \mu[1 - \phi(s)] \tag{84}$$

for $\text{Re}(s) \ge 0$, $\rho = \Phi'(+0) = \mu b$ and $\sigma^2 = -\Phi''(+0) = \mu(b^2 + \sigma_b^2)$.

30. PROBLEMS

1. In the time interval $(0, \infty)$ customers arrive at a counter in accordance with a Poisson process of density λ. The customers are attended by a single server who starts working at time $u = 0$. The service times $\chi_1, \chi_2, \ldots, \chi_r, \ldots$ are mutually independent, identically distributed, positive random variables with distribution function $\mathbf{P}\{\chi_r \le x\} = H(x)$ and independent of the arrival times.

It is supposed that the server is busy if there is at least one customer in the system. Find $G_n(x)$, the probability that a busy period (other than the initial one) consists of n services and has length $\leq x$.

2. Consider Problem 1 and suppose that the initial queue size is $\zeta_0 = i \geq 1$. Find $G_n^{(i)}(x)$, the probability that the initial busy period consists of n services and has length $\leq x$.

3. Consider Problem 1 and suppose that the initial occupation time of the server is $\eta(0) = c > 0$. Find $G_n(x \mid c)$, the probability that the initial busy period consists of n services and has length $\leq x$.

4. Consider Problem 1 and denote by $G(x)$ the probability that a busy period (other than the initial one) has length $\leq x$. Find the moments of $G(x)$.

5. Consider Problem 1. Denote by $\eta(t)$ the virtual waiting time at time t. Find the stationary distribution of $\eta(t)$ and its moments.

6. Consider Problem 1 and denote by ξ_n the queue size immediately before the nth arrival. Find the stationary distribution of ξ_n and its moments.

7. Consider Problem 1 and denote by $\xi(t)$ the queue size at time t. Find the stationary distribution of $\xi(t)$.

8. Consider Problem 1 and suppose that the initial occupation time of the server is $\eta(0) = c$. Denote by $\eta(t)$ the virtual waiting time at time t. Find $\mathbf{P}\{\eta(t) \leq x \mid \eta(0) = c\}$.

9. Consider Problem 1 and suppose that the customers are served in the order of arrival. Denote by η_n the waiting time of the nth arriving customer. Find the limiting distribution of η_n as $n \to \infty$.

10. In the time interval $[0, T]$, n customers arrive at a counter. The arrival times are mutually independent random variables having a uniform distribution over $[0, T]$. Suppose that the customers are attended by a single server. The service times $\chi_1, \chi_2, \ldots, \chi_n$ are mutually independent and identically distributed random variables with distribution function $\mathbf{P}\{\chi_r \leq x\} = H(x)$ and independent of the arrival times. It is supposed that the server is busy if there is at least one customer in the system. Find the distribution of $\eta(t)$ $(0 \leq t \leq T)$, the virtual waiting time at time t.

11. In the time interval $[0, \infty)$ customers arrive at a counter at times τ_0', $\tau_1', \ldots, \tau_r', \ldots$ where $\tau_0' = 0$ and the interarrival times $\tau_r' - \tau_{r-1}'$, $r = 1, 2, \ldots$, are mutually independent, identically distributed, positive random variables with distribution function $\mathbf{P}\{\tau_r' - \tau_{r-1}' \leq x\} = F(x)$. The customers are attended by a single server. The service times, $\chi_1', \chi_2', \ldots, \chi_r', \ldots$ are mutually independent and identically distributed random variables with distribution function $H(x) = 1 - e^{-\mu x}$ $(x \geq 0)$ and independent of the arrival times. It is supposed that the server is busy if there is at least one customer in the system. Suppose that the queue size is 0 immediately before time $u = 0$. Find the probability that the initial busy period consists of n services, and the probability that the initial busy period has length $\leq x$.

12. Consider Problem 11 and suppose that the queue size immediately before time $u = 0$ is $\zeta_0 = i$. Find the probability that the initial busy period has length $\leq x$.

REFERENCES

[1] Bailey, N. T. J. "A continuous time treatment of a simple queue using generating functions," *J. Roy. Statist. Soc. Ser. B* **16** (1954), 288–291.

[2] Bailey, N. T. J. "Some further results in the non-equilibrium theory of a simple queue," *J. Roy. Statist. Soc. Ser. B* **19** (1957), 326–333.

[3] Beneš, V. E. "On queues with Poisson arrivals," *Ann. Math. Statist.* **28** (1957), 670–677.

[4] Beneš, V. E. "General stochastic processes in traffic systems with one server," *Bell System Tech. J.* **39** (1960), 127–160.

[5] Beneš, V. E. "Combinatory methods and stochastic Kolmogorov equations in the theory of queues with one server," *Trans. Amer. Math. Soc.* **94** (1960), 282–294.

[6] Beneš, V. E. "Weakly Markov queues," *Transactions of the Second Prague Conference on Information Theory, Statistical Decision Functions, Random Processes*, Prague, 1960, pp. 9–25.

[7] Beneš, V. E. *General Stochastic Processes in the Theory of Queues*, Addison-Wesley, Reading, Mass., 1963.

[8] Bhat, U. N. "Customer overflow in queues with finite waiting space," *Austral. J. Statist.* **7** (1965), 15–19.

[9] Borel, É. "Sur l'emploi du théorème de Bernoulli pour faciliter le calcul d'un infinité de coefficients. Application au problème de l'attente à un guichet," *Comptes Rendus Acad. Sci. Paris* **214** (1942), 452–456.

[10] Brockmeyer, E., H. L. Halstrøm and A. Jensen, "The Life and Works of A. K. Erlang," *Transactions of the Danish Academy of Technical Sciences No.* 2 (1948), 1–277.

[11] Champernowne, D. G. "An elementary method of solution of the queueing problem with a sinlge server and constant parameters," *J. Roy. Statist. Soc. Ser. B* **18** (1956), 125–128.

[12] Clarke, A. B. "A waiting line process of Markov type," *Ann. Math. Statist.* **27** (1956), 452–459.

[13] Conolly, B. W. "The busy period in relation to the queueing process GI/M/1," *Biometrika* **46** (1959), 246–251.

[14] Cox, D. R. "The analysis of non-Markovian stochastic processes by the inclusion of supplementary variables," *Proc. Cambridge Phil. Soc.* **51** (1955), 433–441.

[15] Cox, D. R. and W. L. Smith, *Queues*, Methuen, London, 1961.

[16] Cramér, H. "On the mathematical theory of risk," *Skandia Jubilee Volume*, Stockholm, 1930.

[17] Crommelin, C. D. "Delay probability formulae when the holding times are constant," *Post Office Electrical Engineers' Journal* **25** (1932), 41–50 and **26** (1934), 266–274.

[18] Daley, D. J. "Single-server queueing processes with uniformly limited queueing time," *J. Austral. Math. Soc.* **4** (1964), 489–505.

[19] Doig, A. "A bibliography on the theory of queues," *Biometrika* **44** (1957), 490–514.

[20] Erlang, A. K. "The theory of probabilities and telephone conversations," (Danish) *Nyt Tidsskrift for Matematik B* **20** (1909), 33–39. [French version: "Calcul des probabilités et conversations téléphoniques," *Revue générale de l'Electricité* **18** (1925), 305–309. English translation in reference [10] pp. 131–137.]

[21] Erlang, A. K. "Solution of some problems in the theory of probabilities of significance in automatic telephone exchanges," (Danish) *Elektroteknikeren* **13** (1917), 5–13. [English translation in the *Post Office Electrical Engineers' Journal* **10** (1917–18), 189–197 and in reference [10] pp. 138–155.]

[22] Erlang, A. K. "Telephone waiting times," (Danish) *Matematisk Tidsskrift B* **31** (1920), 25–42. [French translation: "Calcul des probabilités et conversations téléphoniques," *Revue générale de l'Electricité* **20** (1926) 270–278. English translation in reference [10] pp. 156–171.]

[23] Finch, P. D. "On the distribution of the queue size in queueing problems," *Acta. Math. Acad. Sci. Hungar.* **10** (1959), 327–336.

[24] Finch, P. D. "On the transient behaviour of a simple queue," *J. Roy. Statist. Soc Ser. B* **22** (1960), 277–284.

[25] Finch, P. D. "On the busy period in the queueing system GI/G/1," *J. Austral. Math. Soc.* **2** (1961), 217–228.

[26] Gaver, D. P. "Imbedded Markov chain analysis of a waiting-line process in continuous time," *Ann. Math. Statist.* **30** (1959), 698–720.

[27] Ghosal, A. "Queues with finite waiting time," *Operations Res.* **11** (1963), 919–921.

[28] Hasofer, A. M. "On the integrability, continuity and differentiability of a family of functions introduced by L. Takács," *Ann. Math. Statist.* **34** (1963), 1045–1049.

[29] Hasofer, A. M. "On the single-server queue with non-homogeneous Poisson input and general service times," *J. Appl. Probability* **1** (1964), 369–384.

[30] Heathcote, C. R. "On the queueing process M/G/1," *Ann. Math. Statist.* **32** (1961), 770–773.

[31] Karlin, S. and J. McGregor, "Many server queueing processes with Poisson input and exponential service times," *Pacific J. Math.* **8** (1958), 87–118.

[32] Karlin, S., R. G. Miller and N. U. Prabhu, "Note on a moving single server problem," *Ann. Math. Statist.* **30** (1959), 243–246.

[33] Kawata, T. "On the imbedded queueing process of general type," *Bull. Inst. Internat. Statist.* **38** (1961), 445–455.

[34] Keilson, J. "The use of Green's functions in the study of bounded random walks with application to queuing theory," *J. Math. Phys.* **41** (1962), 42–52.

[35] Keilson, J. "A gambler's ruin type problem in queuing theory," *Operations Res.* **11** (1963), 570–576.

[36] Keilson, J. "Some comments on single-server queuing methods and some new results," *Proc. Cambridge Phil. Soc.* **60** (1964), 237–251.

[37] Keilson, J. and A. Kooharian, "On time dependent queuing processes," *Ann. Math. Statist.* **31** (1960), 104–112.

[38] Keilson, J. and A. Kooharian, "On the general time dependent queue with a single server," *Ann. Math. Statist.* **33** (1962), 767–791.

[39] Kendall, D. G. "Some problems in the theory of queues," *J. Roy. Statist. Soc. Ser. B* **13** (1951), 151–185.

[40] Kendall, D. G. "Stochastic processes occurring in the theory of queues and their analysis by the method of the imbedded Markov chain," *Ann. Math. Statist.* **24** (1953), 338–354.

[41] Kendall, D. G. "Some recent work and further problems in the theory of queues," *Theory of Probability and its Applications* **9** (1964), 1–13.

[42] Khintchine, A. Y. "Mathematical theory of a stationary queue," (Russian) *Matem. Sbornik* **39** *No.* 4 (1932), 73–84.

[43] Khintchine, A. Y. "Mathematical Methods of the Theory of Mass Service," (Russian) *Trudy Mat. Inst. Steklov No.* 49 (1955) 1–122. [English translation: *Mathematical Methods in the Theory of Queueing*, Griffin, London, 1960.]

[44] Kingman, J. F. C. "The use of Spitzer's identity in the investigation of the busy period and other quantities in the queue GI/G/1," *J. Austral. Math. Soc.* **2** (1962), 345–356.

[45] Kolmogoroff, A. "Sur le problème d'attente," *Matem. Sbornik* **38** *No.* 1–2 (1931), 101–106.
[46] Lindley, D. V. "The theory of queues with a single server," *Proc. Cambridge Phil. Soc.* **48** (1952), 277–289.
[47] Loyness, R. M. "A continuous-time treatment of certain queues and infinite dams," *J. Austral. Math. Soc.* **2** (1962), 484–498.
[48] Luchak, G. "The solution of the single-channel queuing equation characterized by a time-dependent Poisson-distributed arrival rate and a general class of holding times," *Operations Res.* **4** (1956), 711–732.
[49] McMillan, B., and J. Riordan. "A moving single server problem," *Ann. Math. Statist.* **28** (1957), 471–478.
[50] Morimura, H. "On the number of served customers in a busy period," *J. Operat. Res. Soc. Japan* **4** (1961–62), 67–75.
[51] Neuts, M. F. "The distribution of the maximum length of a Poisson queue during a busy period," *Operations Res.* **12** (1964), 281–285.
[52] Neuts, M. F. "An alternative proof of a theorem of Takács on the GI/M/1 queue," *Operations Res.* **14** (1966), 313–316.
[53] Pollaczek, F. "Über eine Aufgabe der Wahrscheinlichkeitstheorie," I-II. *Mathem. Zeitschrift* **32** (1930), 64–100 and 729–750.
[54] Pollaczek, F. "Über das Warteproblem," *Matem. Zeitschrift* **38** (1934), 492–537.
[55] Pollaczek, F. "Problèmes stochastiques posés par le phénomène de formation d'une queue d'attente à un guichet et par des phénomènes apparentés," *Mémorial des Sciences Mathématiques*, fasc. 136, Gauthier-Villars, Paris, 1957.
[56] Prabhu, N. U. "Application of storage theory to queues with Poisson arrivals," *Ann. Math. Statist.* **31** (1960), 475–482.
[57] Prabhu, N. U. "Some results for the queue with Poisson arrivals," *J. Roy. Statist. Soc. Ser. B* **22** (1960), 104–107.
[58] Prabhu, N. U. and U. Narayan Bhat, "Some first passage problems and their application to queues," *Sankhyā, Ser. A* **25** (1963), 281–292.
[59] Prabhu, N. U. and U. Narayan Bhat, "Further results for the queue with Poisson arrivals," *Operations Res.* **11** (1963), 380–385.
[60] Reich, E. "On the integrodifferential equation of Takács," I-II. *Ann. Math. Statist.* **29** (1958), 563–570 and **30** (1959), 143–148.
[61] Rice, S. O. "Single server systems-II. Busy periods," *Bell System Tech. J.* **41** (1962), 279–310.
[62] Riordan, J. "Delays for last-come first-served service and the busy period," *Bell System Tech. J.* **40** (1961), 785–793.
[63] Riordan, J. *Stochastic Service Systems*, John Wiley and Sons, New York, 1962.
[64] Runnenburg, Th. J. "Probabilistic interpretation of some formulae in queueing theory," *Bull. Inst. Internat. Statist.* **37** (1960), 405–414.
[65] Runnenburg, Th. J. *On the use of Markov processes in one-server waiting-time problems and renewal theory*, Thesis, Amsterdam, 1960.
[66] Saaty, T. L. *Elements of Queueing Theory with Applications*, McGraw-Hill, New York, 1961.
[67] Shanbag, D. N. "On queues with Poisson service time," *Austral. J. Statist.* **5** (1963), 57–61.
[68] Smith, W. L. "On the distribution of queueing times," *Proc. Cambridge Phil. Soc.* **49** (1953), 449–461.
[69] Spitzer, F. "The Wiener-Hopf equation whose kernel is a probability density," *Duke Math. J.* **24** (1957), 327–343.

[70] Syski, R. *Introduction to Congestion Theory in Telephone Systems*, Oliver and Boyd, Edinburgh, 1960.

[71] Takács, L. "Investigation of waiting time problems by reduction to Markov processes," *Acta Math. Acad. Sci. Hungar.* **6** (1955), 101–129.

[72] Takács, L. "Transient behavior of single-server queuing processes with recurrent input and exponentially distributed service times," *Operations Res.* **8** (1960), 231–245.

[73] Takács, L. "The transient behavior of a single server queueing process with a Poisson input," *Proceedings of the Fourth Berkeley Symposium on Mathematical Statistics and Probability*, Vol. **II**, Univ. California Press, Berkeley, 1961, pp. 535–567.

[74] Takács, L. "The transient behavior of a single server queuing process with recurrent input and gamma service time," *Ann. Math. Statist.* **32** (1961), 1286–1298.

[75] Takács, L. "Transient behavior of single-server queueing processes with Erlang input," *Trans. Amer. Math. Soc.* **100** (1961), 1–28.

[76] Takács, L. "The probability law of the busy period for two types of queuing processes," *Operations Res.* **9** (1961), 402–407.

[77] Takács, L. *Introduction to the Theory of Queues*, Oxford University Press, New York, 1962.

[78] Takács, L. "A generalization of the ballot problem and its application in the theory of queues," *J. Amer. Statist. Assoc.* **57** (1962), 327–337.

[79] Takács, L. "A single-server queue with recurrent input and exponentially distributed service times," *Operations Res.* **10** (1962), 395–399.

[80] Takács, L. "A combinatorial method in the theory of queues," *J. Soc. Indust. Appl. Math.* **10** (1962), 691–694.

[81] Takács, L. "The distribution of the virtual waiting time for a single-server queue with Poisson input and general service times," *Operations Res.* **11** (1963), 261–264.

[82] Takács, L. "The stochastic law of the busy period for a single server queue with Poisson input," *J. Math. Anal. and Appl.* **6** (1963), 33–42.

[83] Takács, L. "The limiting distribution of the virtual waiting time and the queue size for a single-server queue with recurrent input and general service times," *Sankhyā, Ser. A*, **25** (1963), 91–100.

[84] Takács, L. "The time dependence of a single-server queue with Poisson input and general service times," *Ann. Math. Statist.* **33** (1962), 1340–1348.

[85] Takács, L. "Delay distributions for one line with Poisson input, general holding times, and various orders of service," *Bell System Tech. J.* **42** (1963), 487–503.

[86] Takács, L. "A combinatorial method in the theory of Markov chains," *J. Math. Anal. and Appl.* **9** (1964), 153–161.

[87] Takács, L. "Occupation time problems in the theory of queues," *Operations Res.* **12** (1964), 753–767.

[88] Takács, L. "Combinatorial methods in the theory of queues," *Rev. Internat. Statist.* **32** (1964), 207–219.

[89] Takács, L. "Application of ballot theorems in the theory of queues," *Proceedings of the Symposium on Congestion Theory*, Chapel Hill, N.C., August 24–26, 1964, Edited by W. L. Smith and W. E. Wilkinson. University of North Carolina Press, Chapel Hill, North Carolina, 1965, pp. 337–398.

[90] Wold, H. O. A., (Editor). *Bibliography on Time Series and Stochastic Processes*, M.I.T. Press, Cambridge, Mass., 1965.

CHAPTER 6

Dam and Storage Processes

31. DAM AND STORAGE PROCESSES

The mathematical investigation of the theory of dams started in the 1950's by the initiation of P. A. P. Moran [21, 22, 23]. In designing dams or reservoirs, it is necessary to find the mathematical law governing the fluctuations of the content of the dam or reservoir. For example, if we want to build an atomic power plant, we should take into account that the plant needs an enormous amount of water to cool its condensers. Knowing the demand, which may be many million gallons an hour, and the supply provided, for example, by a river, the problem is to find the capacity of the reservoir to be built so that it can satisfy the demand consistently with high probability.

In what follows we shall investigate the law of the random fluctuations of the content of a dam if we know the stochastic properties of the input. We shall consider different mathematical models for reservoirs of unlimited (infinite) capacity and for those of finite capacity. We shall use the terminology of dams; however, the results can be applied for general storage processes. If we consider stores, then the content of the dam corresponds to the stock size. We shall consider cases where the content is a continuous variable which is the case in water storage (reservoirs, dams), liquid storage, or gas storage. We shall also consider cases where the content is a discrete variable such as the number of items of a certain commodity in a warehouse.

32. FLUCTUATIONS OF THE CONTENT OF DAMS OF UNLIMITED CAPACITY

We shall consider the following mathematical model of infinite dams. In the time interval $(0, \infty)$ water is flowing into a dam (reservoir). Denote by $\chi(u)$ the total quantity of water flowing into the reservoir in the time interval $(0, u]$. Denote by $\delta(u)$ the total demand in the interval $(0, u]$.

If there is enough water in the reservoir the demand is satisfied; if there is not enough water in the reservoir the difference is supplied from elsewhere. Let $\zeta(u) = \chi(u) - \delta(u)$. If $\eta(0)$ denotes the initial content of the reservoir, then the content at time t is given by

$$(1) \qquad \eta(t) = \sup \{\eta(0) + \zeta(t) \text{ and } \zeta(t) - \zeta(u) \text{ for } 0 \leq u \leq t\}.$$

This can be seen as follows: If in the interval $(0, t]$ no auxiliary water is needed to satisfy the demand, then $\eta(t) = \eta(0) + \zeta(t)$, and (1) holds. If in the interval $(0, t]$ auxiliary water is needed and u is the last time when auxiliary water is used, that is, $u = \sup \{v : \eta(v) = 0 \text{ and } 0 \leq v \leq t\}$, then $\eta(t) = \zeta(t) - \zeta(u)$, and (1) holds in this case too.

The total quantity of auxiliary water needed in the time interval $[0, t]$ is

$$(2) \qquad \alpha(t) = \sup \{0 \text{ and } -\eta(0) - \zeta(u) \text{ for } 0 \leq u \leq t\}.$$

Evidently

$$(3) \qquad \eta(t) = \eta(0) + \zeta(t) + \alpha(t).$$

Define θ_0 as the time when auxiliary water is needed for the first time in the interval $(0, \infty)$, that is,

$$(4) \qquad \theta_0 = \inf \{u : \eta(0) + \zeta(u) \leq 0 \text{ and } 0 \leq u \leq \infty\},$$

and $\theta_0 = \infty$ if $\eta(0) + \zeta(u) > 0$ for all $u \geq 0$.

In many applications the demand $\delta(u)$ is a linear function of u which, by a suitable normalization, may be chosen as $\delta(u) = u$ for $0 \leq u < \infty$.

If $\chi(u)$, $0 \leq u < \infty$, is a nondecreasing step function for which $\chi(0) = 0$ and $\delta(u) = u$ for $0 \leq u < \infty$, then $\alpha(t)$ is the total time in $[0, t]$ during which the reservoir is empty and θ_0 is the time of first emptiness.

If either the input $\{\chi(u), 0 \leq u < \infty\}$ or the demand $\{\delta(u), 0 \leq u < \infty\}$ or both are stochastic processes and if we consider their separable versions, then $\eta(t)$, $(0 \leq t < \infty)$, $\alpha(t)$, $(0 \leq t < \infty)$, and θ_0 are random variables and our aim is to find the stochastic laws governing the processes $\{\eta(t), 0 \leq t < \infty\}$ and $\{\alpha(t), 0 \leq t < \infty\}$ and to find the distribution of θ_0.

We note that the following relations are generally valid. If $c \geq 0$ and $0 < x \leq t$, then

$$(5) \qquad \mathbf{P}\{\alpha(t) \geq x \mid \eta(0) = c\} = \mathbf{P}\{\theta_0 \leq t \mid \eta(0) = c + x\}$$

and if $c \geq 0$ and $t > 0$, then

$$(6) \qquad \mathbf{P}\{\alpha(t) = 0 \mid \eta(0) = c\} = \mathbf{P}\{\theta_0 \geq t \mid \eta(0) = c\}.$$

These relations immediately follow from (2) and (4).

NOTE. In the important particular case when $\delta(u) = u$ for all $u \geq 0$, we observe that $\eta(t)$, $\alpha(t)$ and θ_0 depend on the input $\{\chi(u), 0 \leq u < \infty\}$

in exactly the same way as the virtual waiting time at time t, the total idle time of the server in $(0, t)$ and the length of the initial busy period depend on the input $\{\chi(u), 0 \leq u < \infty\}$ in the queuing process defined in Section 29. For this reason we used the same notation here as in Section 29.

In what follows we shall see that the general theorems found in Chapters 2, 3, and 4 can also be applied in the theory of dams. We shall consider different mathematical models for dam or storage processes and indicate how the general theorems are applicable. The mathematical models considered can be divided into two main types. We shall speak about a discrete dam process if the random variables $\zeta(u)$, $u = 0, 1, 2, \ldots$, take on only integral values, and we shall speak about a general dam process if the random variables $\{\zeta(u), 0 \leq u < \infty\}$ may take on arbitrary real values. We shall always suppose that $\eta(0)$, the initial content of the dam, and $\{\zeta(u), 0 \leq u < \infty\}$ are independent.

Discrete Dam Processes

(i) Suppose that the initial content of a dam is η_0 where η_0 is a random variable taking on nonnegative integers. Suppose that at times $r = 1, 2, \ldots$ water of quantities $\nu_1, \nu_2, \ldots$ is flowing into the dam, and the release is continuous at a constant unit rate when the dam is not empty. Let $N_r = \nu_1 + \cdots + \nu_r$ for $r = 1, 2, \ldots$ and $N_0 = 0$. Denote by η_n the content of the dam immediately after time n. Denote by θ_0 the time of first emptiness, that is, the smallest value of r such that $\eta_r = 0$. Denote by α_n the total time in $[0, n]$ during which the dam is empty.

In this case $\chi(u) = N_{[u]}$, $\delta(u) = u$ and $\zeta(u) = N_{[u]} - u$ for $u \geq 0$. Now we have $\eta_n = \eta(n + 0)$, $\alpha_n = \alpha(n)$ and θ_0 has the same meaning as in (4). In this case we speak about a dam process of type

$$Q = \{\eta_0; N_r, r = 0, 1, 2, \ldots\}.$$

This dam process has exactly the same stochastic properties as the queuing process Q introduced in Section 27. Now η_0 corresponds to ζ_0, the initial queue size; η_n corresponds to ζ_n, the queue size immediately after the nth departure; α_n has the same meaning in both processes; θ_0 corresponds to ρ_0, the number of customers served in the initial busy period.

If we suppose that $\nu_1, \nu_2, \ldots, \nu_r, \ldots$ are either interchangeable random variables taking on nonnegative integers, or, in particular, mutually independent and identically distributed random variables taking on nonnegative integers, then we can apply the theorems of Section 28 to find the distributions of η_n, α_n and θ_0 and their asymptotic distributions. Now we have

$$(7)\quad \mathbf{P}\{\eta_n \leq k \mid \eta_0 = i\} = \mathbf{P}\{N_r < r + k \text{ for } r = 1, 2, \ldots, n \text{ and } N_n \leq n + k - i\}$$

for $i = 0, 1, 2, \ldots,$

$$(8)\quad \mathbf{P}\{\alpha_n > k - i \mid \eta_0 = i\} = 1 - \mathbf{P}\{r - N_r < k \text{ for } r = 0, 1, \ldots, n-1\}$$

for $0 \leq i \leq k < n$, and

$$(9)\quad \mathbf{P}\{\theta_0 = n \mid \eta_0 = i\} = \mathbf{P}\{N_r < r \text{ for } r = 1, \ldots, n \text{ and } N_n = n - i\}$$

for $i = 1, 2, \ldots$. Theorems 1–6 of Section 28 are now applicable.

If instead of the above process we consider the case where $\zeta(u) = u - N_{[u]}$ for $u \geq 0$, then the theorems of Section 28 can be applied in finding the distributions of η_n, α_n, θ_0 and their asymptotic distributions.

NOTE. Suppose that $\nu_1^*, \nu_2^*, \ldots, \nu_r^*, \ldots$ is the dual sequence of $\nu_1, \nu_2, \ldots, \nu_r, \ldots$ defined above and let $N_r^* = \nu_1^* + \cdots + \nu_r^*$ for $r = 1, 2, , \ldots$ and $N_0^* = 0$. If we consider the dam process

$$Q^* = \{\eta_0;\ N_r^*, r = 0, 1, 2, \ldots\},$$

then Q^* has exactly the same stochastic properties as the dual queuing process Q^* introduced in Section 27. If for Q^* we denote by α_n^* and θ_0^*, the same random variables that α_n and θ_0 denote for Q, then the distributions of α_n^* and θ_0^* can be obtained by Theorems 8–11 of Section 28.

(ii) Suppose that the initial stock size of a store is $\eta(0)$ where $\eta(0)$ is a random variable taking on nonnegative integers. Suppose that $\{\zeta(u),\ 0 \leq u < \infty\}$ is a separable stochastic process either with interchangeable increments or, in particular, with stationary independent increments. Suppose that $\mathbf{P}\{\zeta(0) = 0\} = 1$ and that $\zeta(u)$ takes on only integers. In this case

$$(10)\quad \mathbf{P}\{\eta(t) < k \mid \eta(0) = i\} = \mathbf{P}\left\{\sup_{0\leq u\leq t} \zeta(u) < k \text{ and } \zeta(t) < k - i\right\}.$$

This follows from (1). If we replace $\zeta(t) - \zeta(u)$ by $\zeta(t-u)$ in (1) for $0 \leq u \leq t$, then we obtain a new random variable which has exactly the same distribution as $\eta(t)$. This proves (10). By (2)

$$(11)\quad \mathbf{P}\{\alpha(t) > x - i \mid \eta(0) = i\} = 1 - \mathbf{P}\left\{\sup_{0\leq u\leq t} \zeta^*(u) \leq x\right\}$$

for $0 \leq i < x < t + i$ where $\zeta^*(u) = -\zeta(u)$ and by (3)

$$(12)\quad \mathbf{P}\{\theta_0 \leq t \mid \eta(0) = i\} = 1 - \mathbf{P}\left\{\sup_{0\leq u\leq t} \zeta^*(u) \leq i\right\}$$

for $i > 0$ where $\zeta^*(u) = -\zeta(u)$.

If we suppose that almost all sample functions of the process $\{\zeta(u), 0 \leq u < \infty\}$ have either only jumps of magnitude $1, -1, -2, \ldots$ or only jumps of magnitude $-1, 1, 2, \ldots$, that is, if either $\zeta(u) = \xi(u)$ or $\zeta(u) = \xi^*(u) = -\xi(u)$ for $0 \leq u < \infty$ where the process $\{\xi(u), 0 \leq u < \infty\}$ is defined in Section 21, then we can apply the theorems of Section 21 to find the distributions of $\eta(t)$, $\alpha(t)$, θ_0 and their asymptotic distributions.

General Dam Processes

(i) Suppose that the initial content of a dam is $\eta(0)$ where $\eta(0)$ is a nonnegative random variable. Denote by $\chi(u)$ the total quantity of water flowing into the dam in the time interval $[0, u]$. Suppose that the release is continuous at a constant unit rate when the dam is not empty. In this case $\delta(u) = u$ and $\zeta(u) = \chi(u) - u$ for $u \geq 0$. In this case we speak about a dam process of type

$$W = \{\eta(0); \chi(u), 0 \leq u < \infty\}.$$

This dam process has exactly the same stochastic properties as the queuing process W introduced in Section 27. Now $\eta(t)$, the content of the dam at time t, is the same as the waiting time at time t; $\alpha(t)$, the total time in $(0, t)$ during which auxiliary water is needed (the total time in $(0, t)$ during which the dam is empty) is the same as the total idle time of the server in the interval $(0, t)$; θ_0, the time when auxiliary water is needed for the first time (time of first emptiness), is the same as the length of the initial busy period.

If we suppose that $\{\chi(u), 0 \leq u < \infty\}$ has either interchangeable increments, or, in particular, stationary independent increments, and that almost all sample functions of the process are nondecreasing step functions vanishing at $u = 0$, then we can apply the theorems of Section 29 to find the distributions of $\eta(t)$, $\alpha(t)$, θ_0, and their asymptotic distributions.

If we suppose that $\zeta(u) = u - \chi(u)$ for $u \geq 0$ where $\{\chi(u), 0 \leq u < \infty\}$ is defined as above, then we can apply the theorems of Section 29 to find the distributions of $\eta(t)$, $\alpha(t)$, θ_0 and their asymptotic distributions.

While in queuing processes $\{\chi(u), 0 \leq u < \infty\}$ is usually a simple jump process which with probability 1 has only a finite number of jumps in finite intervals, in dam processes $\{\chi(u), 0 \leq u < \infty\}$ may have an infinite number of jumps in any finite interval with probability 1.

NOTE. If we suppose that $\{\chi^*(u), 0 \leq u < \infty\}$ is the dual processs of $\{\chi(u), 0 \leq u < \infty\}$ defined above and we consider the dam process

$$W^* = \{\eta(0); \chi^*(u), 0 \leq u \leq \infty\},$$

then W^* has exactly the same stochastic properties as the dual queuing process W^* introduced in Section 27. If for W^* we denote by $\alpha^*(t)$ and θ_0^* the same random variables that $\alpha(t)$ and θ_0 are for W, then the distributions of $\alpha^*(t)$ and θ_0^* can be obtained by Theorems 8–11 of Section 29.

(ii) If we use the following equivalent interpretation of the process $\{\eta(t), 0 \leq t < \infty\}$, we can consider more general types of processes $\{\zeta(u), 0 \leq u < \infty\}$ than before. Suppose that the process $\{\zeta(u), 0 \leq u < \infty\}$ describes the fluctuations of the level of a dam if the level may vary in the interval $(-\infty, \infty)$. Then $\eta(0) + \zeta(t)$ is the level of the dam at time t. Now suppose that if it is necessary, auxiliary water is used to achieve that the level never decreases below 0. Then $\eta(t)$ is the level (content) of the dam at time t.

Suppose that the initial content of a dam is $\eta(0)$ where $\eta(0)$ is a non-negative random variable. Suppose that $\{\zeta(u), 0 \leq u < \infty\}$ is a separable stochastic process either with interchangeable increments or, in particular, with stationary independent increments. Suppose that $\mathbf{P}\{\zeta(0) = 0\} = 1$. In this case by (1)

$$(13)\quad \mathbf{P}\{\eta(t) \leq x \mid \eta(0) = c\} = \mathbf{P}\left\{\sup_{0 \leq u \leq t} \zeta(u) \leq x \text{ and } \zeta(t) \leq x - c\right\},$$

by (2)

$$(14)\qquad \mathbf{P}\{\alpha(t) > x - c \mid \eta(0) = c\} = 1 - \mathbf{P}\left\{\sup_{0 \leq u \leq t} \zeta^*(u) \leq x\right\}$$

for $0 \leq c < x < t + c$ where $\zeta^*(u) = -\zeta(u)$, and by (3)

$$(15)\qquad \mathbf{P}\{\theta_0 \leq t \mid \eta(0) = c\} = 1 - \mathbf{P}\left\{\sup_{0 \leq u \leq t} \zeta^*(u) \leq c\right\}$$

for $c > 0$ where $\zeta^*(u) = -\zeta(u)$.

If we suppose that $\{\zeta(u), 0 \leq u < \infty\}$ is a separable stochastic process with stationary independent increments for which almost all sample functions have no negative jumps and vanish at $u = 0$, then we can apply the theorems of Section 24 to find the distributions of $\eta(t)$, $\alpha(t)$, θ_0, and their asymptotic distributions.

If we suppose that $\{\zeta(u), 0 \leq u < \infty\}$ is a separable stochastic process with stationary independent increments for which almost all sample functions have no positive jumps and vanish at $u = 0$, then we can also apply the theorems of Section 24 to find the distributions of $\eta(t)$, $\alpha(t)$, θ_0, and their asymptotic distributions; however, in these theorems $\zeta(u)$ should be replaced by $\zeta^*(u) = -\zeta(u)$.

In the most general case when $\{\zeta(u), 0 \leq u < \infty\}$ is an arbitrary separable stochastic process with stationary independent increments, the methods described in Section 25 can be used.

33. FLUCTUATIONS OF THE CONTENT OF DAMS OF FINITE CAPACITY

Now we shall consider the following mathematical model of finite dams: In the time interval $(0, \infty)$ water is flowing into a dam (reservoir). Denote by $\chi(u)$ the total quantity of water flowing into the dam in the time interval $(0, u]$. The capacity of the dam is a finite positive number m. If the dam becomes full, the excess water overflows. Denote by $\delta(u)$ the total quantity of water demanded in the time interval $(0, u]$. If there is enough water in the reservoir the demand is satisfied, if there is not enough water, the difference is supplied from elsewhere. Define $\zeta(u) = \chi(u) - \delta(u)$ for $u \geq 0$. We suppose that $\zeta(u)$, $0 \leq u < \infty$, has no jumps of negative magnitude. Denote by $\eta(t)$ the content of the dam at time t.

Our first aim is to express $\eta(t)$ with the aid of $\eta(0)$ and $\zeta(u)$, $0 \leq u \leq t$. For simplicity we shall suppose that $\eta(0) = m$ and for a fixed t we shall use the notation $\tilde{\zeta}(u) = \zeta(t) - \zeta(t-u)$ for $0 \leq u \leq t$.

Theorem 1. *If $\eta(0) = m$, if $\zeta(u)$, $0 \leq u \leq t$, has no jumps of negative magnitude, and if*

$$\theta(m - x) = \inf\{u : \tilde{\zeta}(u) \leq x - m \text{ and } 0 \leq u \leq t\} \tag{1}$$

exists for $0 \leq x \leq m$, then $\eta(t) \leq x$ $(0 \leq x \leq m)$ holds if and only if $\tilde{\zeta}(u) \leq x$ for $0 \leq u \leq \theta(m - x)$.

Proof. If $x = m$, the theorem is trivially true. Thus we suppose that $0 \leq x < m$. If $\eta(0) = m$ and u denotes the largest u in the interval $[0, t]$ for which $\eta(u) = m$, then the content of the dam at time t is

$$\eta(t) = \sup\{\zeta(t) - \zeta(v) \text{ for } u \leq v \leq t \text{ and } \zeta(t) - \zeta(u) + m\} \tag{2}$$

and necessarily

$$\eta(z) = \sup\{\zeta(z) - \zeta(v) \text{ for } u \leq v \leq z \text{ and } \zeta(z) - \zeta(u) + m\} < m \tag{3}$$

for $u < z < t$.

If we introduce the notation $\tilde{\zeta}(v) = \zeta(t) - \zeta(t - v)$ for $0 \leq v \leq t$, then by (2) and (3) we can conclude that $\eta(t) \leq x$ $(0 \leq x < m)$ holds if and only if

$$\tilde{\zeta}(z) \leq x \quad \text{for} \quad 0 \leq z \leq t - u \tag{4}$$

and

$$\tilde{\zeta}(t - u) \leq x - m \tag{5}$$

where u is the smallest u in $[0, t)$ satisfying the requirements

$$(6) \qquad \tilde{\zeta}(z) - \tilde{\zeta}(v) < m \qquad \text{for} \quad 0 < v \leq z \leq t - u$$

and

$$(7) \qquad \tilde{\zeta}(t-u) - \tilde{\zeta}(z) < 0 \qquad \text{for} \quad 0 < z < t - u.$$

Now if $\eta(t) \leq x$ $(0 \leq x < m)$, then by (5) there exists a $v \in (0, t-u]$ such that $\tilde{\zeta}(v) \leq x - m$. Let $y = \inf\{v: \tilde{\zeta}(v) \leq x - m \text{ and } 0 < v \leq t - u\}$. Then $\tilde{\zeta}(y) = x - m$ and $y > 0$. We shall show that (4) for $y \leq z \leq t - u$ and (5) are automatically satisfied. Let $v = y$ in (6). Then $\tilde{\zeta}(z) - \tilde{\zeta}(y) < m$ for $0 < y \leq z \leq t - u$, that is, $\tilde{\zeta}(z) < x$ for $0 < y \leq z \leq t - u$. Hence (4) holds for $y \leq z \leq t - u$. If $y = t - u$, then (5) evidently holds. If $y < t - u$, then let $z = y$ in (7). Thus we have $\tilde{\zeta}(t-u) < \tilde{\zeta}(y) = x - m$, that is (5) holds in this case too. Conversely, if (4) holds for $u = t - y$ where y is defined as above, then (4) implies (5), (6) and (7).

Accordingly $\eta(t) \leq x$ $(0 \leq x \leq m)$ holds if and only if there exists a $y \in [0, t]$ such that $\tilde{\zeta}(y) = x - m$ and if y is the smallest y with this property, then $\tilde{\zeta}(z) \leq x$ for $0 \leq z \leq y$. This completes the proof of the theorem.

If we suppose that $\eta(0)$ is a random variable taking on values in $[0, m]$ and $\{\zeta(u), 0 \leq u < \infty\}$ is a real valued, separable stochastic process, then $\eta(t)$ is a random variable for all $t \geq 0$. In what follows we shall always make the assumption that $\{\zeta(u), 0 \leq u < \infty\}$ and $\eta(0)$ are independent and we shall find the distribution of $\eta(t)$ for several types of dam and storage processes.

Discrete Dam Processes

(i) Suppose that m is a positive integer and the initial content of a dam of capacity m is $\eta(0) = \eta_0$ where η_0 is a random variable with possible values $0, 1, 2, \ldots, m$. Suppose that at times $u = 1, 2, \ldots, r, \ldots$ water of quantities $\nu_1, \nu_2, \ldots, \nu_r, \ldots$ flows into the dam and the release is continuous at a constant unit rate when the dam is not empty. Let $N_r = \nu_1 + \cdots + \nu_r$ for $r = 1, 2, \ldots$ and $N_0 = 0$. In this case $\chi(u) = N_{[u]}$, $\delta(u) = u$ and $\zeta(u) = N_{[u]} - u$ for $u \geq 0$. Let $\eta_n = \eta(n + 0)$, $n = 1, 2, \ldots$. For $i \geq 1$ define $\rho(i)$ as the smallest r such that $N_r \leq r - i$ and $r = 1, 2, \ldots$.

If $\nu_1, \nu_2, \ldots, \nu_r, \ldots$ are either interchangeable random variables or, in particular, mutually independent and identically distributed random variables taking on nonnegative integer values then we have

$$(8) \quad \mathbf{P}\{\eta_n \leq k \mid \eta_0 = m\}$$
$$= \mathbf{P}\{N_r < r + k \text{ for } r = 1, \ldots, \rho(m-k) \text{ and } \rho(m-k) \leq n\}$$

for $k = 0, 1, \ldots, m$. This follows from Theorem 1 if we take into consideration that $\{\zeta(u),\ u = 0, 1, \ldots, n\}$ and $\{\zeta(n) - \zeta(n-u),\ u = 0, 1, \ldots, n\}$ have exactly the same joint distribution.

***Theorem* 2.** *If $\nu_1, \nu_2, \ldots, \nu_r, \ldots$ are mutually independent and identically distributed random variables with distribution $\mathbf{P}\{\nu_r = j\} = \pi_j$ for $j = 0, 1, 2, \ldots,$ and $\pi_0 > 0$, then*

$$\lim_{n\to\infty} \mathbf{P}\{\eta_n \leq k\} = \frac{Q_k}{Q_m} \tag{9}$$

for $k = 0, 1, \ldots, m$ where Q_0 is a non-null constant and $Q_1, Q_2, \ldots, Q_m$ can be obtained by the following recurrence relation

$$Q_k = \sum_{j=0}^{k} \pi_j Q_{k+1-j} \qquad (k = 0, 1, \ldots). \tag{10}$$

The limiting distribution (9) *is independent of the initial distribution.*

Proof. The case of $k = m$ is evident. Let $k = 0, 1, \ldots, m-1$. If $n \to \infty$ in (8), then we get

$$\lim_{n\to\infty} \mathbf{P}\{\eta_n \leq k \mid \eta_0 = m\} = \mathbf{P}\{N_r < r + k \text{ for } r = 1, \ldots, \rho(m-k)\}. \tag{11}$$

If $\mathbf{P}\{\rho(m-k) < \infty\} = 1$, then this is evident. If $\mathbf{P}\{\rho(m-k) = \infty\} > 0$, then $\mathbf{P}\{N_r < r + k \text{ for } r = 1, 2, \ldots\} = 0$, and thus (11) holds in this case too. The right-hand side of (11) is given by Theorem 2 of Section 7. It is easy to see that the limit (9) is independent of the distribution of η_0.

If we shall denote by $\pi(z)$ the generating function of ν_r, $r = 1, 2, \ldots,$ then we have

$$\sum_{k=1}^{\infty} Q_k z^k = \frac{Q_0 z}{\pi(z) - z} \tag{12}$$

for $|z| < \delta$ where δ is the smallest nonnegative real root of $\pi(z) = z$. Explicit formulas for Q_k, $k = 1, 2, \ldots,$ are given in Section 7.

NOTE. The sequence of random variables $\{\eta_0, \eta_1, \ldots, \eta_n, \ldots\}$ forms a Markov chain with state space $I = \{0, 1, \ldots, m\}$. If $\pi_0 > 0$ and $\pi_0 + \pi_1 < 1$, then the Markov chain is irreducible and aperiodic. Thus the limiting distribution

$$\lim_{n\to\infty} \mathbf{P}\{\eta_n \leq k\} = Q_k^* \qquad (k = 0, 1, \ldots, m) \tag{13}$$

exists and is independent of the distribution of η_0. Since obviously

$$\eta_{n+1} = \min\{[\eta_n - 1]^+ + \nu_n, m\} \tag{14}$$

for $n = 0, 1, 2, \ldots,$ we have

$$Q_k^* = Q_{k+1}^* \pi_0 + Q_k^* \pi_1 + \cdots + Q_1^* \pi_k \tag{15}$$

for $k = 0, 1, \ldots, m-1$ and $Q_m^* = 1$. If we compare (10) and (15), then we obtain immediately that $Q_k^* = Q_k/Q_m$ for $k = 0, 1, \ldots, m$.

(ii) Suppose that m is a positive integer and that the initial stock size of a store of size m is $\eta(0)$ where $\eta(0)$ is a random variable with possible values $0, 1, \ldots, m$. Suppose that $\zeta(u) = \xi(u)$ for $u \geq 0$ where the stochastic process $\{\xi(u), 0 \leq u < \infty\}$ is defined in Section 21. That is we suppose that $\nu_1, \nu_2, \ldots, \nu_r, \ldots$ are interchangeable random variables or, in particular, mutually independent and identically distributed random variables taking on nonnegative integers. Set $N_r = \nu_1 + \cdots + \nu_r$ for $r = 1, 2, \ldots$ and $N_0 = 0$. Let $\{\nu(u), 0 \leq u < \infty\}$ be a separable Poisson process of density λ and suppose that $\{\nu_r\}$ and $\{\nu(u)\}$ are independent. Define $\xi(u) = N_{\nu(u)} - \nu(u)$ for $u \geq 0$.

Let

(16) $$\theta(i) = \inf\{u : \xi(u) = -i \text{ and } 0 \leq u < \infty\}$$

for $i > 0$.

Now by using Theorem 1 we can write

(17) $$\mathbf{P}\{\eta(t) \leq k \mid \eta(0) = m\} = \mathbf{P}\{\xi(u) \leq k \text{ for } 0 \leq u \leq \theta(m-k) \text{ and } \theta(m-k) \leq t\}$$

for $k = 0, 1, \ldots, m$. It is easy to see that Theorem 1 is applicable to the process $\{\xi(u), 0 \leq u < \infty\}$ if m is a positive integer and $x = 0, 1, \ldots, m$. We obtain (17) if we take into consideration that the stochastic processes $\{\xi(u), 0 \leq u \leq t\}$ and $\{\xi(t) - \xi(t-u), 0 \leq u \leq t\}$ have the same finite dimensional distributions.

Theorem 3. *If $\{\xi(u), 0 \leq u < \infty\}$ has stationary independent increments and if $\pi_0 > 0$, then*

(18) $$\lim_{t\to\infty} \mathbf{P}\{\eta(t) \leq k\} = \frac{Q_k}{Q_m}$$

for $k = 0, 1, \ldots, m$ where $Q_0, Q_1, \ldots, Q_m$ are defined as in Theorem 2. *The limiting distribution* (18) *is independent of the initial distribution.*

Proof. The case of $k = m$ is evident. If $k = 0, 1, \ldots, m-1$, then by (17) we obtain

(19) $$\lim_{t\to\infty} \mathbf{P}\{\eta(t) \leq k \mid \eta(0) = m\} = \mathbf{P}\left\{\sup_{0 \leq u \leq \theta(m-k)} \xi(u) \leq k\right\}$$

and the right-hand side of (19) is given by Theorem 5 of Section 21. It is easy to see that the limit (19) is independent of the distribution of $\eta(0)$. This proves (18).

NOTE. The stochastic process $\{\eta(u), 0 \leq u < \infty\}$ is a Markov process with state space $I = \{0, 1, \ldots, m\}$. If we suppose that $\pi_0 > 0$, then it can easily be seen that $\lim_{t\to\infty} \mathbf{P}\{\eta(t) \le k\} = Q_k{}^*$ $(k = 0, 1, \ldots, m)$ exists and is independent of the distribution of $\eta(0)$. For $t \ge 0$, $u > 0$ and $k = 0, 1, \ldots, m - 1$ we have

$$(20) \quad \mathbf{P}\{\eta(t+u) \le k\} = (1 - \lambda u)\mathbf{P}\{\eta(t) \le k\} + \lambda u \sum_{j=0}^{k} \pi_j \mathbf{P}\{\eta(t) \le k + 1 - j\} + o(u)$$

and $\mathbf{P}\{\eta(t) \le m\} = 1$. If we subtract $\mathbf{P}\{\eta(t) \le k\}$ from both sides of (20), form the limit $t \to \infty$, divide the equation by u and let $u \to 0$, then it follows that

$$(21) \qquad Q_k{}^* = \sum_{j=0}^{k} \pi_j Q^*_{k+1-j}$$

for $k = 0, 1, \ldots, m - 1$ and $Q_m{}^* = 1$. Hence $Q_k{}^* = Q_k/Q_m$ for $k = 0, 1, \ldots, m$ where $Q_k (k = 0, 1, \ldots)$ is defined by (10). This result is in agreement with (18).

General Dam Processes

(i) Suppose that m is a positive real number and the initial content of a dam of capacity m is $\eta(0)$ where $\eta(0)$ is a random variable taking on values in the interval $[0, m]$. Denote by $\chi(u)$ the total quantity of water flowing into the dam in the time interval $(0, u]$. If the dam becomes full, the excess water overflows. If the dam is not empty there is a continuous release at a constant unit rate, that is, $\delta(u) = u$ for $u \ge 0$. We suppose that $\{\chi(u), 0 \le u < \infty\}$ is a separable stochastic process with stationary independent increments for which almost all sample functions are non-decreasing step functions vanishing at $u = 0$. Then

$$(22) \qquad \mathbf{E}\{e^{-s\chi(u)}\} = e^{-u\Phi(s)}$$

for $\text{Re}(s) \ge 0$ with an appropriate $\Phi(s)$. The trivial case $\mathbf{P}\{\chi(u) = 0\} = 1$ for all $u \ge 0$ will be excluded.

For $c \ge 0$ define

$$(23) \qquad \theta(c) = \inf\{u : \chi(u) \le u - c \text{ and } 0 \le u < \infty\}$$

and $\theta(c) = \infty$ if $\chi(u) > u - c$ for all $u \ge 0$.

Now by using Theorem 1 we can write

$$(24) \quad \mathbf{P}\{\eta(t) \le x \mid \eta(0) = m\} = \mathbf{P}\{\chi(u) \le u + x \text{ for } 0 \le u \le \theta(m - x) \text{ and } \theta(m - x) \le t\}$$

for $0 \le x \le m$. For $\{\chi(u), 0 \le u \le t\}$ and $\{\chi(t) - \chi(t - u), 0 \le u \le t\}$ have the same finite dimensional distributions.

Theorem 4. *If $\{\chi(u), 0 \leq u < \infty\}$ is a separable stochastic process with stationary independent increments for which almost all sample functions are nondecreasing step functions vanishing at $u = 0$, then*

$$\lim_{t\to\infty} \mathbf{P}\{\eta(t) \leq x\} = \frac{W(x)}{W(m)} \tag{25}$$

for $0 \leq x \leq m$ where $W(x)$ $(0 \leq x < \infty)$ is defined by

$$\Omega(s) = \int_0^\infty e^{-sx}\, dW(x) = \frac{W(0)s}{s - \Phi(s)} \tag{26}$$

for $\mathrm{Re}(s) > \omega$ *where ω is the largest real root of $\Phi(s) = s$, and $W(0)$ is a non-null constant. The limiting distribution (25) is independent of the initial distribution.*

Proof. By (24)

$$\lim_{t\to\infty} \mathbf{P}\{\eta(t) \leq x \mid \eta(0) = m\} = \mathbf{P}\{\chi(u) \leq u + x \text{ for } 0 \leq u \leq \theta\,(m - x)\} \tag{27}$$

for $0 \leq x \leq m$ and the right-hand side is given by Theorem 1 of Section 16. The process $\{\eta(t), 0 \leq t < \infty\}$ is a Markov process and we can see easily that the limiting distribution $\lim_{t\to\infty} \mathbf{P}\{\eta(t) \leq x\}$ is independent of the distribution of $\eta(0)$. This proves the theorem.

For $W(x)$ explicit formulas are given in Section 16. If $\rho = \Phi'(+0)$ is a finite positive number, then $\Phi(s) = \rho s \psi^*(s)$ where $\psi^*(s)$ is the Laplace-Stieltjes transform of a distribution function $H^*(x)$ of a nonnegative random variable. Then by (12) of Section 16

$$W(x) = W(0) \sum_{n=0}^{\infty} \rho^n H_n^*(x) \tag{28}$$

where $H_n^*(x)$ is the nth iterated convolution of $H^*(x)$ with itself; $H_0^*(x) = 1$ if $x \geq 0$ and $H_0^*(x) = 0$ if $x < 0$.

If $\rho \neq 1$, then by (14) of Section 16

$$W(x) = W(0)\left[\frac{e^{\omega x}}{1 - \Phi'(\omega)} - \int_{+0}^{\infty} d_y \mathbf{P}\{\chi(y) \leq y + x\}\right] \tag{29}$$

for all x where ω is the largest nonnegative real root of $\Phi(s) = s$. If $\rho < 1$, then $\omega = 0$, whereas if $\rho > 1$, then $\omega > 0$.

NOTE. Suppose that the input process $\{\chi(u), 0 \leq u < \infty\}$ is a compound Poisson process, that is, $\lambda = \Phi(\infty)$ is a finite positive number. As above, denote by $\eta(t)$ the content of the dam of capacity m at time t. If $m = \infty$, that is, if the dam has unlimited capacity, then denote by $\eta^*(t)$ the content of the infinite dam at time t. Suppose that $\eta(0) = \eta^*(0) = m$. Then we have

$$w\int_0^\infty e^{-wt}\mathbf{P}\{\eta(t) \leq x\}\,dt = \frac{\displaystyle\int_0^\infty e^{-wt}\mathbf{P}\{\eta^*(t) \leq x\}\,dt}{\displaystyle\int_0^\infty e^{-wt}\mathbf{P}\{\eta^*(t) \leq m\}\,dt} \tag{30}$$

for $\text{Re}(w) > 0$. The distribution function $\mathbf{P}\{\eta^*(t) \leq x\}$ is given explicitly in Section 15 (see Section 32). By inverting (30) we obtain $\mathbf{P}\{\eta(t) \leq x\}$.

Now we shall prove (30). Denote by $m^*(t)$ the expected number of transitions $m \to m - 0$ occurring in the interval $(0, t)$ in the process $\{\eta^*(t),\ 0 \leq t < \infty\}$, and by $m(t)$ the same expectation in the process $\{\eta(t),\ 0 \leq t < \infty\}$. Let $G(t, x) = \mathbf{P}\{\eta^*(u) < m$ for $0 \leq u < t$ and $\eta^*(t) \leq x\}$. Evidently $G(t, x) = \mathbf{P}\{\eta(u) < m$ for $0 \leq u < t$ and $\eta(t) \leq x\}$ also holds. For $0 \leq x \leq m$ we have

$$\mathbf{P}\{\eta^*(t) \leq x\} = \int_0^t G(t - u, x)\,dm^*(u) \tag{31}$$

and

$$\mathbf{P}\{\eta(t) \leq x\} = \int_0^t G(t - u, x)\,dm(u). \tag{32}$$

Let

$$\mu^*(w) = \int_0^\infty e^{-wt}\,dm^*(t) \tag{33}$$

and

$$\mu(w) = \int_0^\infty e^{-wt}\,dm(t) \tag{34}$$

for $\text{Re}(w) > 0$.

If we form the Laplace transforms of (31) and (32) and form their ratio, then we get

$$\int_0^\infty e^{-wt}\mathbf{P}\{\eta(t) \leq x\}\,dt = \frac{\mu(w)}{\mu^*(w)}\int_0^\infty e^{-wt}\mathbf{P}\{\eta^*(t) \leq x\}\,dt \tag{35}$$

for $\text{Re}(w) > 0$ and for $0 \leq x \leq m$. If $x = m$ in (35), then $\mathbf{P}\{\eta(t) \leq m\} = 1$ and consequently

$$\frac{1}{w} = \frac{\mu(w)}{\mu^*(w)}\int_0^\infty e^{-wt}\mathbf{P}\{\eta^*(t) \leq m\}\,dt. \tag{36}$$

If we divide (35) by (36), we get (30) which was to be proved.

(ii) If we use the following equivalent interpretation of the process $\{\eta(t),\ 0 \leq t < \infty\}$, we can consider more general types of processes $\{\zeta(u),\ 0 \leq u < \infty\}$ than before. Suppose that the process $\{\zeta(u),\ 0 \leq u < \infty\}$ describes the fluctuations of the level of a dam if the level may vary in the interval $(-\infty, \infty)$. Then $\eta(0) + \zeta(t)$ is the level of the dam at time t. Now suppose that the level of the dam cannot increase above m and cannot decrease below 0, that is, the excess water overflows and if necessary auxiliary water is used to achieve that the level never decreases below 0. Then $\eta(t)$ denotes the level (content)of the dam at time t.

Suppose that m is a positive real number and the initial content of a dam of capacity m is $\eta(0)$ where $\eta(0)$ is a random variable taking on values in the interval $[0, m]$. Suppose that $\{\zeta(u), 0 \le u < \infty\}$ is a separable stochastic process with stationary independent increments for which almost all sample functions have no negative jumps and vanish at $u = 0$. Then

$$\mathbf{E}\{e^{-s\zeta(u)}\} = e^{u\Psi(s)} \tag{37}$$

for $\operatorname{Re}(s) \ge 0$ with an appropriate $\Psi(s)$. The trivial cases $\mathbf{P}\{\zeta(u) \ge 0\} = 1$ for all $u \ge 0$ and $\mathbf{P}\{\zeta(u) \le 0\} = 1$ for all $u \ge 0$ are excluded.

For $c \ge 0$ define

$$\theta(c) = \inf\{\zeta(u) \le -c \text{ and } 0 \le u < \infty\} \tag{38}$$

and $\theta(c) = \infty$ if $\zeta(u) > -c$ for all $u \ge 0$.

Now by using Theorem 1 we can write

$$\begin{aligned}(39)\quad \mathbf{P}\{\eta(t) \le x \mid \eta(0) = m\} \\ = \mathbf{P}\{\zeta(u) \le x \text{ for } 0 \le u \le \theta(m - x) \text{ and } \theta(m - x) \le t\}\end{aligned}$$

for $0 \le x \le m$. For $\{\zeta(u), 0 \le u \le t\}$ and $\{\zeta(t) - \zeta(t - u), 0 \le u \le t\}$ have exactly the same finite dimensional distributions.

Theorem 5. *Let $\{\zeta(u), 0 \le u < \infty\}$ be a separable stochastic process with stationary independent increments almost all of whose sample functions have no negative jumps and vanish at $u = 0$. Then the limiting distribution*

$$\lim_{t\to\infty} \mathbf{P}\{\eta(t) \le x\} = \frac{W(x)}{W(m)} \tag{40}$$

exists for $0 \le x \le m$, is independent of the distribution of $\eta(0)$ and

$$\int_0^\infty e^{-sx} W(x)\, dx = \frac{C}{\Psi(s)} \tag{41}$$

for $\operatorname{Re}(s) > \omega$ where ω is the largest nonnegative real root of $\Psi(s) = 0$ and C is a non-null constant.

Proof. By (39)

$$\lim_{t\to\infty} \mathbf{P}\{\eta(t) \le x \mid \eta(0) = m\} = \mathbf{P}\{\zeta(u) \le x \text{ for } 0 \le u \le \theta(m - x)\} \tag{42}$$

for $0 \le x \le m$ and the right-hand side is given by Theorem 5 of Section 24. The process $\{\eta(t), 0 \le t < \infty\}$ is a Markov process and we can see easily that the limit $\lim_{t \to \infty} \mathbf{P}\{\eta(t) \leq x\}$ is independent of the distribution of $\eta(0)$. This proves the theorem.

34. PROBLEMS

1. Consider a dam of unlimited capacity. Denote by $\chi(u)$ the total quantity of water flowing into the dam in the time interval $(0, u]$. It is supposed that $\{\chi(u), 0 \leq u < \infty\}$ is a separable stochastic process with stationary independent increments and that

$$\mathbf{E}\{e^{-s\chi(u)}\} = \left(\frac{\mu}{\mu + s}\right)^u$$

for $u \geq 0$ where μ is a positive constant. Let us suppose that the release is continuous at a constant unit rate when the dam is not empty. Denote by $\eta(t)$ the content of the dam at time t and by $\alpha(t)$ the total time in the interval $(0, t)$ during which the dam is empty. Find $\mathbf{P}\{\eta(t) \leq x \mid \eta(0) = c\}$, $\lim_{t\to\infty} \mathbf{P}\{\eta(t) \leq x\}$, $\mathbf{P}\{\alpha(t) \leq x - c \mid \eta(0) = c\}$, and the asymptotic distribution of $\alpha(t)$ as $t \to \infty$.

2. Consider Problem 1 in the case where water flows into the dam in accordance with a process $\{\chi^*(u), 0 \leq u < \infty\}$ identical with the dual process of $\{\chi(u), 0 \leq u < \infty\}$ defined in Problem 1. Denote by $\theta_0{}^*$ the time of the first emptiness and by $\beta^*(t)$ the total time in the interval $(0, t)$ during which the dam is not empty. Find the distributions of $\theta_0{}^*$ and $\beta^*(t)$ and the asymptotic distribution of $\beta^*(t)$ as $t \to \infty$.

3. Consider a dam of finite capacity m where m is a positive real number. Suppose that the input $\{\chi(u), 0 \leq u < \infty\}$ is a separable stochastic process with stationary independent increments and for $\mathrm{Re}(s) \geq 0$

$$\mathbf{E}\{e^{-s\chi(u)}\} = e^{-u\Phi(s)}$$

where

$$\Phi(s) = \int_0^\infty (1 - e^{-sx})\, dN(x).$$

Suppose that the demand, $\delta(u) = u$ for $u \geq 0$. Find the distribution of the content of the dam for a stationary process in the following case

$$N(x) = \frac{-1}{\sqrt{4\pi}} \int_x^\infty e^{-\mu y} \frac{dy}{y^{3/2}}$$

for $x > 0$ and μ is a positive constant.

4. Consider Problem 3. Find the distribution of the content of the dam for a stationary process in the case where

$$N(x) = -\int_x^\infty e^{-\mu y} \frac{dy}{y}$$

for $x > 0$ and μ is a positive constant.

5. Consider Problem 3. Find the distribution of the content of the dam for a stationary process in the case where $N(x) = -1/\sqrt{\pi x}$ for $x > 0$.

6. Consider a dam of capacity m where m is a positive real number. Suppose that $\{\zeta(u), 0 \leq u < \infty\}$ is a separable Brownian motion process for which $\mathbf{E}\{\zeta(u)\} = au$ and $\mathbf{Var}\{\zeta(u)\} = \sigma^2 u$ if $u \geq 0$. Find the distribution of the content of the dam for a stationary process.

7. Consider a dam of capacity m where m is a positive real number. Suppose that $\{\zeta(u), 0 \leq u < \infty\}$ is a separable stochastic process with stationary independent increments and for $\text{Re}(s) \geq 0$

$$\mathbf{E}\{e^{-s\zeta(u)}\} = e^{u\Psi(s)}$$

where

$$\Psi(s) = as - \int_0^\infty \left(1 - e^{-sx} - \frac{sx}{1 + x^2}\right) \frac{dx}{x^2}.$$

Find the distribution of the content of the dam for a stationary process.

REFERENCES

[1] Downton, F. "A note on Moran's theory of dams," *Quart. J. Math. Oxford, Sec. Ser.* **8** (1957), 282–286.

[2] Gani, J. "Some problems in the theory of provisioning and of dams," *Biometrika* **42** (1956), 179–200.

[3] Gani, J. "Problems in the probability theory of storage systems," *J. Roy. Statist. Soc. Ser. B* **19** (1957), 181–206.

[4] Gani, J. "Elementary methods for an occupancy problem of storage," *Math. Annalen* **136** (1958), 454–465.

[5] Gani, J. "A stochastic dam process with non-homogeneous Poisson inputs," *Studia Mathematica* **21** (1962), 307–315.

[6] Gani, J. and N. U. Prabhu, "Stationary distributions of the negative exponential type for the infinite dam," *J. Roy. Statist. Soc. Ser. B* **19** (1957), 342–351.

[7] Gani, J. and N. U. Prabhu, "Continuous time treatment of a storage problem," *Nature* **182** (1958), 39–40.

[8] Gani, J. and N. U. Prabhu, "Remarks on the dam with Poisson type inputs," *Austral. J. Appl. Sci.* **10** (1959), 113–122.

[9] Gani, J. and N. U. Prabhu, "The time dependent solution of a storage model with Poisson input," *J. Math. Mech.* **8** (1959), 653–663.

[10] Gani, J. and N. U. Prabhu, "A storage model with continuous infinitely divisible inputs," *Proc. Cambridge Phil. Soc.* **59** (1963), 417–429.

[11] Gani, J. and R. Pyke, "The content of a dam as the supremum of an infinitely divisible process," *J. Math. Mech.* **9** (1960), 639–651.

[12] Ghosal, A. "Emptiness in the finite dam," *Ann. Math. Statist.* **31** (1960), 803–808.

[13] Hasofer, A. M. "On the distribution of the time to first emptiness of a store with stochastic input," *J. Austral. Math. Soc.* **4** (1964), 506–517.

[14] Hasofer, A. M. "A dam with inverse Gaussian input," *Proc. Cambridge Phil. Soc.* **60** (1964), 931–933.

[15] Kendall, D. G. "Some problems in the theory of dams," *J. Roy. Statist. Soc. Ser. B* **19** (1957), 207–212.

[16] Kingman, J. F. C. "On continuous time models in the theory of dams," *J. Austral. Math. Soc.* **3** (1963), 480–487.

[17] Kinney, J. R. "A transient discrete time queue with finite storage," *Ann. Math. Statist.* **33** (1962), 130–136.

[18] Lloyd, E. H. "The epochs of emptiness of a semi-infinite discrete reservoir," *J. Roy. Statist. Soc. Ser. B* **25** (1963), 131–136.

[19] Lloyd, E. H. and S. Odon, "A note on the solution of dam equations," *J. Roy. Stat. Soc. Ser. B* **26** (1964), 338–344.

[20] Loyness, R. M. "A continuous-time treatment of certain queues and infinite dams," *J. Austral. Math. Soc.* **2** (1962), 484–498.

[21] Moran, P. A. P. "A probability theory of dams and storage systems," *Austral. J. Appl. Sci.* **5** (1954), 116–124.

[22] Moran, P. A. P. "A probability theory of dams and storage systems: modifications of the release rules," *Austral. J. Appl. Sci.* **6** (1955), 117–130.

[23] Moran, P. A. P. "A probability theory of a dam with continuous release," *Quart. J. Math. Oxford. Sec. Ser.* **7** (1956), 130–137.

[24] Moran, P. A. P. *The Theory of Storage*, Methuen, London, 1959.

[25] Mott, J. L. "The distribution of the time-to-emptiness of a discrete dam under steady demand," *J. Roy. Statist. Soc. Ser. B* **25** (1963), 137–139.

[26] Prabhu, N. U. "Some exact results for the finite dam." *Ann. Math. Statist.* **29** (1958), 1234–1243.

[27] Prabhu, N. U. "On the integral equation for the finite dam," *Quart. J. Math. Oxford. Sec. Ser* **9** (1958), 183–188.

[28] Prabhu, N. U. "Application of generating functions to a problem in finite dam theory," *J. Austral. Math. Soc.* **1** (1959), 116–120.

[29] Prabhu, N. U. "Time-dependent results in storage theory," *J. Appl. Probability* **1** (1964), 1–46.

[30] Prabhu, N. U. *Queues and Inventories*, John Wiley and Sons, New York, 1964.

[31] Prabhu, N. U. "Unified results and methods for queues and dams," *Proceedings of the Symposium on Congestion Theory*, Chapel Hill, North Carolina, August 24–26, 1964. Edited by W. L. Smith and W. E. Wilkinson. University of North Carolina Press, Chapel Hill, North Carolina, 1965, pp. 317–336.

[32] Takács, L. "The distribution of the content of a dam when the input process has stationary independent increments," *J. Math. Mech.* **15** (1966), 101–112.

[33] Takács, L. "Combinatorial methods in the theory of dams," *J. Appl. Probability* **1** (1964), 69–76.

[34] Takács, L. "The distribution of the content of finite dams," *J. Appl. Probability* **4** (1967) to appear.

[35] Takács, L. "On dams of finite capacity," *J. Austral. Math. Soc.* **9** (1967) to appear.

[36] Weesakul, B. "First emptiness in a finite dam," *J. Roy. Statist. Soc. Ser. B* **23** (1961), 343–351.

[37] Weesakul, B. and G. F. Yeo, "Some problems in finite dams with an application to insurance risk," *Zeitschr. Wahrscheinlichkeitstheorie* **2** (1963), 135–146.

[38] Yeo, G. F. "The time dependent solution for an infinite dam with discrete additive inputs," *J. Roy. Statist. Soc. Ser. B* **23** (1961), 173–179.

CHAPTER 7

Risk Processes

35. INSURANCE RISK PROCESSES

The mathematical theory of risk processes arising in insurance business was initiated in 1903 by F. Lundberg [21, 22], and further developed between 1926 and 1955 by F. Lundberg [23, 24, 25], H. Cramér [9, 10, 11 12, 13, 14], F. Escher [17], C.-O. Segerdahl [31, 32, 33, 34], S. Täcklind [36], T. Saxén [29, 30], H. Ammeter [1], G. Arfwedson [2, 3, 4, 5, 6] and others.

Suppose that a company deals with ordinary insurance business (straight life, disability, accident and health, casualty, liability, fire, and so on). The policyholders pay premiums regularly. The company collects the premiums in a fund called the risk reserve and, if a claim occurs, the company pays the risk sum of the claim. The insurance company can be considered as an adjustment institution for the policyholders. The individual risks of the policyholders are taken over by the company at the price of the premium. The premiums are so calculated that in the long run (on the average) they cover the company's payments for claims. The risk premium determined in this way is the net risk premium. In addition to the net risk premiums, the policyholders pay certain security risk premiums to cover unfavorable random deviations from the average. The sum of the net risk premium and the security risk premium is the gross risk premium. This is the case of insurance with positive premiums and with positive risk sums only.

There are certain types of insurance in which the circumstances are reversed. A typical case is that of the life annuity business. Here the company is continuously paying out annuities to the policyholders, while the random event of the death of a policyholder places the corresponding reserve at the disposal of the company, thus implying a payment from the policyholder to the company, or a payment of a negative amount by the company to the policyholder. Also the annuities can be regarded as negative risk premiums. This is the case of insurance with negative risk premiums and with negative risk sums only.

The cases of only positive risk sums (no annuities) and only negative risk sums (pure annuity business) constitute important particular cases. In general, however, the company may deal with insurance business which includes insurances of both types. The amount paid by the company in settlement of a claim will then be allowed to take positive as well as negative values, and the same will hold for the risk premiums collected by the company, annuities being regarded as negative risk premiums.

The object of the theory of risk is to study the probability laws governing the random fluctuations of the risk reserve. It is important to know these laws in order to be able to find satisfactory protections against inconvenient effects.

The Mathematical Model of the Risk Reserve Process

Suppose that in the time interval $(0, \infty)$ claims occur according to a Poisson process of density $\lambda(\tau)$, $0 \leq \tau < \infty$, and the risk sums (positive or negative) paid by the company are mutually independent, identically distributed random variables with distribution function $H(x)$ and independent of the times when a claim occurs.

Instead of considering the claim process in real time, it is convenient to introduce a new time variable (operational time, transformed time) $u = u(\tau)$ by assuming that

(1) $$u = \frac{1}{\lambda}\int_0^\tau \lambda(v)\, dv$$

where λ is a positive constant. In this case if we denote by $\tilde{\chi}(u)$ the total amount of claims occurring in the time interval $(0, u]$, then $\{\tilde{\chi}(u), 0 \leq u < \infty\}$ is a stochastic process with stationary independent increments and distribution function

(2) $$\mathbf{P}\{\tilde{\chi}(u) \leq x\} = \sum_{n=0}^{\infty} e^{-\lambda u}\frac{(\lambda u)^n}{n!} H_n(x)$$

where $H_n(x)$ denotes the nth iterated convolution of $H(x)$ with itself; $H_0(x) = 1$ if $x \geq 0$ and $H_0(x) = 0$ if $x < 0$. The process $\{\tilde{\chi}(u), 0 \leq u < \infty\}$ is a so-called compound Poisson process.

If

(3) $$a = \int_{-\infty}^{\infty} x\, dH(x)$$

exists, then the expected amount of total risk sums paid by the company in the interval $(0, u]$ is

(4) $$\mathbf{E}\{\tilde{\chi}(u)\} = \lambda a u.$$

In the case of a fair game, the accumulated net risk premium (premiums less annuities paid) in the interval $(0, u]$ is λau. If security loading is applied, then the gross risk premium is $(\lambda a + b)u$ where $b > 0$ if $a > 0$ (for example, positive risk sums) and $b < 0$ if $a < 0$ (for example, negative risk sums).

Suppose that, at time $u = 0$, the company has at its disposal a certain initial capital x, which is available for covering the losses due to random fluctuations. In this case the size of the risk reserve at time u is

$$\gamma(u) = x + cu - \tilde{\chi}(u) \tag{5}$$

for $0 \leq u < \infty$ where $\gamma(0) = x$ is the initial risk reserve at time $u = 0$ and c is a constant.

One of the fundamental problems of the theory of risk is to determine the probability of ruin, that is, the probability that some time in the future the risk reserve becomes negative or more precisely the probability that ruin occurs before time t.

Denote by θ_x the time when the risk reserve becomes negative for the first time in $(0, \infty)$, that is,

$$\theta_x = \inf\{u : \gamma(u) < 0 \text{ for } 0 \leq u < \infty\} \tag{6}$$

and $\theta_x = \infty$ if $\gamma(u) \geq 0$ for $u \geq 0$.

Then the probability that ruin occurs in $(0, t]$ is

$$\mathbf{P}\{\theta_x \leq t\} = 1 - \mathbf{P}\left\{\sup_{0 \leq u \leq t} [\tilde{\chi}(u) - cu] \leq x\right\} \tag{7}$$

and the probability that ruin occurs some time in the future

$$\mathbf{P}\{\theta_x < \infty\} = 1 - \mathbf{P}\left\{\sup_{0 \leq u < \infty} [\tilde{\chi}(u) - cu] \leq x\right\}. \tag{8}$$

If we know the probabilities $\mathbf{P}\{\theta_x < \infty\}$ and $\mathbf{P}\{\theta_x \leq t\}$, then we may decide which precautions (reinsurance, loading of the premium, etc.) should be taken in order to make the probability of ruin so small that in practice no ruin is to be expected.

Let

$$W(t, x) = \mathbf{P}\left\{\sup_{0 \leq u \leq t} [\tilde{\chi}(u) - cu] \leq x\right\} \tag{9}$$

and

$$W(x) = \mathbf{P}\left\{\sup_{0 \leq u < \infty} [\tilde{\chi}(u) - cu] \leq x\right\}. \tag{10}$$

Most of the investigations are concerned with determining the distribution functions $W(x)$ and $W(t, x)$ and finding asymptotic expressions for these probabilities for large x values.

Positive Risk Sums

Suppose that the insurance company pays only positive risk sums, that is, $H(x) = 0$ if $x < 0$. In this case we shall write $\tilde{\chi}(u) = \chi(u)$ for $u \geq 0$ where now $\{\chi(u), 0 \leq u < \infty\}$ is a compound Poisson process for which

$$\mathbf{P}\{\chi(u) \leq x\} = \sum_{n=0}^{\infty} e^{-\lambda u} \frac{(\lambda u)^n}{n!} H_n(x) \tag{11}$$

and for $\mathrm{Re}(s) \geq 0$

$$\mathbf{E}\{e^{-s\chi(u)}\} = e^{-u\Phi(s)} \tag{12}$$

where

$$\Phi(s) = \lambda[1 - \psi(s)] \tag{13}$$

if $\psi(s)$ denotes the Laplace-Stieltjes transform of $H(x)$. If

$$a = \int_0^{\infty} x \, dH(x), \tag{14}$$

then $\mathbf{E}\{\chi(u)\} = \rho u$ with $\rho = \lambda a$, and if

$$\sigma_a^2 = \int_0^{\infty} (x - a)^2 \, dH(x), \tag{15}$$

then $\mathbf{Var}\,\{\chi(u)\} = \sigma^2 u$ with $\sigma^2 = \lambda(a^2 + \sigma_a^2)$.

In this case c is a positive constant and by choosing a suitable monetary unit we can achieve that $c = 1$. Now our problem reduces to finding

$$W(t, x) = \mathbf{P}\left\{\sup_{0 \leq u \leq t} [\chi(u) - u] \leq x\right\} \tag{16}$$

for finite t values as well as

$$W(x) = \mathbf{P}\left\{\sup_{0 \leq u < \infty} [\chi(u) - u] \leq x\right\}. \tag{17}$$

To find these probabilities we can apply the theorems of Section 15. By Theorem 1 of Section 15 we have

$$\begin{aligned} W(t, x) &= \mathbf{P}\{\chi(t) \leq t + x\} \\ &\quad - \iint\limits_{0 < y \leq z \leq t} \left(\frac{t - z}{t - y}\right) d_y\mathbf{P}\{\chi(y) \leq y + x\}\, d_z\mathbf{P}\{\chi(t - y) \leq z - y\} \end{aligned} \tag{18}$$

and

$$W(t, 0) = \int_0^t \left(1 - \frac{y}{t}\right) d_y \mathbf{P}\{\chi(t) \le y\}. \tag{19}$$

If

$$\Omega(t, s) = \int_0^\infty e^{-sx}\, d_x W(t, x) \tag{20}$$

for $\operatorname{Re}(s) \ge 0$, then by (14) of Section 15

$$\int_0^\infty e^{-zt}\Omega(t, s)\, dt = \frac{1}{z - s + \Phi(s)}\left(1 - \frac{s}{\omega(z)}\right) \tag{21}$$

for $\operatorname{Re}(z) > 0$ where $s = \omega(z)$ is the only root of $\Phi(s) = s - z$ in the domain $\operatorname{Re}(s) \ge 0$. We can obtain $W(t, x)$ by inversion from (21).

If $\rho < 1$, then by Theorem 3 of Section 15

$$W(x) = 1 - (1 - \rho)\int_{+0}^\infty d_y \mathbf{P}\{\chi(y) \le y + x\} \tag{22}$$

for all x. If $x < 0$, then $W(x) = 0$ and $W(0) = 1 - \rho$. If $\rho \ge 1$, then $W(x) = 0$ for all x.

If $\rho < 1$, then by Theorem 4 of Section 15 we have

$$\Omega(s) = \int_0^\infty e^{-sx}\, dW(x) = \frac{W(0)s}{s - \Phi(s)} \tag{23}$$

for $\operatorname{Re}(s) > 0$, whence $W(x)$ can be obtained by inversion.

By Theorem 9 of Section 29 we can conclude that if $\rho > 1$ and $\sigma^2 < \infty$, then

$$\lim_{x\to\infty} \mathbf{P}\left\{\frac{\theta_x - \dfrac{x}{\rho - 1}}{\sqrt{\sigma^2 x/(\rho - 1)^3}} \le z\right\} = \frac{1}{\sqrt{2\pi}}\int_{-\infty}^z e^{-y^2/2}\, dy. \tag{24}$$

EXAMPLE 1. Suppose that

$$H(x) = \begin{cases} 1 & \text{if } x \ge a, \\ 0 & \text{if } x < a. \end{cases} \tag{25}$$

Then $\psi(s) = e^{-sa}$, $\Phi(s) = \lambda(1 - e^{-sa})$, $\rho = \lambda a$, $\sigma^2 = \lambda a^2$ and

$$\mathbf{P}\{\chi(u) = ak\} = e^{-\lambda u}\frac{(\lambda u)^k}{k!} \tag{26}$$

for $k = 0, 1, 2, \ldots$. Then by (18)

$$W(t, x) = \mathbf{P}\{\chi(t) \le t + x\} - \sum_{x < aj \le ak \le t+x}\sum \left(\frac{t + x - ak}{t + x - aj}\right) \cdot \mathbf{P}\{\chi(aj - x) = aj\}\, \mathbf{P}\{\chi(t + x - aj) = a(k - j)\} \tag{27}$$

and by (19)

$$W(t, 0) = \sum_{0 \le aj \le t} \left(1 - \frac{aj}{t}\right) \mathbf{P}\{\chi(t) = aj\}. \tag{28}$$

If $\rho = \lambda a < 1$, then by inverting (23) we get

$$W(x) = (1 - \lambda a) \sum_{j=0}^{[\frac{x}{a}]} e^{-\lambda(aj-x)} \frac{[\lambda(aj - x)]^j}{j!}. \tag{29}$$

EXAMPLE 2. Suppose that

$$H(x) = \begin{cases} 1 - e^{-\mu x} & \text{if } x \ge 0, \\ 0 & \text{if } x < 0. \end{cases} \tag{30}$$

Then $\psi(s) = \mu/(\mu + s)$, $\Phi(s) = \lambda s/(\mu + s)$, $\rho = \lambda/\mu$ and $\sigma^2 = 2\lambda/\mu^2$. In this case $\mathbf{P}\{\chi(u) = 0\} = e^{-\lambda u}$ for $u \ge 0$ and

$$\frac{\partial \mathbf{P}\{\chi(u) \le x\}}{\partial x} = \lambda\mu u e^{-\lambda u - \mu x} J'(\lambda\mu u x) \tag{31}$$

for $u > 0$ and $x > 0$ where

$$J(x) = \sum_{n=0}^{\infty} \frac{x^n}{(n!)^2} \tag{32}$$

is the Bessel function. Now we have

$$\begin{aligned} (33)\quad W(t, x) &= 1 - \lambda e^{-\mu x} \int_0^t \frac{e^{-(\lambda+\mu)y}}{x + y} [xJ(\lambda\mu y(x + y)) + yJ'(\lambda\mu y(x + y))]\, dy \end{aligned}$$

for $x \ge 0$ and if $\rho = \lambda/\mu < 1$, then

$$W(x) = 1 - \frac{\lambda}{\mu} e^{-(\mu-\lambda)x} \tag{34}$$

for $x > 0$.

Negative Risk Sums

Suppose that the insurance company deals with annuities only. In this case the total amount of risk sums paid by the company in the interval $(0, u]$ is $\tilde{\chi}(u) = -\chi(u)$ where $\{\chi(u), 0 \le u < \infty\}$ is a compound Poisson process which has the same properties as the process introduced in the previous point. The distribution of $\chi(u)$ is given by (11) and we use the notations (12), (13), (14), (15) unchangeably for the process $\{\chi(u), 0 \le u < \infty\}$.

In this case c is a negative number and by choosing a suitable monetary unit we can achieve that $c = -1$.

Now our problem reduces to finding

$$W(t, x) = \mathbf{P}\left\{\sup_{0 \le u \le t} [u - \chi(u)] \le x\right\} \tag{35}$$

for finite t values, as well as

$$W(x) = \mathbf{P}\left\{\sup_{0 \le u < \infty} [u - \chi(u)] \le x\right\}. \tag{36}$$

To find these probabilities we can apply the theorems of Section 17. By Theorem 1 of Section 17 we have

$$W(t, x) = 1 - \int_x^t \frac{x}{y}\, d_y \mathbf{P}\{\chi(y) \le y - x\} \tag{37}$$

for $0 < x \le t$ and by Theorem 3 of Section 17

$$W(x) = 1 - \int_x^\infty \frac{x}{y}\, d_y \mathbf{P}\{\chi(y) \le y - x\} = 1 - e^{-\omega x} \tag{38}$$

for $x > 0$ where ω is the largest nonnegative real root of the equation $\Phi(s) = s$. If $0 \le \rho \le 1$, then $\omega = 0$, whereas if $\rho > 1$, then $\omega > 0$.

Now

$$\mathbf{E}\{e^{-z\theta_x}\} = e^{-x\omega(z)} \tag{39}$$

for $x > 0$ and $\mathrm{Re}(z) > 0$ where $s = \omega(z)$ is the only root of $\Phi(s) = s - z$ in the domain $\mathrm{Re}(s) \ge 0$. Hence we get

$$\mathbf{E}\{\theta_x\} = \frac{x}{1 - \rho} \tag{40}$$

if $\rho < 1$ and

$$\mathbf{Var}\,\{\theta_x\} = \frac{\sigma^2 x}{(1 - \rho)^3} \tag{41}$$

if $\rho < 1$ and $\sigma^2 < \infty$. By Theorem 9 of Section 29 we can prove that

$$\lim_{x \to \infty} \mathbf{P}\left\{\frac{\theta_x - \dfrac{x}{1 - \rho}}{\sqrt{\sigma^2 x/(1 - \rho)^3}} \le z\right\} = \frac{1}{\sqrt{2\pi}} \int_{-\infty}^z e^{-y^2/2}\, dy \tag{42}$$

if $\rho < 1$ and $\sigma^2 < \infty$.

EXAMPLE 1. Suppose that

$$H(x) = \begin{cases} 1 & \text{if} \quad x \ge a, \\ 0 & \text{if} \quad x < a. \end{cases} \tag{43}$$

Then

$$\mathbf{P}\{\chi(u) = ak\} = e^{-\lambda u} \frac{(\lambda u)^k}{k!} \tag{44}$$

for $k = 0, 1, 2, \ldots$. In this case by (37)

$$(45)\quad W(t, x) = 1 - \sum_{j=0}^{[(t-x)/a]} \frac{x}{aj + x} \mathbf{P}\{\chi(aj + x) = aj\}$$

$$= 1 - \mathbf{P}\{\chi(x) = 0\} - \lambda x \sum_{j=1}^{[(t-x)/a]} \frac{1}{j} \mathbf{P}\{\chi(aj + x) = a(j - 1)\}$$

for $0 < x \leq t$ and by (38)

$$(46)\qquad W(x) = 1 - e^{-\omega x}$$

for $x > 0$ where ω is the largest nonnegative real root of the equation $\lambda(1 - e^{-a\omega}) = \omega$.

NOTE. By (45) we have

$$(47)\qquad W(t, x) = 1 - e^{-\lambda x} - \lambda x \sum_{j=1}^{[(t-x)/a]} e^{-\lambda(aj+x)} \frac{[\lambda(aj + x)]^{j-1}}{j!}$$

for $0 < x \leq t$. T. Saxén [29] found that

$$(48)\quad W(t, x) = 1 - e^{-\lambda x} - e^{-\lambda x} \sum_{k=1}^{[(t-x)/a]} e^{-\lambda ak}(\lambda a)^k \sum_{\substack{\sum_i j_i = k \\ j_i > 0}} \left(\frac{x}{a}\right)^{j_1} \frac{j_1^{\,j_2} j_2^{\,j_3} \cdots}{j_1!\, j_2!\, j_3! \cdots}.$$

If we compare (47) and (48), then we get the interesting identity

$$(49)\qquad z \frac{(k + z)^{k-1}}{k!} = \sum_{\substack{\sum_i j_i = k \\ j_i > 0}} z^{j_1} \frac{j_1^{\,j_2} j_2^{\,j_3} \cdots}{j_1!\, j_2! \cdots}$$

which holds for $k = 1, 2, \ldots$ and for all z.

EXAMPLE 2. Suppose that

$$(50)\qquad H(x) = \begin{cases} 1 - e^{-\mu x} & \text{if} \quad x \geq 0, \\ 0 & \text{if} \quad x < 0. \end{cases}$$

Then by (37)

$$(51)\qquad W(t, x) = 1 - e^{-\lambda x} + \int_x^t \frac{x}{y} \frac{\partial \mathbf{P}\{\chi(y) \leq y - x\}}{\partial x} dy$$

$$= 1 - e^{-\lambda x} - \lambda\mu x e^{\mu x} \int_x^t e^{-(\lambda+\mu)y} J'(\lambda\mu y(y - x))\, dy$$

for $0 < x \leq t$ where $J(x)$ is defined by (32).

If $\rho = \lambda/\mu < 1$, then $\omega = 0$, whereas if $\rho = \lambda/\mu > 1$, then $\omega = \lambda - \mu$. Thus by (38) we get

$$(52)\qquad W(x) = 1 - e^{-(\lambda-\mu)x}$$

if $x > 0$ and $\lambda > \mu$.

Arbitrary Risk Sums

Now suppose that the risk sums may take on positive values as well as negative values. That is, $\{\tilde{\chi}(u), 0 \leq u < \infty\}$ is a compound Poisson process with distribution (2). Then $\tilde{\chi}(u)$ can be represented as a sum of a random number of random variables as follows:

$$\tilde{\chi}(u) = \sum_{0 \leq \tau_i \leq u} \chi_i \tag{53}$$

where $\chi_1, \chi_2, \ldots, \chi_i, \ldots$ are mutually independent and identically distributed random variables with distribution function $H(x)$ and $\tau_1, \tau_2, \ldots, \tau_i, \ldots$ are the times when an event occurs in the underlying Poisson process. The random variables $\{\chi_i\}$ and $\{\tau_i\}$ are independent. Furthermore, $\tau_i - \tau_{i-1}$ $(i = 1, 2, \ldots; \tau_0 = 0)$ are mutually independent and identically distributed random variables with distribution function $F(x) = 1 - e^{-\lambda x}$ for $x \geq 0$. We shall write $a = \mathbf{E}\{\chi_i\}$.

If we introduce the notation $\zeta(u) = \tilde{\chi}(u) - cu$ for $u \geq 0$, then

$$W(t, x) = \mathbf{P}\left\{\sup_{0 \leq u \leq t} \zeta(u) \leq x\right\} \tag{54}$$

and

$$W(x) = \mathbf{P}\left\{\sup_{0 \leq u < \infty} \zeta(u) \leq x\right\} \tag{55}$$

are to be determined.

For $x \geq 0$ we have

$$W(t, x) = e^{-\lambda t}\epsilon(x + ct) + \int_0^{\delta(t,x,c)} \int_{-\infty}^{x+cu} W(t - u, x + cu - y)e^{-\lambda u}\lambda \, du \, dH(y) \tag{56}$$

where $\epsilon(x) = 1$ if $x \geq 0$ and $\epsilon(x) = 0$ if $x < 0$ and $\delta(t, x, c) = t$ if $c \geq 0$ and $\delta(t, x, c) = \min(t, -x/c)$ if $c < 0$. This can be seen as follows:

$$\mathbf{P}\left\{\sup_{0 \leq u \leq t} \zeta(u) \leq x \mid \tau_1 = u \text{ and } \chi_1 = y\right\} = \begin{cases} \epsilon(x + ct) & \text{if } u > t, \\ W(t - u, x + cu - y) & \text{if } u < \delta(t, x, c), \\ 0 & \text{otherwise.} \end{cases} \tag{57}$$

If we form the expectation of (57) with respect to τ_1 and χ_1, then we get (56). $W(t, x)$ can be obtained by solving the integral equation (56).

From (56) we can deduce the following integro-differential equation

$$(58)\qquad \frac{\partial W(t, x)}{\partial t} = c\,\frac{\partial W(t, x)}{\partial x} - \lambda\left[W(t, x) - \int_{-\infty}^{x} W(t, x - y)\, dH(y)\right]$$

which holds for almost all (t, x) $(t \geq 0, x \geq 0)$.

By using similar reasoning as in deducing (56) we can prove that

$$(59)\qquad W(x) = \int_{0}^{\delta(x,c)} \int_{-\infty}^{x+cu} W(x + cu - y)e^{-\lambda u}\lambda\, du\, dH(y)$$

holds for $x \geq 0$ where $\delta(x, c) = \infty$ if $c \geq 0$ and $\delta(x, c) = -x/c$ if $c < 0$. If $\lambda a < c$, then $W(\infty) = 1$ and $W(x)$ can be determined by (59). If $\lambda a \geq c$, then $W(\infty) = 0$ and thus $W(x) = 0$ for all x.

In a similar way as (58) we obtain

$$(60)\qquad cW'(x) = \lambda\left[W(x) - \int_{-\infty}^{x} W(x - y)\, dH(y)\right]$$

for almost all $x \geq 0$. If we integrate (60) from x to ∞, then we get

$$(61)\qquad c[1 - W(x)] = \lambda\int_{x}^{\infty} [1 - H(u)]\, du + \lambda\int_{0}^{x} [1 - W(u)]\, du - \lambda\int_{0}^{\infty} [1 - W(u)]H(x - u)\, du$$

for $x \geq 0$.

If $\lambda a < c$ and $c \geq 0$, then

$$(62)\qquad \int_{0}^{\infty} e^{-sx} dW(x) = A(s)$$

for $\text{Re}(s) \geq 0$, and if $\lambda a < c$ and $c \leq 0$, then

$$(63)\qquad \int_{0}^{\infty} e^{-sx}\, dW(x) = A(s)\left(\frac{\lambda}{\lambda - cs}\right)$$

for $\text{Re}(s) \geq 0$ where

$$(64)\qquad A(s) = \exp\left\{-\int_{0}^{\infty} e^{-sx}\, dM(x)\right\}$$

and

$$(65)\qquad M(x) = \sum_{n=1}^{\infty} \frac{\lambda^n}{n!} \int_{0}^{\infty} e^{-\lambda u}\, u^{n-1}[1 - H_n(x + cu)]\, du,$$

or equivalently

$$(66)\qquad M(x) = \int_{0}^{\infty} \frac{\mathbf{P}\{\zeta(u) > x\}}{u}\, du$$

for $x \geq 0$.

Formulas (62) and (63) can easily be proved by using (23) of Section 11. Let $\zeta = \sup_{0 \leq u < \infty} \zeta(u)$. If $c \geq 0$, then we have

(67) $$\zeta = \sup_{0 \leq r < \infty} \zeta(\tau_r + 0) = \sup_{0 \leq r < \infty} (\chi_1 + \cdots + \chi_r - c\tau_r)$$

and if $c \leq 0$, then we have

(68) $$\zeta = \sup_{1 \leq r < \infty} \zeta(\tau_r - 0) = \sup_{1 \leq r < \infty} (\chi_1 + \cdots + \chi_{r-1} - c\tau_r).$$

Accordingly if $\xi_r = \chi_r - c(\tau_r - \tau_{r-1})$ for $r = 1, 2, \ldots$, then in the case of $c \geq 0$ by (67) we have

(69) $$\zeta = \sup (0, \xi_1, \xi_1 + \xi_2, \ldots, \xi_1 + \cdots + \xi_r, \ldots)$$

where $\xi_1, \xi_2, \ldots, \xi_r, \ldots$ are mutually independent and identically distributed random variables. If $\mathbf{E}\{\xi_r\} = a - \dfrac{c}{\lambda} < 0$, then ζ is a proper random variable and the Laplace-Stieltjes transform of the distribution $\mathbf{P}\{\zeta \leq x\} = W(x)$ is given by (23) of Section 11. If $\mathbf{E}\{\xi_r\} = a - \dfrac{c}{\lambda} \geq 0$, then $\mathbf{P}\{\zeta = \infty\} = 1$, that is, $W(x) = 0$ for all x.

If $\xi_r = \chi_r - c(\tau_{r+1} - \tau_r)$ for $r = 1, 2, \ldots$, then in the case of $c \leq 0$ by (68) we have

(70) $$\zeta = -c\tau_1 + \sup (0, \xi_1, \xi_1 + \xi_2, \ldots, \xi_1 + \cdots + \xi_r, \ldots).$$

Hence $\zeta = -c\tau_1 + \zeta^*$ where ζ^* has the same distribution as (69) and ζ^* is independent of τ_1. This proves (63).

NOTE. In what follows we would like to say a few words about the historical development of the theory of mathematical risk.

The asymptotic distribution of the risk process $\{\tilde{\chi}(u), 0 \leq u < \infty\}$ was studied first in 1903 by F. Lundberg [21] and further developed by himself in his works [22, 23, 24, 25, 26]. F. Lundberg noticed that if $\mathbf{E}\{\tilde{\chi}(u)\} = \rho u$ and $\mathbf{Var}\{\tilde{\chi}(u)\} = \sigma^2 u$ where σ^2 is a finite positive number, then

(71) $$\lim_{u \to \infty} \mathbf{P}\left\{\frac{\tilde{\chi}(u) - \rho u}{\sqrt{\sigma^2 u}} \leq x\right\} = \frac{1}{\sqrt{2\pi}} \int_{-\infty}^{x} e^{-y^2/2}\, dy.$$

The error of the normal approximation has been estimated by H. Cramér [9, 10] and C. G. Esseen [18]. An approximate formula for $\mathbf{P}\{\tilde{\chi}(u) - \rho u \leq xu\}$, where $x < 0$, has been given by F. Esscher [17] and his method was further developed by H. Cramér [11] and W. Feller [19].

The ruin function $\mathbf{P}\{\theta_x < \infty\} = 1 - W(x)$, defined by (55), was introduced by F. Lundberg [23, 25, 26]. In the case of positive risk sums ($H(0) = 0$) F. Lundberg found that $1 - W(x) \leq e^{-Rx}$ if $x \geq 0$ and $1 - W(x) \sim Ce^{-Rx}$ for $x \to \infty$ where R and C are positive constants.

In 1926 H. Cramér [9] found that if $\lambda a < c$ and $H(0) = 0$, then $W(x)$ satisfies the following integral equation of the Volterra type

$$c[1 - W(x)] = \lambda a - \lambda \int_0^x W(u)[1 - H(x - u)]\, du \tag{72}$$

for $x \geq 0$. In 1930 H. Cramér [10] found the Fourier transform of $W(x)$ (Pollaczek-Khintchine formula in the theory of queues). For constant risk sums $W(x)$ has been given explicitly by W. Feller (cf. C.-O. Segerdahl [31], p. 88). In this case $W(x)$ has also been found earlier by A. K. Erlang (cf. reference [20] in Chapter 5). For arbitrary risk sums C.-O. Segerdahl [31, 32, 33] proved that $1 - W(x) \leq e^{-Rx}$ if $x \geq 0$ and $1 - W(x) \sim Ce^{-Rx}$ if $x \to \infty$. For the case of arbitrary risk sums, in 1937, H. Cramér [12] showed that $W(x)$ satisfies the integral equation (61). The solution of the integral equation (61) was given by S. Täcklind [36] and by H. Cramér [13] in the forms of (62) and (63).

The moments of the random variable θ_x, defined by (6), have been calculated by F. Lundberg [23] and C.-O. Segerdahl [31].

The ruin function $\mathbf{P}\{\theta_x \leq t\} = 1 - W(t, x)$ defined by (54), has been studied first by T. Saxén [29, 30]. In the case of negative risk sums T. Saxén [29] deduced the integro-differential equation (58) and for negative and constant risk sums he found the solution (48). In 1950 G. Arfwedson [2] deduced the integro-differential equation (58) and found an explicit expression for $W(t, x)$ in the cases where the risk sums are positive and exponentially distributed random variables [formula (33)] or the risk sums are negative and exponentially distributed random variables [formula (51)]. See also G. Arfwedson [3]. In the case of positive and constant risk sums, $W(t, x)$ was found by T. Saxén [30] and G. Arfwedson [4] when $t = m/c$ and $x = n$ (m, n are nonnegative integers). G. Arfwedson [4] found also $W(m/c, n)$ in the case of negative and constant risk sums. For both only positive and only negative risk sums the double Laplace-Stieltjes transform of $W(t, x)$ was found by G. Arfwedson [6]. For arbitrary risk sums a method of finding $W(t, x)$ was given in 1955 by H. Cramér [14]. (See also G. Baxter and M. D. Donsker [1] in Chapter 4.)

36. PROBLEMS

1. Consider Example 2 in Positive Risk Sums. Find $\Omega(t, s)$ defined by (20).

2. Prove that

$$z\frac{(k+z)^{k-1}}{k!} = \sum_{\substack{\Sigma j_i = k \\ j_i > 0}} z^{j_1} \frac{j_1^{\,j_2} j_2^{\,j_3} \cdots}{j_1!\, j_2! \cdots}$$

holds for $k = 1, 2, \ldots$ and for all z (cf. G. Arfwedson [4]).

3. Prove (40), (41), and (42).

4. Prove (58).

5. Find $W(x)$ defined by (10) where

$$H(x) = \begin{cases} 1 - e^{-x} & \text{if } x \geq 0, \\ 0 & \text{if } x < 0, \end{cases}$$

and c is a positive constant

6. Find $W(x)$ defined by (10) where

$$H(x) = \begin{cases} 1 - e^{-2x}(1 + 2x) & \text{if } x \geq 0, \\ 0 & \text{if } x < 0, \end{cases}$$

and c is a positive constant.

7. Find $W(x)$ defined by (10) where

$$H(x) = \begin{cases} 1 - \alpha e^{-x} & \text{if } x \geq 0, \\ (1 - \alpha)e^{x} & \text{if } x \leq 0, \end{cases}$$

and $0 < \alpha < 1$.

8. Let

$$\Omega(t, s) = \int_0^\infty e^{-sx}\, d_x W(t, x)$$

for Re(s) ≥ 0 where $W(t, x)$ is defined by (54) and

$$\mathbf{E}\{e^{-s\zeta(u)}\} = e^{csu - \lambda u[1 - \psi(s)]}$$

for $\text{Re}(s) = 0$ where $\psi(s)$ is the Laplace-Stieltjes transform of $H(x)$. Prove that

$$w\int_0^\infty e^{-wt}\, \Omega(t, s)\, dt = \begin{cases} A(s, w) & \text{if } c \geq 0, \\ A(s, w)\left(\dfrac{\lambda + w}{\lambda + w - cs}\right) & \text{if } c \leq 0 \end{cases}$$

for $0 < w < \infty$ where

$$A(s, w) = \exp\left\{ -\int_0^\infty e^{-sx}\, d_x M(x, w)\right\}$$

and

$$\begin{aligned} M(x, w) &= \sum_{n=1}^{\infty} \frac{\lambda^n}{n!} \int_0^\infty e^{-(\lambda+w)u} u^{n-1}[1 - H_n(x + cu)]\, du \\ &= \int_0^\infty \frac{e^{-wu}}{u}\, \mathbf{P}\{\zeta(u) > x\}\, du \end{aligned}$$

for $x \geq 0$. (See H. Cramér [14].)

REFERENCES

[1] Ammeter, H. "A generalisation of the collective theory of risk in regard to fluctuating basic-probabilities," *Skand. Aktuarietids.* **31** (1948), 171–198.

[2] Arfwedson, G. "Some problems in the collective theory of risk," *Skand. Aktuarietids.* **33** (1950), 1–38.

[3] Arfwedson, G. "A semi-convergent series with application to the collective theory of risk," *Skand. Aktuarietids.* **35** (1952), 16–35.

[4] Arfwedson, G. "Research in collective risk theory. The case of equal risk sums," *Skand. Aktuarietids.* **36** (1953), 1–15.

[5] Arfwedson, G. "On the collective theory of risk," *Trans. Internat. Congress of Actuaries*, Madrid, 1954.

[6] Arfwedson, G. "Research in collective risk theory," Part I. *Skand. Akturaietids.* **37** (1954), 191–223; Part II. *Skand. Aktuarietids.* **38** (1955), 53–100.

[7] Arfwedson, G. "Notes on collective risk theory," *Skand. Aktuarietids.* **40** (1957), 46–59.

[8] Brans, J. P. "Quelques aspects du problème de la ruine en théorie collective du risque," *Cahiers Centre Études Rech. Opér.* **5** (1963), 139–159.

[9] Cramér, H. Review of F. Lundberg, "Försäkringsteknisk Riskutjämning I. Teori," *Skand. Aktuarietids.* **9** (1926), 223–245.

[10] Cramér, H. "On the mathematical theory of risk," *Skandia Jubilee Volume*, Stockholm, 1930.

[11] Cramér, H. "Sur un nouveau théorème-limite de la théorie des probabilités," *Actualités Scientifiques, No.* 736, Hermann, Paris, 1938.

[12] Cramér, H. "Deux conférences sur la théorie des probabilités," *Skand. Aktuarietids* **24** (1941), 34–69.

[13] Cramér, H. "On some questions connected with mathematical risk," *University of California Publications in Statistics* **2** (1954), 99–124.

[14] Cramér, H. "Collective Risk Theory. A survey of the theory from the point of view of the theory of stochastic processes," *Jubilee Volume of Försäkringsaktiebolaget Skandia* (Skandia Insurance Company), Nordiska Bokhandeln, Stockholm, (1955), 1–92.

[15] Davidson, Å. "Om ruinproblemet i den kollektiva riskteorien under antagande av variabel säkerhetsbelastning," *F. Lundberg Jubilee Volume*, Stockholm, 1946 pp. 32–47.

[16] Dubourdieu, J. *Théorie mathématique des assurances. I. Théorie mathématique du risque dans les assurances de répartition*, Gautheir-Villars, Paris, 1952.

[17] Esscher, F. "On the probability function in the collective theory of risk," *Skand. Aktuarietids.* **15** (1932), 175–195.

[18] Esseen, C. G. "Fourier analysis of distribution functions," *Acta Mathematica* **77** (1954), 1–125.

[19] Feller, W. "Generalization of a probability limit theorem by Cramér," *Trans. Amer. Math. Soc.* **54** (1943), 361–372.

[20] Laurin, I. "An introduction into Lundberg's theory of risk," *Skand. Aktuarietids.* **13** (1930), 84–111.

[21] Lundberg, F. "Approximerad framställning av sannolikhetsfunktionen. Återförsäkring av kollektivrisker," *Akad. Afhandling, Almqvist o Wiksell*, Uppsala, 1903.

[22] Lundberg, F. "Zur Theorie der Rückversicherung," *Verhandl. Kongr. Versicherungsmath.*, Wien, 1909.

[23] Lundberg, F. *Försäkringsteknisk Riskutjämning, I-II*, F. Englund, Stockholm, 1926–1928.

[24] Lundberg, F. "Über die Wahrscheinlichkeitsfunktion einer Risikenmasse," *Skand. Aktuarietids.* **13** (1390), 1–83.

[25] Lundberg, F. "Some supplementary researches on the collective risk theory," *Skand. Aktuarietids.* **15** (1932), 137–158.

[26] Lundberg, F. "On the numerical application of the collective risk theory," *De Förenade Jubilee Volume*, Stockholm, 1934.

[27] Philipson, C. "A note on different models of stochastic processes dealt with in the collective theory of risk," *Skand. Aktuarietids.* **39** (1956), 26–37.

[28] Prabhu, N. U. "On the ruin problem of collective risk theory," *Ann. Math. Statist.* **32** (1961), 757–764.

[29] Saxén, T. "On the probability of ruin in the collective risk theory for insurance enterprises with only negative risk sums," *Skand. Aktuarietids.* **31** (1948), 199–228.

[30] Saxén, T. "Sur les mouvements aléatoires et le problème de ruine de la théorie du risque collective," *Soc. Sci. Fenn. Comm. Phys. Math.* **16** (1951), 1–55.

[31] Segerdahl, C. -O. *On homogeneous Random Processes and Collective Risk Theory*, Thesis, Stockholm, 1939.

[32] Segerdahl, C. -O. "Über einige risikotheoretische Fragestellungen," *Skand. Aktuarietids.* **25** (1942) 43–83.

[33] Segerdahl, C. -O. "Some properties of the ruin function in the collective theory of risk," *Skand. Aktuarietids.* **31** (1948), 46–87.

[34] Segerdahl, C. -O. "When does ruin occur in the collective theory of risk?," *Skand. Aktuarietids.* **38** (1955), 22–36.

[35] Segerdahl, C. -O. "A survey of results in the collective theory of risk," *Probability and Statistics*, The Harald Cramér Volume, Edited by U. Grenander, Almqvist and Wiksell, Stockholm; John Wiley and Sons, New York, 1959, pp. 276–299.

[36] Täcklind, S. "Sur le risque de ruine dans des jeux inéquitables," *Skand. Aktuarietids.* **25** (1942), 1–42.

CHAPTER 8

Order Statistics

37. ANOTHER EXTENSION OF THE BALLOT THEOREM

The classical ballot theorem which we mentioned in Section 2 can also be formulated as follows:

Suppose that in a ballot candidate A scores a votes and candidate B scores b votes and that all the possible $\binom{a+b}{a}$ voting records are equally probable. Denote by α_r and β_r the number of votes registered for A and B respectively among the first r votes recorded. Denote by P_j the probability that the inequality $\alpha_r > \mu\beta_r$ holds for exactly j subscripts $r = 1, 2, \ldots, a + b$. If μ is a nonnegative integer and $a \geq \mu b$, then by Theorem 1 of Section 2

$$P_{a+b} = \frac{a - \mu b}{a + b}. \tag{1}$$

However, it is of some interest to find the complete distribution $\{P_j\}$.

In what follows we shall prove two combinatorial theorems and by using them we shall be able to find P_j, $j = 0, 1, \ldots, a + b$, in the case when μ is a nonnegative integer.

Theorem 1. *Let $k_1, k_2, \ldots, k_n$ be integers with sum $k_1 + k_2 + \cdots + k_n = 1$. Among the n cyclic permutations of $(k_1, k_2, \ldots, k_n)$ there is exactly one for which exactly j $(j = 1, 2, \ldots, n)$ of its successive partial sums are positive.*

Proof. Let $k_{j+n} = k_j$ for $j = 1, 2, \ldots$ and define

$$d_j = n(k_1 + \cdots + k_j) - j$$

for $j = 1, 2, \ldots$. Then $d_{j+n} = d_j$ for $j = 1, 2, \ldots$. The numbers d_1, $d_2, \ldots, d_n$ are distinct and $d_n = 0$. We shall prove that if d_i is the rth $(r = 1, 2, \ldots, n)$ largest number among $d_1, d_2, \ldots, d_n$, then the cyclic permutation $(k_{i+1}, \ldots, k_{i+n})$ has exactly $n + 1 - r$ positive partial sums. This implies the theorem.

Evidently $(k_{i+1}, k_{i+1} + k_{i+2}, \ldots, k_{i+1} + \cdots + k_{i+n})$ has the same number of positive terms as $(d_{i+1} - d_i, d_{i+2} - d_i, \ldots, d_{i+n} - d_i)$ has nonnegative elements. For if $k_{i+1} + \cdots + k_{i+j} > 0$, then $d_{i+j} - d_i = n(k_{i+1} + \cdots + k_{i+j}) - j \geq 0$ for $j = 1, 2, \ldots, n$. Conversely, if $d_{i+j} - d_i \geq 0$, then $k_{i+1} + \cdots + k_{i+j} > 0$ for $j = 1, 2, \ldots, n$. Thus $(k_{i+1}, k_{i+1} + k_{i+2}, \ldots, k_{i+1} + \cdots + k_{i+n})$ has the same number of positive terms as $(d_1 - d_i, d_2 - d_i, \ldots, d_n - d_i)$ has nonnegative elements. If d_i is the rth largest number among $d_1, d_2, \ldots, d_n$, then the latter sequence contains $n + 1 - r$ nonnegative elements. This proves the theorem.

This theorem can also be proved by using Theorem 2.1 of F. Spitzer [26] or Theorem 3 of E. Sparre Andersen [3].

Theorem 1 immediately implies the following theorem.

Theorem 2. *If $\gamma_1, \gamma_2, \ldots, \gamma_n$ are cyclically interchangeable random variables taking on integer values and if Δ_n denotes the number of positive partial sums among $\gamma_1 + \cdots + \gamma_r$, $r = 1, 2, \ldots, n$, then*

$$\mathbf{P}\{\Delta_n = j \mid \gamma_1 + \cdots + \gamma_n = 1\} = \frac{1}{n} \tag{2}$$

for $j = 1, 2, \ldots, n$, provided that the conditional probability is defined.

Now by using Theorem 2, and Theorem 1 of Section 4 we shall prove the following general theorem.

Theorem 3. *Let $\nu_1, \nu_2, \ldots, \nu_n$ be interchangeable random variables taking on nonnegative integers, and set $N_r = \nu_1 + \cdots + \nu_r$, $r = 1, 2, \ldots, n$. Let Δ_n denote the number of indices $r = 1, 2, \ldots, n$ for which $N_r < r$. If $k < n - 1$, we have*

$$\mathbf{P}\{\Delta_n = j \mid N_n = k\} \tag{3}$$

$$= \begin{cases} 0 & \text{if } j = 0, 1, \ldots, n-k-1, \\ \displaystyle\sum_{i=n-j+1}^{k+1} \frac{\binom{n-k-1}{}}{i(n-i)} \mathbf{P}\{N_i = i - 1 \mid N_n = k\} & \text{if } j = n-k, \ldots, n-1, \\ 1 - \dfrac{k}{n} & \text{if } j = n. \end{cases}$$

Further,

$$\mathbf{P}\{\Delta_n = j \mid N_n = n - 1\} = \frac{1}{n} \tag{4}$$

for $j = 1, 2, \ldots, n$, *and*

(5) $\mathbf{P}\{\Delta_n = j \mid N_n = n\}$

$$= \begin{cases} 1 - \sum_{i=1}^{n-1} \frac{1}{i} \mathbf{P}\{N_i = i - 1 \mid N_n = n\} & \textit{for} \quad j = 0, \\ \sum_{i=1}^{n-j} \frac{1}{i(n-i)} \mathbf{P}\{N_i = i - 1 \mid N_n = n\} & \textit{for} \quad j = 1, 2, \ldots, n-1. \end{cases}$$

Proof. We note that

$$\mathbf{P}\{\Delta_n = n \mid N_n = k\} = 1 - \frac{k}{n} \tag{6}$$

for $k = 0, 1, \ldots, n$. This is exactly Theorem 1 of Section 4. Further,

$$\mathbf{P}\{\Delta_n = j \mid N_n = n - 1\} = \frac{1}{n} \tag{7}$$

for $j = 1, 2, \ldots, n$. This follows from Theorem 2 if we apply it to the random variables $\gamma_i = 1 - \nu_i$, $i = 1, 2, \ldots, n$. In what follows we shall denote by Δ_j the number of indices $r = 1, 2, \ldots, j$ for which $N_r < r$.

First we shall prove (3). Without loss of generality we may suppose that $N_n = k$ is fixed. Let $j \leq n - 1$. If $\Delta_n = j < n$ and $N_n = k < n - 1$, then there exists an r such that $N_r = r - 1$. Denote by $r = i$ ($i = 1, \ldots, k + 1$) the greatest r with this property. Then $N_i = i - 1$ and $N_r - N_i < r - i$ for $r = i + 1, \ldots, n$. Thus

$$\mathbf{P}\{\Delta_n = j\} = \sum_{i=1}^{k+1} \mathbf{P}\{N_i = i - 1\} \mathbf{P}\{\Delta_i = i + j - n \mid N_i = i - 1\} \cdot \mathbf{P}\{\Delta_n - \Delta_i = n - i \mid N_i = i - 1\}. \tag{8}$$

Now by (7) $\mathbf{P}\{\Delta_i = i + j - n \mid N_i = i - 1\} = 1/i$ for $n - j < i \leq n$ and 0 otherwise. By (6)

$$\begin{aligned} \mathbf{P}\{\Delta_n - \Delta_i = n - i \mid N_i = i - 1\} &= \mathbf{P}\{\Delta_n - \Delta_i = n - i \mid N_n - N_i = k - i + 1\} \\ &= \frac{n - k - 1}{n - i} \quad \text{for} \quad i = 1, \ldots, k + 1. \end{aligned} \tag{9}$$

Thus (3) follows for $j \leq n - 1$. If $j < n - k$, then $\mathbf{P}\{\Delta_n = j\} = 0$. If $j = n$, then (3) reduces to (6). This completes the proof of (3). Formula (4) is identical with (7).

It remains to prove (5). Suppose that $N_n = n$ is fixed. If $\Delta_n = j$, $j = 1, 2, \ldots, n - 1$, then there is an $r = 1, 2, \ldots, n$ for which $N_r < r$. Denote by i the smallest r with this property. Then necessarily $N_i = i - 1$,

$N_r \geq r$ for $r = 1, 2, \ldots, i-1$ and $N_r < r$ holds for j indices among $r = i, i+1, \ldots, n$. Thus

$$\text{(10)} \qquad \mathbf{P}\{\Delta_n = j\} = \sum_{i=1}^{n-j} \mathbf{P}\{N_i = i-1\}\mathbf{P}\{\Delta_i = 0 \mid N_i = i-1\} \cdot \mathbf{P}\{\Delta_n - \Delta_i = j \mid N_n - N_i = n-i+1\}.$$

Now by (7) $\mathbf{P}\{\Delta_i = 0 \mid N_i = i-1\} = 1/i$ for $i = 1, 2, \ldots, n-1$. If we apply Theorem 2 to the random variables $(\nu_{i+1} - 1), \ldots, (\nu_n - 1)$, then we get $\mathbf{P}\{\Delta_n - \Delta_i = j \mid N_n - N_i = n-i+1\} = 1/(n-i)$ for $i = 1, 2, \ldots, n-j$. Thus

$$\text{(11)} \qquad \mathbf{P}\{\Delta_n = j\} = \sum_{i=1}^{n-j} \frac{1}{i(n-i)} \mathbf{P}\{N_i = i-1\}$$

for $j = 1, 2, \ldots, n-1$. If we add (11) for $j = 1, 2, \ldots, n-1$, then we get

$$\text{(12)} \qquad 1 - \mathbf{P}\{\Delta_n = 0\} = \sum_{i=1}^{n-1} \frac{1}{i} \mathbf{P}\{N_i = i-1\}.$$

Now (5) follows from (11) and (12). This completes the proof of the theorem.

By using Theorem 3 we can find the distribution $P_j, j = 0, 1, \ldots, a+b$, in the case where $\mu \geq 0$ is an integer and $a \geq \mu b$.

Theorem 4. *If $a > \mu b + 1$, then*

(13)
$$P_j = \frac{1}{\binom{a+b}{a}} \sum_{\frac{a+b-j}{\mu+1} \leq s \leq b} \frac{(a-b\mu-1)}{s(b-s)} \binom{s\mu+s}{s-1} \binom{a+b-s\mu-s-2}{b-s-1}$$

for $j = 0, 1, \ldots, a+b-1$ and $P_{a+b} = (a-b\mu)/(a+b)$. If $a = \mu b + 1$, then

$$\text{(14)} \qquad P_j = \frac{1}{a+b}$$

for $j = 1, 2, \ldots, a+b$. If $a = \mu b$, then

(15)
$$P_j = \frac{1}{\binom{a+b}{a}} \sum_{0 \leq s \leq \frac{a+b-j-1}{\mu+1}} \frac{1}{s(b-s)} \binom{s\mu+s}{s-1} \binom{a+b-s\mu-s-2}{b-s-1}$$

for $j = 1, 2, \ldots, a+b-1$ and

$$\text{(16)} \quad P_0 = 1 - \frac{1}{\binom{a+b}{a}} \sum_{0 \leq s \leq \frac{a+b-2}{\mu+1}} \frac{1}{s} \binom{s\mu+s}{s-1} \binom{a+b-s\mu-s-1}{b-s}.$$

Proof. Define the random variables $\nu_r, r = 1, 2, \ldots, a + b$, as follows: $\nu_r = 0$ if the rth vote is cast for A and $\nu_r = (\mu + 1)$ if the rth vote is cast for B. Set $N_r = \nu_1 + \cdots + \nu_r$ for $r = 1, 2, \ldots, a + b$ and $N_0 = 0$. Now $\nu_1, \nu_2, \ldots, \nu_{a+b}$ are interchangeable random variables taking on nonnegative integers for which $\nu_1 + \nu_2 + \cdots + \nu_{a+b} = b(\mu + 1)$. Since $N_r = \beta_r(\mu + 1)$ and $r = \alpha_r + \beta_r$ for $r = 1, 2, \ldots, a + b$, the inequality $\alpha_r > \mu\beta_r$ holds if and only if $N_r < r$. Thus $P_j = \mathbf{P}\{\Delta_n = j \mid N_n = k\}$ is given by Theorem 3 where now $n = a + b$, $k = b(\mu + 1)$, and

$$(17) \qquad \mathbf{P}\{N_i = s(\mu + 1)\} = \frac{\binom{a}{i-s}\binom{b}{s}}{\binom{a+b}{i}} = \frac{\binom{i}{s}\binom{a+b-i}{b-s}}{\binom{a+b}{a}}$$

for $s = 0, 1, \ldots, \min(i, b)$ and $\mathbf{P}\{N_i = j\} = 0$ otherwise. Formulas (13), (14), (15), and (16) can be obtained by the corresponding formulas of Theorem 3.

There is another method of finding the distribution $P_j, j = 0, 1, \ldots, a + b$. This method is based on the following theorem of E. Sparre Andersen [4] and W. Feller [19].

Theorem 5. *Let $c_1, c_2, \ldots, c_n$ be n given real numbers and consider the $n!$ permutations of $(c_1, c_2, \ldots, c_n)$. Then there are as many permutations in which precisely k among the n successive partial sums are strictly positive (nonnegative) as there are permutations in which the first (last) maximal element in the sequence of 0 and the n successive partial sums occurs at the kth place.*

Proof. For the proof it is convenient to give an equivalent probabilistic formulation of this theorem.

Let $(\xi_1, \xi_2, \ldots, \xi_n)$ be a random permutation of $(c_1, c_2, \ldots, c_n)$, and suppose that all the $n!$ permutations are equally probable. Define $\zeta_r = \xi_1 + \cdots + \xi_r$ for $r = 1, 2, \ldots, n$ and $\zeta_0 = 0$. Denote by Δ_n the number of strictly positive terms in $\zeta_1, \zeta_2, \ldots, \zeta_n$ and by $\Delta_n{}^*$ the number of nonnegative terms in $\zeta_1, \zeta_2, \ldots, \zeta_n$. Denote by ρ_n the index of the first maximal term in the sequence $\zeta_0, \zeta_1, \ldots, \zeta_n$; that is, $\rho_n = j$ if j is the smallest index such that $\zeta_j = \max(\zeta_0, \zeta_1, \ldots, \zeta_n)$. Denote by $\rho_n{}^*$ the index of the last maximal term in the sequence $\zeta_0, \zeta_1, \ldots, \zeta_n$; that is, $\rho_n{}^* = j$ if j is the largest index such that $\zeta_j = \max(\zeta_0, \zeta_1, \ldots, \zeta_n)$. Then

$$(18) \qquad \mathbf{P}\{\Delta_n = k\} = \mathbf{P}\{\rho_n = k\}$$

and

$$(19) \qquad \mathbf{P}\{\Delta_n{}^* = k\} = \mathbf{P}\{\rho_n{}^* = k\}$$

for $k = 0, 1, \ldots, n$.

First we observe that if we replace $(c_1, c_2, \ldots, c_n)$ by $(-c_1, -c_2, \ldots, -c_n)$, then the random variables $\Delta_n, \Delta_n^*, \rho_n, \rho_n^*$ are replaced by $n - \Delta_n^*$, $n - \Delta_n, n - \rho_n^*, n - \rho_n$ respectively. The mapping $(c_{i_1}, c_{i_2}, \ldots, c_{i_n}) \to (-c_{i_1}, -c_{i_2}, \ldots, -c_{i_n})$ proves the first two relations, and the mapping $(c_{i_1}, c_{i_2}, \ldots, c_{i_n}) \to (-c_{i_n}, -c_{i_{n-1}}, \ldots, -c_{i_1})$ proves the last two relations.

Now we shall prove the theorem by induction. If $n = 1$, then (18) and (19) are evidently true. We suppose that (18) and (19) are true for $n - 1$ and we shall prove that they are true for n too.

First let $c_1 + \cdots + c_n < 0$. Then $\zeta_n < 0$. Since $\zeta_0 = 0$, no maximum can occur at the last place. Therefore all four variables $\Delta_n, \Delta_n^*, \rho_n, \rho_n^*$ depend only on the permutations of $n - 1$ elements and so (18) and (19) are true by the induction hypothesis. If $c_1 + \cdots + c_n = 0$, then Δ_n and ρ_n depend only on the permutations of $n - 1$ elements and thus (18) holds by the induction hypothesis.

Now let $c_1 + \cdots + c_n > 0$. Then the variables $n - \Delta_n^*$, $n - \Delta_n$, $n - \rho_n^*$, $n - \rho_n$ depend only on the permutations of $n - 1$ elements and so (18) and (19) are true by the induction hypothesis. If $c_1 + \cdots + c_n = 0$, then $n - \Delta_n^*$ and $n - \rho_n^*$ depend only on the permutations of $n - 1$ elements and thus (19) holds by the induction hypothesis.

This completes the proof of the theorem. Theorem 5 can also be formulated in the following more general form.

Theorem 6. *Let $\xi_1, \xi_2, \ldots, \xi_n$ be interchangeable random variables taking on real values. Define $\zeta_r = \xi_1 + \cdots + \xi_r$ for $r = 1, 2, \ldots, n$ and $\zeta_0 = 0$. Denote by Δ_n the number of positive terms in the sequence $\zeta_1, \zeta_2, \ldots, \zeta_n$ and by Δ_n^* the number of nonnegative terms in the sequence $\zeta_1, \zeta_2, \ldots, \zeta_n$. Denote by ρ_n the index of the first maximal term in the sequence $\zeta_0, \zeta_1, \ldots, \zeta_n$ and by ρ_n^* the index of the last maximal term in the sequence $\zeta_0, \zeta_1, \ldots, \zeta_n$. Then we have*

$$\mathbf{P}\{\Delta_n = k\} = \mathbf{P}\{\rho_n = k\} \tag{20}$$

and

$$\mathbf{P}\{\Delta_n^* = k\} = \mathbf{P}\{\rho_n^* = k\} \tag{21}$$

for $k = 0, 1, \ldots, n$.

By using Theorem 6 we shall prove the following theorem.

Theorem 7. *Let $\nu_1, \nu_2, \ldots, \nu_n$ be interchangeable random variables taking on nonnegative integers. Define $N_r = \nu_1 + \cdots + \nu_r$ for $r = 1, 2, \ldots, n$ and $N_0 = 0$. Denote by Δ_n the number of subscripts $r = 1, 2, \ldots, n$ for which the inequality $N_r < r$ holds. We have*

$$\mathbf{P}\{\Delta_n = 0\} = 1 - \sum_{i=1}^{n} \frac{1}{i} \mathbf{P}\{N_i = i - 1\} \tag{22}$$

and

$$(23)\quad \mathbf{P}\{\Delta_n = j\} = \sum_{l=0}^{j}\left(1 - \frac{l}{j}\right) \cdot \left[\mathbf{P}\{N_j = l\} - \sum_{i=j+1}^{n} \frac{1}{(i-j)}\mathbf{P}\{N_j = l, N_i - N_j = i - j - 1\}\right]$$

for $j = 1, 2, \ldots, n.$

Proof. Now

$$(24)\quad \mathbf{P}\{\Delta_n = 0\} = \mathbf{P}\{N_r \geq r \text{ for } r = 1, 2, \ldots, n\}$$

and the right-hand side is given by Theorem 1 of Section 8. Thus we obtain (22). If $j = 1, 2, \ldots, n$, then by using Theorem 6 we can write

$$(25)\quad \mathbf{P}\{\Delta_n = j\} = \mathbf{P}\{r - N_r < j - N_j \text{ for } r = 0, \ldots, j-1 \text{ and } r - N_r \leq j - N_j \text{ for } r = j, \ldots, n\},$$

whence

$$(26)\quad \mathbf{P}\{\Delta_n = j\} = \sum_{l=0}^{j} \mathbf{P}\{N_j - N_r < j - r \text{ for } r = 0, \ldots, j-1 \mid N_j = l\} \cdot \mathbf{P}\{N_j - N_r \leq j - r \text{ for } r = j, \ldots, n \text{ and } N_j = l\}.$$

By Theorem 1 of Section 4, the first factor in the sum is $(j - l)/j$ and by (3) of Section 8, the second factor in the sum is equal to

$$(27)\quad \mathbf{P}\{N_j = l\} - \sum_{i=j+1}^{n} \frac{1}{(i-j)}\mathbf{P}\{N_j = l, N_i - N_j = i - j - 1\}.$$

Thus we obtain (23). This completes the proof of the theorem.

NOTE. If we denote by Δ_j, $j = 1, 2, \ldots, n$, the number of subscripts $r = 1, 2, \ldots, j$ for which $N_r < r$ holds, then by (26) we obtain

$$(28)\quad \mathbf{P}\{\Delta_n = j \mid N_n = k\} = \sum_{l=0}^{j}\left(1 - \frac{l}{j}\right)\mathbf{P}\{N_j = l\}\mathbf{P}\{\Delta_{n-j} = 0 \mid N_{n-j} = k - l\}$$

for $j = 1, 2, \ldots, n$.

Theorem 7 makes it possible to find the distribution P_j, $j = 0, 1, \ldots, a + b$ if $\mu \geq 0$ is an integer. If we use the same notation as in the proof of Theorem 4 and we take into consideration that in this case

$$(29)\quad \mathbf{P}\{N_j = s(\mu + 1), N_i - N_j = r(\mu + 1)\} = \frac{\binom{j}{s}\binom{i-j}{r}\binom{a+b-i}{b-s-r}}{\binom{a+b}{a}}$$

for $0 \leq j \leq i \leq a + b$, then by Theorem 7 we obtain the following result.

Theorem 8. *If $\mu \geq 0$, then*

$$(30)\quad P_0 = 1 - \frac{1}{\binom{a+b}{a}} \cdot \left[\sum_{0 \le s \le \frac{a+b-1}{\mu+1}} \frac{1}{[s(\mu+1)+1]} \binom{s\mu+s+1}{s} \binom{a-b-s\mu-s-1}{b-s} \right]$$

and

$$(31)\quad P_j = \frac{1}{\binom{a+b}{a}} \left[\sum_{0 \le s \le \frac{j}{\mu+1}} \frac{(j-s\mu-s)}{j} \binom{j}{s} \binom{a+b-j}{b-s} - \sum_{0 \le s \le \frac{j}{\mu+1},\ 0 \le r \le \frac{a+b-1-j}{\mu+1}} \frac{(j-s\mu-s)}{j(r\mu+r+1)} \cdot \binom{j}{s} \binom{r\mu+r+1}{r} \binom{a-b-1-j-r\mu-r}{b-s-r} \right]$$

for $j = 1, 2, \ldots, a+b$. We have $P_j = 0$ if $j < a - b\mu$ or $j \geq a(\mu+1)/\mu$.

If we use the notation $P_j = P_j(a, b)$ indicating the number of votes registered for A and the number of votes registered for B, then by Theorem 8 we obtain that

$$(32)\quad P_j(a,b) = \frac{1}{\binom{a+b}{a}} \sum_{0 \le s \le \frac{j}{\mu+1}} \left(1 - \frac{s\mu+s}{j}\right) \binom{j}{s} \binom{a+b-j}{b-s} P_0(a+s-j, b-s).$$

38. ORDER STATISTICS

Let $\xi_1, \xi_2, \ldots, \xi_n$ be mutually independent random variables having a common distribution function $\mathbf{P}\{\xi_r \leq x\} = F(x)$ $(r = 1, 2, \ldots, n)$. The random variables $(\xi_1, \xi_2, \ldots, \xi_n)$ form a *sample* of size n. Denote by $(\xi_1^*, \xi_2^*, \ldots, \xi_n^*)$ the random variables $\xi_1, \xi_2, \ldots, \xi_n$ arranged in increasing order of magnitude. The random variable ξ_r^* is called the rth *order statistic* of the sample $(\xi_1, \xi_2, \ldots, \xi_n)$. We define $F_n(x)$, the empirical distribution function of the sample $(\xi_1, \xi_2, \ldots, \xi_n)$, as the number of variables $\leq x$ divided by n. For each x the empirical distribution function, $F_n(x)$, is a random variable with distribution

$$(1)\quad \mathbf{P}\left\{F_n(x) = \frac{k}{n}\right\} = \binom{n}{k} [F(x)]^k [1 - F(x)]^{n-k} \qquad (k = 0, 1, \ldots, n).$$

If we consider an infinite sequence of mutually independent and identically distributed random variables $\xi_1, \xi_2, \ldots, \xi_n, \ldots$ with distribution function $\mathbf{P}\{\xi_n \leq x\} = F(x)$, $n = 1, 2, \ldots$, and if for every $n = 1, 2, \ldots$ we form $F_n(x)$, the *empirical distribution function* of the sample $(\xi_1, \xi_2, \ldots, \xi_n)$, then by the weak law of large numbers

$$\lim_{n\to\infty} F_n(x) = F(x) \tag{2}$$

in probability for each x, and by the strong law large numbers

$$\lim_{n\to\infty} F_n(x) = F(x) \tag{3}$$

with probability 1 for each x. If we define the random variable

$$\delta_n = \sup_{-\infty<x<\infty} |F_n(x) - F(x)|, \tag{4}$$

then by a theorem of V. Glivenko [43]

$$\mathbf{P}\left\{\lim_{n\to\infty} \delta_n = 0\right\} = 1. \tag{5}$$

A. N. Kolmogorov [50] proved that if $F(x)$ is a continuous distribution function, then

$$\lim_{n\to\infty} \mathbf{P}\{\sqrt{n}\,\delta_n \leq z\} = K(z) \tag{6}$$

where $K(z)$ is a distribution function independent of $F(x)$ and is given by

$$K(z) = \begin{cases} \sum_{j=-\infty}^{\infty} (-1)^j e^{-2j^2z^2} & \text{for } z > 0, \\ 0 & \text{for } z \leq 0. \end{cases} \tag{7}$$

If

$$\delta_n^+ = \sup_{-\infty<x<\infty} [F_n(x) - F(x)], \tag{8}$$

and

$$\delta_n^- = \sup_{-\infty<x<\infty} [F(x) - F_n(x)], \tag{9}$$

and $F(x)$ is a continuous distribution function, then

$$\lim_{n\to\infty} \mathbf{P}\{\sqrt{n}\,\delta_n^+ \leq z\} = \lim_{n\to\infty} \mathbf{P}\{\sqrt{n}\,\delta_n^- \leq z\} = 1 - e^{-2z^2} \tag{10}$$

for $z \geq 0$ independently of the distribution function $F(x)$. The random variables $\delta_n, \delta_n^+, \delta_n^-$ are so called *distribution-free statistics*.

Now consider two independent sequences of mutually independent and identically distributed random variables $\xi_1, \xi_2, \ldots, \xi_m, \ldots$ and η_1,

$\eta_2, \ldots, \eta_n, \ldots$ for which $\mathbf{P}\{\xi_m \le x\} = \mathbf{P}\{\eta_n \le x\} = F(x)$ $(m = 1, 2, \ldots; n = 1, 2, \ldots)$. Denote by $F_m(x)$ the empirical distribution function of the sample $(\xi_1, \xi_2, \ldots, \xi_m)$ and by $G_n(x)$ the empirical distribution function of the sample $(\eta_1, \eta_2, \ldots, \eta_n)$.

Define the following random variables

$$\delta(m, n) = \sup_{-\infty < x < \infty} |F_m(x) - G_n(x)| \tag{11}$$

and

$$\delta^+(m, n) = \sup_{-\infty < x < \infty} [F_m(x) - G_n(x)]. \tag{12}$$

If $F(x)$ is a continuous distribution function, then $\delta(m, n)$ and $\delta^+(m, n)$ are distribution-free statistics.

N. V. Smirnov [56] proved that if $F(x)$ is a continuous distribution function, then

$$\lim_{\substack{m\to\infty\\ n\to\infty}} \mathbf{P}\left\{\sqrt{\frac{mn}{m+n}}\,\delta(m, n) \le z\right\} = K(z) \tag{13}$$

where $K(z)$ is defined by (7) and

$$\lim_{\substack{m\to\infty\\ n\to\infty}} \mathbf{P}\left\{\sqrt{\frac{mn}{m+n}}\,\delta^+(m, n) \le z\right\} = 1 - e^{-2z^2} \tag{14}$$

for $z \ge 0$.

The random variables δ_n, δ_n^+, δ_n^-, $\delta(m, n)$, $\delta^+(m, n)$ are of great importance in mathematical statistics. Since they are distribution-free statistics, they make it possible to devise statistical tests in cases when the distribution function of the observed random variables is unknown.

In what follows we shall be dealing with problems connected with the deviations $F_n(x) - F(x)$ $(-\infty < x < \infty)$ and the deviations $F_m(x) - G_n(x)$ $(-\infty < x < \infty)$.

39. DISCRETE DISTRIBUTIONS

The Comparison of a Theoretical Distribution and an Empirical Distribution. Let $\xi_1, \xi_2, \ldots, \xi_n$ be mutually independent random variables having a common continuous distribution function $F(x)$. Let $F_n(x)$ be the empirical distribution function of the sample $(\xi_1, \xi_2, \ldots, \xi_n)$, that is, $F_n(x)$ is defined as the number of variables $\xi_1, \xi_2, \ldots, \xi_n$ less than or equal to x divided by n. Denote by $\xi_1^*, \xi_2^*, \ldots, \xi_n^*$ the random variables $\xi_1, \xi_2, \ldots, \xi_n$ arranged in increasing order of magnitude.

Consider the deviations $\delta_n(r) = F_n(\xi_r^*) - F(\xi_r^*)$, $r = 1, 2, \ldots, n$. Obviously the random variables $\delta_n(r)$, $r = 1, 2, \ldots, n$, are continuous, and distinct with probability 1. The joint distribution of the random variables $\delta_n(r)$, $r = 1, 2, \ldots, n$, does not depend on $F(x)$. If we want to find the distribution of a random variable depending only on $\delta_n(1)$, $\delta_n(2), \ldots, \delta_n(n)$, then we may assume, without loss of generality, that $\xi_1, \xi_2, \ldots, \xi_n$ are mutually independent random variables having a uniform distribution over the interval (0, 1), that is, $F(x) = x$ for $0 \leq x \leq 1$. In this case

$$(1) \qquad \delta_n(r) = \frac{r}{n} - \xi_r^* \qquad (r = 1, 2, \ldots, n).$$

We shall introduce the following random variables and determine their distributions.

Let $\delta_n = \max_{1 \leq r \leq n} \delta_n(r)$. Denote by ρ_n the number of nonnegative elements among $\delta_n(r)$, $r = 1, 2, \ldots, n$. Define ρ_n^* as the value of r for which $\delta_n(r)$, $r = 1, 2, \ldots, n$, attains its maximum. The random variable ρ_n^* is defined with probability 1.

The following theorem is due to P. Cheng [35].

Theorem 1. *We have*

$$(2) \qquad \mathbf{P}\{\rho_n = j\} = \frac{1}{n} \sum_{i=1}^{j} \frac{1}{i} \binom{n}{i-1} \left(\frac{i}{n}\right)^{i-1} \left(1 - \frac{i}{n}\right)^{n-i}$$

for $j = 1, 2, \ldots, n$.

Proof. Denote by ν_r, $r = 1, 2, \ldots, n$, the number of variables $\xi_1, \xi_2, \ldots, \xi_n$ falling in the interval $((r-1)/n, r/n]$ and define $N_r = \nu_1 + \cdots + \nu_r$ for $r = 1, 2, \ldots, n$. By (1) $\delta_n(r) \geq 0$ if and only if $N_r \geq r$. Consequently ρ_n is equal to the number of indices $r = 1, 2, \ldots, n$ for which $N_r \geq r$. Now $\nu_1, \nu_2, \ldots, \nu_n$ are interchangeable random variables taking on nonnegative integers and $N_n = \nu_1 + \cdots + \nu_n = n$. Accordingly $\mathbf{P}\{\rho_n = j\} = \mathbf{P}\{\Delta_n = n - j \mid N_n = n\}$ is given by (5) of Section 37. Since in this case

$$(3) \qquad \mathbf{P}\{N_r = j\} = \binom{n}{j} \left(\frac{r}{n}\right)^j \left(1 - \frac{r}{n}\right)^{n-j}$$

for $j = 0, 1, \ldots, n$, we get (2) by (5) of Section 37.

Theorem 2. *We have*

$$(4) \qquad \mathbf{P}\{\rho_n^* = j\} = \mathbf{P}\{\rho_n = j\}$$

for $j = 1, 2, \ldots, n$ *where the right-hand side is given by* (2).

Proof. By Theorem 6 of Section 37 we can conclude that the position of the maximum in $\delta_n(r)$, $r = 1, 2, \ldots, n$, has the same distribution as the number of nonnegative terms in $\delta_n(r)$, $r = 1, 2, \ldots, n$. Hence (4) follows.

The distribution of ρ_n^* has been found directly by Z. Birnbaum and R. Pyke [31].

Theorem 3. *If $k = 1, 2, \ldots, n$, then*

$$(5)\qquad \mathbf{P}\left\{\delta_n \le \frac{k}{n}\right\} = 1 - \sum_{j=1}^{n-k} \frac{k}{(n-j)} \binom{n}{j+k} \left(\frac{j}{n}\right)^{j+k} \left(1 - \frac{j}{n}\right)^{n-j-k}.$$

Proof. If we use the same notation as in the proof of Theorem 1, then for $k = 1, 2, \ldots, n$ we have

$$(6)\quad \mathbf{P}\left\{\delta_n \le \frac{k}{n}\right\} = \mathbf{P}\left\{\max_{1 \le r \le n} (N_r - r) < k\right\}$$

$$= 1 - \sum_{j=1}^{n-k} \frac{k}{(n-j)} \mathbf{P}\{N_j = j + k\}$$

where the extreme right expression follows from (1) of Section 8.

The Comparison of Two Empirical Distribution Functions. Let $\xi_1, \xi_2, \ldots, \xi_m, \eta_1, \eta_2, \ldots, \eta_n$ be mutually independent random variables having a common continuous distribution function. Denote by $F_m(x)$ and $G_n(x)$ the empirical distribution functions of the samples $(\xi_1, \xi_2, \ldots, \xi_m)$ and $(\eta_1, \eta_2, \ldots, \eta_n)$ respectively. That is, $F_m(x)$ is equal to the number of variables $\xi_1, \xi_2, \ldots, \xi_m$ less than or equal to x divided by m, and $G_n(x)$ is equal to the number of variables $\eta_1, \eta_2, \ldots, \eta_n$ less than or equal to x divided by n. Denote by $\eta_1^*, \eta_2^*, \ldots, \eta_n^*$ the random variables $\eta_1, \eta_2, \ldots, \eta_n$ arranged in increasing order of magnitude.

Let $\gamma(m, n)$ be the number of subscripts $r = 1, 2, \ldots, n$ for which $F_m(\eta_r^*) \le G_n(\eta_r^* - 0)$, that is, $\gamma(m, n)$ is equal to the number of positive jumps of $G_n(x)$ relative to $F_m(x)$. Further let

$$(7)\qquad \delta^+(m, n) = \sup_{-\infty < x < \infty} [F_m(x) - G_n(x)].$$

It is easy to see that $\gamma(m, n)$ and $\delta^+(m, n)$ are distribution-free statistics.

Theorem 4. *If $n = mp$ where p is a positive integer, then*

$$(8)\qquad \mathbf{P}\{\gamma(m, n) = j\} = \frac{1}{n+1}$$

for $j = 0, 1, \ldots, n$.

Proof. Let ν_r, $r = 1, 2, \ldots, n + 1$, be p times the number of variables $\xi_1, \xi_2, \ldots, \xi_m$ falling in the interval $(\eta_{r-1}^*, \eta_r^*]$ where $\eta_0^* = -\infty$ and $\eta_{n+1}^* = \infty$. Set $N_r = \nu_1 + \cdots + \nu_r$ for $r = 1, \ldots, n + 1$. In this case $\nu_1, \nu_2, \ldots, \nu_{n+1}$ are interchangeable random variables taking on nonnegative integers and their sum is $N_{n+1} = \nu_1 + \cdots + \nu_{n+1} = mp$. We have

$$(9)\qquad \mathbf{P}\{N_i = sp\} = \frac{\binom{i+s-1}{s}\binom{m+n-i-s}{m-s}}{\binom{m+n}{m}}$$

for $i = 1, 2, \ldots, n$. Evidently $F_m(\eta_r^*) = N_r/mp$ and $G_n(\eta_r^* - 0) = (r-1)/n$ for $r = 1, 2, \ldots, n$. If $n = mp$, then $N_{n+1} = n$ and $\gamma(m, n)$ equals the number of subscripts $r = 1, 2, \ldots, n$ for which $N_r < r$. Since $N_{n+1} < n + 1$ also holds, we obtain (8) by Theorem 2 of Section 37 if we apply it to the random variables $(1 - \nu_1), (1 - \nu_2), \ldots, (1 - \nu_{n+1})$.

For the case $p = 1$ Theorem 4 has been proved by B. V. Gnedenko and V. S. Mihalevič [45] and for $p \geq 1$ by B. V. Gnedenko and V. S. Mihalevič [46].

Theorem 5. *If $n = mp$ where p is a positive integer, and c is a non-negative integer, then*

$$(10)\quad \mathbf{P}\left\{\delta^+(m, n) \leq \frac{c}{n}\right\} = 1 - \frac{1}{\binom{m+n}{m}} \sum_{\frac{c+1}{p} \leq s \leq m} \frac{c+1}{n+c+1-sp} \cdot \binom{sp+s-c-1}{s}\binom{m+n+c-sp-s}{m-s}.$$

Proof. Using the same notation as in the proof of Theorem 4 we can write that if $n = mp$, then

$$(11)\quad \delta^+(m, n) = \max_{1\leq r\leq n} [F_m(\eta_r^*) - G_n(\eta_r^* - 0)] = \frac{1}{n} \max_{1\leq r\leq n+1} (N_r - r + 1).$$

Thus

$$(12)\quad \mathbf{P}\left\{\delta^+(m, n) \leq \frac{c}{n}\right\} = \mathbf{P}\{N_r < r + c \text{ for } r = 1, 2, \ldots, n+1\}$$

and the right-hand side can be obtained by Theorem 1 of Section 6 if we apply it to the random variables $\nu_1, \nu_2, \ldots, \nu_{n+1}$ defined in the proof of Theorem 4. The distribution of N_i is given by (9) and $N_{n+1} = n$.

If $p = 1$, then (10) reduces to

$$(13)\quad \mathbf{P}\left\{\delta^+(m, m) \leq \frac{c}{m}\right\} = 1 - \binom{2m}{m+1+c} \Big/ \binom{2m}{m}.$$

The distribution of the random variable $\delta^+(m, n)$ for $n = m$ was found by B. V. Gnedenko and V. S. Koroljuk [44] and for $n = mp$ where p is a positive integer, by V. S. Koroljuk [51].

40. CONTINUOUS DISTRIBUTIONS

The Comparison of a Theoretical Distribution and an Empirical Distribution. Let $\xi_1, \xi_2, \ldots, \xi_n$ be mutually independent random variables with a common continuous distribution function $F(x)$. Let $F_n(x)$ denote the empirical distribution function of the sample $(\xi_1, \xi_2, \ldots, \xi_n)$, that is, $F_n(x)$ is the number of variables $\leq x$ divided by n. Let

$$(1) \qquad \delta_n^+ = \sup_{-\infty < x < \infty} [F_n(x) - F(x)]$$

and

$$(2) \qquad \delta_n^- = \sup_{-\infty < x < \infty} [F(x) - F_n(x)].$$

They are distribution-free statistics. To find the distributions of δ_n^+ and δ_n^- we may suppose, without loss of generality, that $F(x) = x$ for $0 \leq x \leq 1$. In this case we can write

$$(3) \qquad \mathbf{P}\{\delta_n^+ \leq x\} = \mathbf{P}\left\{\sup_{0 \leq u \leq 1} [\chi_n(u) - u] \leq x\right\}$$

and

$$(4) \qquad \mathbf{P}\{\delta_n^- \leq x\} = \mathbf{P}\left\{\sup_{0 \leq u \leq 1} [u - \chi_n(u)] \leq x\right\}$$

where $\{\chi_n(u), 0 \leq u \leq 1\}$ is a stochastic process defined in the following way. We choose n points independently in the interval $(0, 1)$ such that each point has a uniform distribution over $(0, 1)$. Denote by $\chi_n(u)$ the ratio of the number of points in the interval $(0, u]$ to n. Then $\{\chi_n(u), 0 \leq u \leq 1\}$ has interchangeable increments, $\chi_n(u)$, $0 \leq u \leq 1$, is a nondecreasing step function, $\mathbf{P}\{\chi_n(0) = 0\} = 1$, and $\mathbf{P}\{\chi_n(1) = 1\} = 1$. We have

$$(5) \qquad \mathbf{P}\left\{\chi_n(u) = \frac{j}{n}\right\} = \binom{n}{j} u^j (1 - u)^{n-j}$$

for $0 \leq u \leq 1$ and $j = 0, 1, \ldots, n$, and

$$(6) \qquad \mathbf{P}\left\{\chi_n(u) = \frac{j}{n}, \chi_n(v) = \frac{k}{n}\right\} = \frac{n!}{j!\,(k-j)!\,(n-k)!} u^j (v-u)^{k-j} (1-v)^{n-k}$$

for $0 \leq u \leq v \leq 1$ and $0 \leq j \leq k \leq n$.

In finding the distributions of δ_n^+ and δ_n^- we can apply Theorem 1 of Section 15 and Theorem 1 of Section 17 respectively.

Theorem 1. *If* $0 < x \leqq 1$, *then*

$$(7) \qquad \mathbf{P}\{\delta_n^+ \leq x\} = \mathbf{P}\{\delta_n^- \leq x\} = 1 - \sum_{nx \leq j \leq n} \left(\frac{nx}{nx + n - j}\right) \binom{n}{j} \left(\frac{j}{n} - x\right)^j \left(1 + x - \frac{j}{n}\right)^{n-j}.$$

Proof. By (1) of Section 15

$$(8)\quad \mathbf{P}\left\{\sup_{0\le u\le 1}[\chi_n(u)-u]\le x\right\}=1-\sum_{0\le y\le 1-x}\frac{x}{1-y}\mathbf{P}\{\chi_n(y)=y+x\}$$

for $x>0$ and by (1) of Section 17

$$(9)\quad \mathbf{P}\left\{\sup_{0\le u\le 1}[u-\chi_n(u)]\le x\right\}=1-\sum_{x\le y\le 1}\frac{x}{y}\mathbf{P}\{\chi_n(y)=y-x\}$$

for $x>0$. Since $\mathbf{P}\{\chi_n(y)=x\}=0$, except if $x=j/n$, $j=0,1,\ldots,n$, (8) reduces to

$$(10)\quad \mathbf{P}\left\{\sup_{0\le u\le 1}[\chi_n(u)-u]\le x\right\}$$
$$=1-\sum_{nx\le j\le n}\left(\frac{nx}{nx+n-j}\right)\mathbf{P}\left\{\chi_n\left(\frac{j}{n}-x\right)=\frac{j}{n}\right\},$$

and (9) reduces to

$$(11)\quad \mathbf{P}\left\{\sup_{0\le u\le 1}[u-\chi_n(u)]\le x\right\}$$
$$=1-\sum_{0\le j\le n(1-x)}\left(\frac{nx}{nx+j}\right)\mathbf{P}\left\{\chi_n\left(\frac{j}{n}+x\right)=\frac{j}{n}\right\}.$$

The distribution of $\chi_n(u)$, $0\le u\le 1$, is given by (5). Thus (7) follows. Evidently (10) and (11) are identical.

The distributions of the random variables δ_n^+ and δ_n^- have been found by N. V. Smirnov [57]. See also A. Wald and J. Wolfowitz [66], Z. Birnbaum and F. H. Tingey [32], B. L. Van der Waerden [65] and A. P. Dempster [37].

In a similar way we can determine the distributions of the following statistics

$$(12)\quad \delta_n^+(\alpha,\beta,\gamma)=\sup_{\alpha\le F(x)\le\beta}[F_n(x)-\gamma F(x)]$$

and

$$(13)\quad \rho_n^+(\alpha,\beta,\gamma)=\sup_{\alpha\le F(x)\le\beta}\left[\frac{F_n(x)-\gamma F(x)}{F(x)}\right]$$

where $0\le\alpha<\beta\le 1$ and $\gamma\ge 1$.

It is easy to see that $\delta_n^+(\alpha,\beta,\gamma)$ and $\rho_n^+(\alpha,\beta,\gamma)$ are distribution-free statistics. Thus in finding their distributions we may assume that $F(x)=x$ for $0\le x\le 1$. Then

$$(14)\quad \mathbf{P}\{\delta_n^+(\alpha,\beta,\gamma)\le x\}=\mathbf{P}\left\{\sup_{\alpha\le u\le\beta}[\chi_n(u)-\gamma u]\le x\right\}$$

and

(15) $$\mathbf{P}\{\rho_n^+(\alpha, \beta, \gamma) \le x\} = \mathbf{P}\left\{\sup_{\alpha \le u \le \beta}\left[\frac{\chi_n(u) - \gamma u}{u}\right] \le x\right\}$$

where the stochastic process $\{\chi_n(u), 0 \le u \le 1\}$ is defined as above.

If we take into consideration that $\chi_n(u)$ is a discrete random variable for $0 \le u \le 1$, then by a slight modification of Theorem 1 of Section 15 we obtain that

(16) $$\mathbf{P}\left\{\sup_{\alpha \le u \le \beta}[c\chi_n(u) - u] \le a\right\} = \mathbf{P}\{c\chi_n(\beta) - \beta \le a\} - \sum_{\alpha < y \le z \le \beta}\sum \left(\frac{\beta - z}{\beta - y}\right) \mathbf{P}\{c\chi_n(y) = a + y, c\chi_n(\beta) = a + z\}$$

for $0 \le \alpha < \beta \le 1$, $a \ge 0$ and $c \ge 0$. By using (16) we can easily obtain the distributions of (14) and (15).

Theorem 2. *For $x \ge 0$ we have*

(17) $$\mathbf{P}\{\delta_n^+(\alpha, \beta, \gamma) \le x\} = \sum_{k \le n(x+\beta\gamma)} \mathbf{P}\left\{\chi_n(\beta) = \frac{k}{n}\right\} - \sum_{n(x+\alpha\gamma) < j \le k \le n(x+\beta\gamma)}\sum \left(\frac{n(x + \beta\gamma) - k}{n(x + \beta\gamma) - j}\right) \mathbf{P}\left\{\chi_n\left(\frac{j - nx}{n\gamma}\right) = \frac{j}{n}, \chi_n(\beta) = \frac{k}{n}\right\}$$

where the probabilities on the right-hand side are given by (5) *and* (6). *If, in particular, $\beta = 1$, then for $x \ge 0$*

18) $$\mathbf{P}\{\delta_n^+(\alpha, 1, \gamma) \le x\} = 1 - \sum_{n(x+\alpha\gamma) < j \le n} \left(\frac{n(x + \gamma) - n}{n(x + \gamma) - j}\right) \mathbf{P}\left\{\chi_n\left(\frac{j - nx}{n\gamma}\right) = \frac{j}{n}\right\}.$$

Proof. If $a = x/\gamma$ and $c = 1/\gamma$ in (16), then we get the right-hand side of (14). We get (17) if we take into consideration that $\mathbf{P}\{c\chi_n(y) = a + y, c\chi_n(\beta) = a + z\} = 0$ except if $y = (j - nx)/n\gamma$ and $z = (k - nx)/n\gamma$ where $0 \le j \le k \le n$. If $\beta = 1$, then (17) reduces to (18) because $\mathbf{P}\{\chi_n(1) = 1\} = 1$.

Theorem 3. *For $x \ge 0$ we have*

(19) $$\mathbf{P}\{\rho_n^+(\alpha, \beta, \gamma) \le x\} = \sum_{k \le n\beta(x+\gamma)} \mathbf{P}\left\{\chi_n(\beta) = \frac{k}{n}\right\} - \sum_{n\alpha(x+\gamma) < j \le k \le n\beta(x+\gamma)}\sum \left(\frac{n\beta(x + \gamma) - k}{n\beta(x + \gamma) - j}\right) \mathbf{P}\left\{\chi_n\left(\frac{j}{n(x + \gamma)}\right) = \frac{j}{n}, \chi_n(\beta) = \frac{k}{n}\right\}$$

where the probabilities on the right-hand side are given by (5) *and* (6). *If, in particular,* $\beta = 1$, *then for* $x \geq 0$

$$\text{(20)}\quad \mathbf{P}\{\rho_n^+(\alpha, 1, \gamma) \leq x\} = 1 - \sum_{n\alpha(x+\gamma)<j\leq n} \binom{n(x+\gamma)-n}{n(x+\gamma)-j} \mathbf{P}\left\{\chi_n\left(\frac{j}{n(x+\gamma)}\right) = \frac{j}{n}\right\}.$$

Proof. If $a = 0$ and $c = 1/(x+\gamma)$ in (16), then we get the right-hand side of (15). We get (19) if we take into consideration that $\mathbf{P}\{c\chi_n(y) = a + y, c\chi_n(\beta) = a + z\} = 0$ except if $y = j/n(x+\gamma)$ and $z = k/n(x+\gamma)$ where $0 \leq j \leq k \leq n$.

NOTE. If $\alpha = 0$ and $x = 0$, then (20) further reduces to

$$\text{(21)}\qquad \mathbf{P}\{\rho_n^+(0, 1, \gamma) \leq 0\} = \mathbf{P}\left\{\sup_{0\leq u\leq 1} [\chi(u) - \gamma u] \leq 0\right\} = 1 - \frac{1}{\gamma}$$

by Theorem 1 of Section 13.

If we define the random variables $\delta_n^-(\alpha, \beta, \gamma)$ and $\rho_n^-(\alpha, \beta, \gamma)$ similarly to (12) and (13), then their distributions can be obtained in a similar way as those of (12) and (13).

We note that in various particular cases several authors determined the distributions of $\delta_n^+(\alpha, \beta, \gamma)$ and $\rho_n^+(\alpha, \beta, \gamma)$ as well as their asymptotic distributions. The distribution for $\delta_n^+(0, 1, 1)$ was found by N. V. Smirnov [57] and by Z. Birnbaum and F. H. Tingey [32], for $\delta_n^+(\alpha, 1, 1)$ by N. V. Smirnov [58], and for $\delta_n^+(0, 1, \gamma)$ by A. P. Dempster [37] and M. Dwass [41]. The distribution for $\rho_n^+(0, \beta, 0)$ was found by L. Chang [34] and for $\rho_n^+(\alpha, 1, 1)$ by G. Ishii [48] and N. V. Smirnov [58]. The particular result (21) was found by H. E. Daniels [36], H. Robbins [55], L. Chang [34], and others.

Theorem 4. *Let*

$$\text{(22)}\qquad \mathbf{P}\left\{\frac{k}{n} - \delta_n^+ \leq \frac{x}{n} \text{ and } \rho_n^* = k\right\} = G_k(x).$$

If $0 < x < k$, *then*

$$\text{(23)}\quad \frac{dG_k(x)}{dx} = \binom{n}{k}\frac{(k-x)(n-x)^{n-k-1}}{n^n}\left[kx^{k-1} - \sum_{j=1}^{[x]}\binom{k}{j} j^{j-1}(x-j)^{k-j}\right].$$

Proof. We have $\delta_n^+ = (k-x)/n$ and $\rho_n^* = k$ if and only if $\xi_k^* = x/n$ and $\chi_n(u) - \chi_n(x/n) \leq u - (x/n)$ for $0 \leq u \leq 1$. The condition $\xi_k^* = x/n$ is equivalent to $\chi_n(x/n) = k/n$ and $\chi_n[(x/n) - 0] = (k-1)/n$. By (2) of Section 13

$$\text{(24)}\quad \mathbf{P}\left\{\chi_n(u) - \chi_n\left(\frac{x}{n}\right) \leq u - \frac{x}{n} \text{ for } \frac{x}{n} \leq u \leq 1 \mid \chi_n\left(\frac{x}{n} - 0\right) = \frac{k-1}{n}, \right.$$
$$\left. \chi_n\left(\frac{x}{n}\right) = \frac{k}{n}\right\} = \frac{k-x}{n-x} \qquad \text{if } 0 \leq x \leq k$$

and by (1) of Section 17

$$(25)\quad \mathbf{P}\left\{\chi_n(u) - \chi_n\left(\frac{x}{n}\right) \leq u - \frac{x}{n} \text{ for } 0 \leq u \leq \frac{x}{n} \,\middle|\, \chi_n\left(\frac{x}{n} - 0\right) = \frac{k-1}{n}, \chi_n\left(\frac{x}{n}\right) = \frac{k}{n}\right\}$$

$$= \mathbf{P}\left\{u - \chi_n(u) \leq \frac{1}{n} \text{ for } 0 \leq u \leq \frac{x}{n} \,\middle|\, \chi_n\left(\frac{x}{n} - 0\right) = \frac{k-1}{n}\right\}$$

$$= 1 - \sum_{j=1}^{[x]} \frac{1}{j} \mathbf{P}\left\{\chi_n\left(\frac{j}{n}\right) = \frac{j-1}{n} \,\middle|\, \chi_n\left(\frac{x}{n} - 0\right) = \frac{k-1}{n}\right\}$$

for in (25) we can replace $\chi_n\left(\frac{x}{n} - 0\right) - \chi_n(u)$ by $\chi_n\left(\frac{x}{n} - u\right)$ for $0 \leq u \leq x/n$ without changing the probability in question. Further we have

$$(26)\qquad \frac{d\mathbf{P}\{\xi_k^* \leq x/n\}}{dx} = \frac{d\mathbf{P}\{\chi_n(x/n) \geq k/n\}}{dx}.$$

If we form the product of (24), (25), (26), then we get

$$(27)\quad \frac{dG_k(x)}{dx} = \left(\frac{k-x}{n-x}\right)\left[\frac{d\mathbf{P}\{\chi_n(x/n) \geq k/n\}}{dx} - \sum_{j=1}^{[x]} \frac{1}{j} \frac{d\mathbf{P}\{\chi_n(j/n) = (j-1)/n, \chi_n(x/n) \geq k/n\}}{dx}\right]$$

for $0 < x < k$. Since

$$(28)\qquad \frac{d\mathbf{P}\{\chi_n(x/n) \geq k/n\}}{dx} = \binom{n-1}{k-1}\left(\frac{x}{n}\right)^{k-1}\left(1 - \frac{x}{n}\right)^{n-k}$$

and

$$(29)\quad \frac{d\mathbf{P}\{\chi_n(j/n) = (j-1)/n, \chi_n(x/n) \geq k/n\}}{dx} = \binom{n-1}{k-1}\binom{k-1}{j-1}\left(\frac{j}{n}\right)^{j-1}\left(\frac{x-j}{n}\right)^{k-j}\left(1 - \frac{x}{n}\right)^{n-k}$$

for $1 \leq j \leq x \leqq n$ and $1 \leq j \leq k \leq n$, we obtain (23) by (27).

The joint distribution of δ_n^+ and ρ_n^+ has been found by Z. Birnbaum and R. Pyke [31].

Theorem 5. *The random variable* $\dfrac{\rho_n^*}{n} - \delta_n^+$ *has a uniform distribution over the interval* (0, 1).

Proof. If $\dfrac{\rho_n^*}{n} - \delta_n^+ = x$ $(0 < x < 1)$, then necessarily x is an element of the sample $(\xi_1, \xi_2, \ldots, \xi_n)$, that is, $\chi_n(x) - \chi_n(x - 0) = 1/n$ and

$\chi_n(u) - \chi_n(x) \le u - x$ for $0 \le u \le 1$. Define $\chi_n^*(u) = \chi_n(u + x) - \chi_n(x)$ for $0 \le u \le 1 - x$ and $\chi_n^*(u) = 1 + \chi_n(u + x - 1) - \chi_n(x)$ for $1 - x \le u \le 1$. Then

$$(30)\quad \mathbf{P}\left\{\chi_n(u) - \chi_n(x) \le u - x \text{ for } 0 \le u \le 1 \mid \chi_n(x) - \chi_n(x - 0) = \frac{1}{n}\right\}$$

$$= \mathbf{P}\left\{\chi_n^*(u) \le u \text{ for } 0 \le u \le 1 \mid \chi^*(1 - 0) = \frac{n-1}{n}\right\} = \frac{1}{n}.$$

For it can easily be seen that Theorem 1 of Section 13 is applicable to the process $\{\chi_n^*(u), 0 \le u \le 1\}$ and by (2) of Section 13 we obtain the extreme right member. Since the probability that the sample $(\xi_1, \xi_2, \ldots, \xi_n)$ has at least one element in the interval $(x, x + \Delta x)$ is $n\Delta x + o(\Delta x)$ if $0 \le x \le 1 - \Delta x$, we obtain that the density function of $\dfrac{\rho_n^*}{n} - \delta_n^+$ is 1 in the interval (0, 1). This proves the theorem.

This theorem is due to Z. Birnbaum and R. Pyke [31]. Other proofs have been given by M. Dwass [40] and N. H. Kuiper [52].

Samples of Random Size. Let $\xi_1, \xi_2, \ldots, \xi_r, \ldots$ be an infinite sequence of mutually independent random variables having a common continuous distribution function $F(x)$. Let ν be a random variable having a Poisson distribution with parameter λ, that is,

$$(31)\qquad \mathbf{P}\{\nu = j\} = e^{-\lambda}\frac{\lambda^j}{j!}$$

for $j = 0, 1, 2, \ldots$, and let ν be independent of $\{\xi_n\}$. Denote by $F_\lambda(x)$, $-\infty < x < \infty$, the empirical distribution function of the sample of random size $(\xi_1, \xi_2, \ldots, \xi_\nu)$; $F_\lambda(x) \equiv 0$ if $\nu = 0$.

Define

$$(32)\qquad \gamma^+(\lambda) = \sup_{-\infty < x < \infty}\left[\frac{\nu}{\lambda}F_\lambda(x) - F(x)\right],$$

$$(33)\qquad \gamma^-(\lambda) = \sup_{-\infty < x < \infty}\left[F(x) - \frac{\nu}{\lambda}F_\lambda(x)\right],$$

$$(34)\qquad \delta^+(\lambda) = \sup_{-\infty < x < \infty}[F_\lambda(x) - F(x)],$$

and

$$(35)\qquad \delta^-(\lambda) = \sup_{-\infty < x < \infty}[F(x) - F_\lambda(x)].$$

It is easy to see that $\gamma^+(\lambda)$, $\gamma^-(\lambda)$, $\delta^+(\lambda)$, and $\delta^-(\lambda)$ are distribution-free statistics. Thus in finding the distributions of (32), (33), (34), and (35) we may suppose that $F(x) = x$ for $0 \le x \le 1$. Then $\nu F_\lambda(x) = \nu(u)$ for

$0 \le u \le 1$ where $\{\nu(u), 0 \le u \le 1\}$ is a Poisson process of density λ, and $\nu = \nu(1)$. In this case

$$\mathbf{P}\{\nu(u) = j\} = e^{-\lambda u}\frac{(\lambda u)^j}{j!} \tag{36}$$

for $j = 0, 1, 2, \ldots$. To obtain the distributions of (32), (33), (34), and (35), we shall use the following theorems. If $a \ge 0$ and $c \ge 0$, then

$$\mathbf{P}\left\{\sup_{0\le u\le 1}[c\nu(u) - u] \le a\right\} = \mathbf{P}\{c\nu(1) \le a + 1\} - \sum_{0<y\le z\le 1}\sum \left(\frac{1-z}{1-y}\right)\mathbf{P}\{c\nu(y) = a + y,\ c\nu(1) = a + z\} \tag{37}$$

which follows from Theorem 1 of Section 15, and

$$\mathbf{P}\left\{\sup_{0\le u\le 1}[u - c\nu(u)] \le a\right\} = 1 - \sum_{a\le y\le 1}\frac{a}{y}\mathbf{P}\{c\nu(y) = y - a\} \tag{38}$$

which follows from Theorem 1 of Section 17.

Theorem 6. *For* $x \ge 0$

$$\mathbf{P}\{\gamma^+(\lambda) \le x\} = \mathbf{P}\{\nu(1) \le \lambda(x+1)\} - \sum_{\lambda x<j\le k\le\lambda(x+1)}\sum\left(\frac{\lambda(x+1)-k}{\lambda(x+1)-j}\right)\mathbf{P}\left\{\nu\left(\frac{j}{\lambda} - x\right) = j\right\} \cdot \mathbf{P}\left\{\nu\left(x + 1 - \frac{j}{\lambda}\right) = k - j\right\} \tag{39}$$

where the distribution of $\nu(u)$, $0 \le u \le 1$, *is given by* (36).

Proof. Now

$$\mathbf{P}\{\gamma^+(\lambda) \le x\} = \mathbf{P}\{\nu(u) \le \lambda(u + x) \text{ for } 0 \le u \le 1\} \tag{40}$$

and the right-hand side is given by (37) if $a = x$ and $c = 1/\lambda$ in it.

Theorem 7. *For* $x > 0$

$$\mathbf{P}\{\gamma^-(\lambda) \le x\} = 1 - \sum_{0\le j\le\lambda(1-x)}\left(\frac{\lambda x}{\lambda x + j}\right)\mathbf{P}\left\{\nu\left(\frac{j}{\lambda} + x\right) = j\right\} \tag{41}$$

where the distribution of $\nu(u)$, $0 \le u \le 1$, *is given by* (36).

Proof. Now

$$\mathbf{P}\{\gamma^-(\lambda) \le x\} = \mathbf{P}\{\lambda u - \nu(u) \le \lambda x \text{ for } 0 \le u \le 1\} \tag{42}$$

and the right-hand side is given by (38) if $a = x$ and $c = 1/\lambda$ in it.

Theorem 8. *For* $0 < x \leq 1$

$$\text{(43)}\quad \mathbf{P}\{\delta^+(\lambda) \leq x\} = 1 - \sum_{k=1}^{\infty} \sum_{kx \leq j \leq k} \left(\frac{kx}{k(x+1)-j}\right) \cdot \mathbf{P}\left\{\nu\left(\frac{j}{k} - x\right) = j\right\}\mathbf{P}\left\{\nu\left(x + 1 - \frac{j}{k}\right) = k - j\right\}$$

where the distribution of $\nu(u)$, $0 \leq u \leq 1$, *is given by* (36).

Proof. Now

$$\text{(44)}\qquad \mathbf{P}\{\delta^+(\lambda) \leq x\} = \mathbf{P}\{\nu(u) \leq (u + x)\nu(1) \text{ for } 0 \leq u \leq 1\}.$$

If $\nu(1) = k$, $k = 1, 2, \ldots$, and if $a = x$ and $c = 1/k$ in (37), then we get

$$\text{(45)}\quad \mathbf{P}\{\delta^+(\lambda) \leq x \mid \nu(1) = k\} = 1 - \sum_{kx \leq j \leq k} \left(\frac{kx}{k(x+1)-j}\right)\mathbf{P}\left\{\nu\left(\frac{j}{k} - x\right) = j \mid \nu(1) = k\right\}.$$

Hence

$$\text{(46)}\quad \mathbf{P}\{\delta^+(\lambda) \leq x\} = \mathbf{P}\{\nu(1) = 0\} + \sum_{k=1}^{\infty}\mathbf{P}\{\nu(1) = k\}\mathbf{P}\{\delta^+(\lambda) \leq x \mid \nu(1) = k\}$$

which proves (43).

Theorem 9. *For* $0 < x < 1$

$$\text{(47)}\quad \mathbf{P}\{\delta^-(\lambda) \leq x\} = \mathbf{P}\{\nu(1) > 0\} - \sum_{k=1}^{\infty} \sum_{0 \leq j \leq k(1-x)} \left(\frac{kx}{kx + j}\right) \cdot \mathbf{P}\left\{\nu\left(\frac{j}{k} + x\right) = j\right\}\mathbf{P}\left\{\nu\left(1 - x - \frac{j}{k}\right) = k - j\right\}$$

where the distribution of $\nu(u)$, $0 \leq u \leq 1$, *is given by* (36).

Proof. Now

$$\text{(48)}\quad \mathbf{P}\{\delta^-(\lambda) \leq x\} = \mathbf{P}\{u\nu(1) - \nu(u) \leq x\nu(1) \text{ for } 0 \leq u \leq 1\} - \mathbf{P}\{\nu(1) = 0\}.$$

If $\nu(1) = k$, $k = 1, 2, \ldots$, and if $a = x$ and $c = 1/k$ in (38), then we get

$$\text{(49)}\quad \mathbf{P}\{\delta^-(\lambda) \leq x \mid \nu(1) = k\} = 1 - \sum_{0 \leq j \leq k(1-x)} \left(\frac{kx}{kx + j}\right)\mathbf{P}\left\{\nu\left(\frac{j}{k} + x\right) = j \mid \nu(1) = k\right\}.$$

Hence

$$\text{(50)}\qquad \mathbf{P}\{\delta^-(\lambda) \leq x\} = \sum_{k=1}^{\infty}\mathbf{P}\{\nu(1) = k\}\mathbf{P}\{\delta^-(\lambda) \leq x \mid \nu(1) = k\}$$

which proves (47).

NOTE. Define

$$\gamma(\lambda) = \sup_{-\infty < x < \infty} \left| \frac{\nu}{\lambda} F_\lambda(x) - F(x) \right| . \tag{51}$$

Then $\gamma(\lambda)$ is a distribution-free statistic. M. Kac [49] proved that

$$\lim_{\lambda \to \infty} \mathbf{P}\{\sqrt{\lambda}\, \gamma(\lambda) \leq z\} = L(z) \tag{52}$$

where

$$L(z) = \begin{cases} \dfrac{4}{\pi} \sum_{j=0}^{\infty} \dfrac{(-1)^j}{2j+1} \exp\left(-\dfrac{(2j+1)^2\pi^2}{8z^2}\right) & \text{if } z > 0, \\ 0 & \text{if } z \leq 0. \end{cases} \tag{53}$$

41. PROBLEMS

1. In a ballot candidate A scores a votes and candidate B scores b votes and all the possible voting records are equally probable. Denote by α_r and β_r the number of votes registered for A and B respectively among the first r votes recorded. Denote by $Q_j(a, b)$ the probability that the inequality $\alpha_r \geq \mu\beta_r$ holds for exactly j subscripts among $r = 1, 2, \ldots, a + b$, and denote by $P_j(a, b)$ the probability that the inequality $\alpha_r > \mu\beta_r$ holds for exactly j subscripts among $r = 1, 2, \ldots, a + b$.

Find $Q_j(a, b)$ if a and b are relatively prime numbers and $\mu = a/b$. (See M. T. L. Bizley and H. D. Grossman [9].)

2. Consider Problem 1 and find $Q_j(a, b)$ if $b = a$ and $\mu = 1$. (See O. Engelberg [15].)

3. Consider Problem 1 and find $Q_j(a, b)$ if $a \geq \mu b$ and $\mu \geq 0$ is an integer. (See O. Engelberg [15].)

4. Consider Problem 1 and find $Q_j(a, b)$ if μ is a nonnegative integer.

5. In Problem 1 find $Q_{a+b}(a, b)$ and $P_{a+b-1}(a, b)$ if $a = km$, $b = kn$, $(m, n) = 1$, and $\mu = a/b$. (See H. D. Grossman [21] and M. T. L. Bizley [8].)

6. In Problem 1 find $P_j(a, b)$, $j = 0, 1, \ldots, a + b$, if $a = km$, $b = kn$, $(m, n) = 1$, and $\mu = a/b$.

7. In a ballot candidate A scores a votes and candidate B scores b votes and all the possible voting records are equally probable. Denote by α_r and β_r the number of votes registered for A and B respectively among the first r votes recorded and let $\alpha_0 = \beta_0 = 0$. For $0 \leq u \leq a + b$ define $\alpha(u)$ and $\beta(u)$ as follows: $\alpha(u) = \alpha_r(r + 1 - u) + \alpha_{r+1}(u - r)$ if $r \leq u \leq r + 1$, and $\beta(u) = \beta_r(r + 1 - u) + \beta_{r+1}(u - r)$ if $r \leq u \leq r + 1$. If the votes are recorded at times $u = 1, 2, \ldots, a + b$, then $\alpha(u)$ and $\beta(u)$ $(0 \leq u \leq a + b)$ describe the temporal fluctuations of the number of votes registered for A and B respectively. Denote by $\delta_{a,b}$ the total time in $(0, a + b)$ during which A is in leading position, that is, $\delta_{a,b}$ is the measure of the set: $\{u\colon \alpha(u) > \beta(u) \text{ and } 0 \leq u \leq a + b\}$. Find the distribution of the random variable $\delta_{a,b}$. (See K. L. Chung and W. Feller [13].)

8. Let $\xi_1, \xi_2, \ldots, \xi_n$ be mutually independent random variables having a common continuous and symmetric distribution (that is, $\mathbf{P}\{\xi_r = x\} = 0$ and

$\mathbf{P}\{\xi_r \leq x\} = \mathbf{P}\{\xi_r \geq -x\}$ for every x). Define $\zeta_0 = 0$ and $\zeta_r = \xi_1 + \cdots + \xi_r$ for $r = 1, 2, \ldots, n$. Denote by Δ_n the number of nonnegative (positive) terms in $\zeta_1, \zeta_2, \ldots, \zeta_n$. Find $\mathbf{P}\{\Delta_n = j\}$ for $j = 0, 1, \ldots, n$. (See E. Sparre Andersen [1] and D. A. Darling [14].)

9. Consider Problem 8 and let $(\alpha_0(n), \alpha_1(n), \ldots, \alpha_n(n))$ be that permutation of $(0, 1, \ldots, n)$ for which $\zeta_{\alpha_0(n)} < \zeta_{\alpha_1(n)} < \cdots < \zeta_{\alpha_n(n)}$. Find $\mathbf{P}\{\alpha_k(n) = j\}$, $j = 0, 1, \ldots, n$. (See D. A. Darling [14] and E. Sparre Andersen [4].)

10. Let $\xi_1, \xi_2, \ldots, \xi_n$ be mutually independent and identically distributed random variables having a continuous distribution function $F(x)$. Let $F_n(x)$ be the empirical distribution function of the sample $(\xi_1, \xi_2, \ldots, \xi_n)$. Prove that

$$\delta_n = \sup_{-\infty < x < \infty} |F_n(x) - F(x)|$$

is a distribution-free statistic.

11. Let $\xi_1, \xi_2, \ldots, \xi_n, \eta_1, \eta_2, \ldots, \eta_n$ be mutually independent random variables having a common continuous distribution function. Denote by $F_n(x)$ and $G_n(x)$ the empirical distribution functions of the samples $(\xi_1, \xi_2, \ldots, \xi_n)$ and $(\eta_1, \eta_2, \ldots, \eta_n)$ respectively. Define

$$\delta^+(n, n) = \sup_{-\infty < x < \infty} [F_n(x) - G_n(x)]$$

and

$$\delta(n, n) = \sup_{-\infty < x < \infty} |F_n(x) - G_n(x)|.$$

Find the distribution and the asymptotic distribution of $\delta^+(n, n)$.

12. Consider Problem 11. Find the asymptotic distribution of $\delta(n, n)$.

13. Let $\xi_1, \xi_2, \ldots, \xi_m, \eta_1, \eta_2, \ldots, \eta_n$ be mutually independent random variables having a common continuous distribution function. Denote by $F_m(x)$ and $G_n(x)$ the empirical distribution functions of the samples $(\xi_1, \xi_2, \ldots, \xi_m)$ and $(\eta_1, \eta_2, \ldots, \eta_n)$ respectively. Find the probability that

$$\inf_{0 < G_n(x) < 1} [F_m(x) - G_n(x)] > 0.$$

(See E. F. Drion [39].)

14. Let $\{\nu(u), 0 \leq u \leq 1\}$ be a Poisson process of density λ. Find

$$\lim_{\lambda \to \infty} \mathbf{P}\left\{ \sup_{0 \leq u \leq 1} \left| \frac{\nu(u) - \lambda u}{\sqrt{\lambda}} \right| \leq z \right\}.$$

(See M. Kac [49].)

REFERENCES

Fluctuation Theory

[1] Andersen, E. S. "On the number of positive sums of random variables," *Skand. Aktuarietids.* **32** (1949), 27–36.

[2] Andersen, E. S. "On the frequency of positive partial sums of a series of random variables," *Math. Tidskrift B* (1950), 33–35.

[3] Andersen, E. S. "On the fluctuations of sums of random variables," *Math. Scand.* **1** (1953) 263–285.

[4] Andersen, E. S. "On sums of symmetrically dependent random variables," *Skand. Aktuarietids.* **36** (1953), 123–138.

[5] Andersen, E. S. "On the fluctuations of sums of random variables," *Math. Scand.* **2** (1954), 195–223.

[6] Baxter, G. "An analytic approach to finite fluctuation problems in probability," *J. d'Analyse Math.* **9** (1961), 37–70.

[7] Baxter, G. "Combinatorial methods in fluctuation theory." *Zeitschrift für Wahrscheinlichkeitstheorie* **1** (1963), 263–270.

[8] Bizley, M. T. L. "Derivation of a new formula for the number of minimal lattice paths from (0, 0) to (km, kn) having just t contacts with the line $my = nx$ and having no points above this line; and a proof of Grossman's formula for the number of paths which may touch but do not rise above this line," *J. Inst. Actuaries* **80** (1954), 55–62.

[9] Bizley, M. T. L. and H. D. Grossman, "Fun with lattice points 25. Paths having a given number of lattice points in a given region," *Scripta Math.* **20** (1954), 203–204.

[10] Brandt, A. "A generalization of a combinatorial theorem of Sparre Andersen about sums of random variables," *Math. Skand.* **9** (1961), 352–358.

[11] Brunk, H. D. "On a theorem of E. Sparre Andersen and its application to tests against trend," *Math. Scand.* **8** (1960), 305–326.

[12] Brunk, H. D. "A generalization of Spitzer's combinatorial lemma," *Zeitschrift für Wahrscheinlichkeitstheorie* **2** (1964), 395–405.

[13] Chung, K. L. and W. Feller, "On fluctuations in coin tossing," *Proc. Nat. Acad. Sci. U.S.A.* **35** (1949), 605–608.

[14] Darling, D. A. "Sums of symmetrical random variables," *Proc. Amer. Math. Soc.* **2** (1951), 511–517.

[15] Engelberg, O. "Exact and limiting distributions of the number of lead positions in 'unconditional' ballot problems," *J. Appl. Probability* **1** (1964), 168–172.

[16] Engelberg, O. "On some problems concerning a restricted random walk," *J. Appl. Probability* **2** (1965), 369–404.

[17] Engelberg, O. "Generalization of the ballot problem," *Zeitschrift für Wahrscheinlichkeitstheorie* **3** (1965), 271–275.

[18] Erdös, P. and M. Kac, "On the number of positive sums of independent random variables," *Bull. Amer. Math. Soc.* **53** (1947), 1011–1020.

[19] Feller, W. "On combinatorial methods in fluctuation theory," *Probability and Statistics*, The Harald Cramér Volume, Edited by U. Grenander, Almqvist and Wiksell, Stockholm, and John Wiley and Sons, New York, 1959, pp. 75–91.

[20] Feller, W. "*An Introduction to Probability Theory and its Applications*," Vol. I, Second edition, John Wiley and Sons, New York, 1957; Vol. II, John Wiley and Sons, New York, 1966.

[21] Grossman, H. D. "Fun with lattice-points 22. Paths in a lattice triangle," *Scripta Math.* **16** (1950), 207–212.

[22] Hobby, Ch. and R. Pyke, "Combinatorial results in multi-dimensional fluctuation theory," *Ann. Math. Statist.* **34** (1963), 402–404.

[23] Lipschutz, M. "Generalization of a theorem of Chung and Feller," *Proc. Amer. Math. Soc.* **3** (1952), 659–670.

[24] Riordan, J. "The enumeration of election returns by number of lead positions," *Ann. Math. Statist.* **35** (1964), 369–379.

[25] Sarkadi, K. "On Galton's rank order test," *Publ. Math. Inst. Hungar. Acad. Sci.* **6** (1961), 127–131; **7** (1962), 223 (addendum).

[26] Spitzer, F. "A combinatorial lemma and its applications to probability theory," *Trans. Amer. Math. Soc.* **82** (1956), 323–339.

[27] Takács, L. "Ballot problems," *Zeitschrift für Wahrscheinlichkeitstheorie* **1** (1962), 154–158.

[28] Takács, L. "The distribution of majority times in a ballot," *Zeitschrift für Wahrscheinlichkeitstheorie* **2** (1963), 118–121.

[29] Takács, L. "Fluctuations in the ratio of scores in counting a ballot," *J. Appl. Probability* **1** (1964), 393–396.

[30] Wendel, J. G. "Order statistics of partial sums," *Ann. Math. Statist.* **31** (1960), 1034–1044.

Order Statistics

[31] Birnbaum, Z. W. and R. Pyke, "On some distributions related to the statistic D_n^+," *Ann. Math. Statist.* **29** (1958), 179–187.

[32] Birnbaum, Z. W. and F. H. Tingey, "One sided confidence contours for probability distribution functions," *Ann. Math. Statist.* **22** (1951), 592–596.

[33] Borovkov, A. A. "On the two-sample problem," (Russian) *Izv. Akad. Nauk SSSR. Ser. Mat.* **26** (1962), 605–624. [English translation: *Selected Translations in Mathematical Statistics and Probability, IMS and AMS,* **5** (1965), 285–307.]

[34] Chang, Li-chien. "On the ratio of an empirical distribution function to the theoretical distribution function," (Chinese) *Acta Math. Sinica* **5** (1955), 347–368. [English translation: *Selected Translations in Mathematical Statistics and Probability, IMS and AMS,* **4** (1963), 17–38.]

[35] Cheng, P. "Non-negative jump points of an empirical distribution function relative to a theoretical distribution function," (Chinese), *Acta Math. Sinica* **8** (1958), 333–347. [English translation: *Selected Translations in Mathematical Statistics and Probability, IMS and AMS,* **3** (1962), 205–224.]

[36] Daniels, H. E. "The statistical theory of the strengths of bundles of threads, I." *Proc. Roy. Soc. A* **183** (1945), 405–435.

[37] Dempster, A. "Generalized D_n^+ statistics," *Ann. Math. Statist.* **30** (1959), 593–597.

[38] Doob, J. L. "Heuristic approach to the Kolmogorov-Smirnov theorems," *Ann. Math. Statist.* **20** (1949), 393–403.

[39] Drion, E. F. "Some distribution-free tests for the difference between two empirical cumulative distribution functions," *Ann. Math. Statist.* **23** (1952), 563–574.

[40] Dwass, M. "On several statistics related to empirical distribution functions," *Ann. Math. Statistics* **29** (1958), 188–191.

[41] Dwass, M. "The distribution of a generalized D_n^+ statistic." *Ann. Math. Statist.* **30** (1959), 1024–1028.

[42] Feller, W. "On the Kolmorogov-Sminov theorems." *Ann. Math. Statist.* **19** (1948), 177–189.

[43] Glivenko, V. "Sulla determinazione empirica delle leggi di probabilitá," *Giornale dell'Istituto Italiano degli Attuari* **4** (1933), 92–99.

[44] Gnedenko, B. V. and V. S. Koroljuk, "On the maximum discrepancy between two empirical distribution functions," (Russian) *Dokl. Akad. Nauk SSSR.* **80** (1951), 525–528. [English translation: *Selected Translations in Mathematical Statistics and Probability, IMS and AMS,* **1** (1961), 13–16.]

[45] Gnedenko, B. V. and V. S. Mihalevič, "On the distribution of the number of excesses of one empirical distribution function over another," (Russian) *Dokl. Akad. Nauk SSSR* **82** (1952), 841–843. [English translation: *Selected Translations in Mathematical Statistics and Probability, IMS and AMS* **1**, (1961), 83–85.]

[46] Gnedenko, B. V. and V. S. Mihalevič, "Two theorems on the behavior of empirical distribution functions," (Russian) *Dokl. Akad. Nauk SSSR* **85** (1952), 25–27. [English translation: *Selected Translations in Mathematical Statistics and Probability, IMS and AMS*, **1** (1961), 55–57.]

[47] Hobby, Ch. and R. Pyke, "A combinatorial theorem related to comparisons of empirical distribution functions," *Zeitschrift für Wahrscheinlichkeitstheorie* **2** (1963), 85–89.

[48] Ishii, G. "On the exact probabilities of Rényi's tests," *Ann. Inst. Statist. Math. Tokyo* **11** (1959), 17–24.

[49] Kac, M. "On deviations between theoretical and empirical distributions," *Proc. Nat. Acad. Sci. U.S.A.* **35** (1949), 252–257.

[50] Kolmogoroff, A. "Sulla determinazione empirica di una legge di distribuzione," *Giornale dell'Istituto Italiano degli Attuari* **4** (1933), 83–91.

[51] Koroljuk, V. S. "On the discrepancy of empirical distribution functions for the case of two independent samples," *Izv. Akad. Nauk SSSR. Ser. Math.* **19** (1955), 81–96. [English translation: *Selected Translations in Mathematical Statistics and Probability, IMS and AMS*, **4** (1963), 105–121.]

[52] Kuiper, N. H. "Alternative proof of a theorem of Birnbaum and Pyke," *Ann. Math. Statist.* **30** (1959), 251–252.

[53] Malmquist, S. "On a property of order statistics from a rectangular distribution," *Skand. Aktuarietids.* **33** (1950), 214–222.

[54] Massey, F. J. "The distribution of the maximum deviation between two sample cumulative step functions," *Ann. Math. Statist.* **22** (1951), 125–128.

[55] Robbins, H. "A one-sided confidence interval for an unknown distribution function" (Abstract), *Ann. Math. Statist.* **25** (1954), 409.

[56] Smirnov, N. "On the estimation of the discrepancy between empirical curves of distribution for two independent samples," *Bulletin Mathématique de l'Université de Moscov, Ser. A* **2** No. 2, (1939), 3–14.

[57] Smirnov, N. V. "Approximate laws of distribution of random variables from empirical data," (Russian) *Uspehi Mat. Nauk.* **10** (1944), 179–206.

[58] Smirnov, N. V. "Probabilities of large values of nonparametric one-sided goodness of fit statistics," (Russian) *Trudy Mat. Inst. Steklov* **64** (1961), 185–210. [English translation: *Selected Translations in Mathematical Statistics and Probability, IMS and AMS*, **5** (1965), 210–239.]

[59] Takács, L. "On random walk problems," (Hungarian) *Magyar Tud. Akad. Mat. Kut. Int. Közl.* **2** (1957), 81–90.

[60] Takács, L. "Remarks on random walk problems," *Magyar Tud. Akad. Mat. Kut. Int. Közl.* **2** (1957), 175–182.

[61] Takács, L. "The use of a ballot theorem in order statistics," *J. Appl. Probability* **1** (1964), 389–392.

[62] Takács, L. "An application of a ballot theorem in order statistics," *Ann. Math. Statist.* **35** (1964), 1356–1358.

[63] Takács, L. "Applications of a ballot theorem in physics and in order statistics," *J. Roy. Statist. Soc. Ser. B* **27** (1965), 130–137.

[64] Takács, L. "The distributions of some statistics depending on the deviations between empirical and theoretical distribution functions," *Sanhkyā, Ser. A* **27** (1965), 93–100.

[65] van der Waerden, B. L. "Testing a distribution function," *Indagationes Mathematicae* **15** (1953), 201–207.

[66] Wald, A. and J. Wolfowitz, "Confidence limits for continuous distribution functions," *Ann. Math. Statist.* **10** (1939), 105–118.

Appendix

1. SOME GENERAL NOTIONS AND THEOREMS

Random Trials. If we speak about a random trial, then we suppose that a probability space $(\Omega, \mathscr{A}, \mathbf{P})$ is associated with the random trial. Ω is the sample space, the set of all possible outcomes of the random trial. $\mathscr{A}$ is a σ-field (σ-algebra) of subsets of Ω. The elements of $\mathscr{A}$ are called events. $\mathbf{P}$ is a probability measure defined on $\mathscr{A}$.

Continuity Theorem for Probabilities. If $A_1, A_2, \ldots, A_r, \ldots$ is an infinite sequence of events, then $\limsup_{n\to\infty} A_n = \prod_{n=1}^{\infty} \sum_{r=n}^{\infty} A_r$ is the event that infinitely many events occur among $A_1, A_2, \ldots, A_r, \ldots$ and $\liminf_{n\to\infty} A_n = \sum_{n=1}^{\infty} \prod_{r=n}^{\infty} A_r$ is the event that all but a finite number of events occur among $A_1, A_2, \ldots, A_r, \ldots$. If $\limsup_{n\to\infty} A_n = \liminf_{n\to\infty} A_n$, then we say that $\lim_{n\to\infty} A_n$ exists and is equal to the common event of the superior limit and the inferior limit. If $A_1, A_2, \ldots, A_r, \ldots$ is either a nondecreasing sequence of events or a nonincreasing sequence of events, then $\lim_{n\to\infty} A_n$ exists. If $\lim_{n\to\infty} A_n$ exists, then

$$(1) \qquad \mathbf{P}\left\{\lim_{n\to\infty} A_n\right\} = \lim_{n\to\infty} \mathbf{P}\{A_n\}.$$

Random Variables. If we speak about a real-valued random variable ξ concerning a random trial, then by this we understand a function $\xi = \xi(\omega)$ defined on Ω and measurable with respect to $\mathscr{A}$, that is, for every x the event $\{\xi(\omega) \leq x\} \in \mathscr{A}$. A random variable $\xi(\omega)$ may be finite or infinite-valued.

If $\xi(\omega)$, $\omega \in \Omega$, is a finite-valued random variable, then the function $F(x) = \mathbf{P}\{\xi(\omega) \leq x\}$ is called the distribution function of the random variable ξ. If $F(x)$ is an absolutely continuous function of x, then $F(x)$ can be represented in the form

$$(2) \qquad F(x) = \int_{-\infty}^{x} f(y)\, dy$$

for all x. Such an $f(x)$ is called the density function of ξ. The spectrum of a random variable ξ is defined as the set $R = \{x : F(x + \epsilon) - F(x - \epsilon) > 0$ for all $\epsilon > 0\}$.

If it is not specified otherwise, then by a random variable ξ we mean a finite-valued random variable.

The Expectation. The expectation of a finite-valued random variable ξ is defined as the integral

$$\mathbf{E}\{\xi\} = \int_\Omega \xi(\omega)\, d\mathbf{P} = \int_{-\infty}^{\infty} x\, dF(x). \tag{3}$$

If $\xi(\omega)$ is absolutely integrable, then we say that ξ has a finite expectation. If the integral of $|\xi(\omega)|$ over Ω is infinite, then $\mathbf{E}\{\xi\} = \infty$ or $\mathbf{E}\{\xi\} = -\infty$ or $\mathbf{E}\{\xi\}$ does not exist.

If $g(x)$ is a Borel-measurable function of x, then $\eta = g(\xi)$ is also a random variable and its expectation is

$$\mathbf{E}\{\eta\} = \int_\Omega g(\xi(\omega))\, d\mathbf{P} = \int_{-\infty}^{\infty} g(x)\, dF(x) \tag{4}$$

provided that it exists.

Generating Functions. If ξ is a real and finite-valued random variable, then the expectation $G(z) = \mathbf{E}\{z^\xi\}$ exists for $|z| = 1$ and it is called the generating function of the random variable ξ. The distribution of the random variable ξ is uniquely determined by its generating function. If R, the spectrum of ξ, contains only nonnegative integers, then we frequently use the generating function. Then $G(z)$ is always convergent for $|z| \leq 1$ and is a regular function of z for $|z| < 1$.

Laplace-Stieltjes Transforms. If ξ is a real and finite-valued random variable, then the expectation $\phi(s) = \mathbf{E}\{e^{-s\xi}\}$ exists for $\mathrm{Re}(s) = 0$ and it is called the Laplace-Stieltjes transform of the distribution function of the random variable ξ. The distribution of the random variable ξ is uniquely determined by its Laplace-Stieltjes transform. If R, the spectrum of ξ, contains only nonnegative numbers, then we frequently use the Laplace-Stieltjes transform. In this case $\phi(s)$ is always convergent for $\mathrm{Re}(s) \geq 0$ and regular for $\mathrm{Re}(s) > 0$.

Characteristic Functions. If ξ is a real and finite-valued random variable, then the expectation $\psi(\omega) = \mathbf{E}\{e^{i\omega\xi}\}$ always exists if $-\infty < \omega < \infty$ and is called the characteristic function of the random variable ξ. Clearly $\psi(\omega) = \phi(-i\omega)$. The distribution of the random variable ξ is uniquely determined by its characteristic function.

Conditional Probabilities. Let $(\Omega, \mathscr{A}\ \mathbf{P})$ be a probability space, $A \in \mathscr{A}$ an event, and $\mathscr{B}$ a σ-field of sets belonging to $\mathscr{A}$ (σ-subalgebra of $\mathscr{A}$). The conditional probability of A relative to $\mathscr{B}$, denoted by $\mathbf{P}\{A \mid \mathscr{B}\}$, is defined as any function of ω which is measurable with respect to $\mathscr{B}$ and which satisfies the equation

$$\int_B \mathbf{P}\{A \mid \mathscr{B}\}\, d\mathbf{P} = \mathbf{P}\{AB\} \tag{5}$$

for all $B \in \mathscr{B}$. By the Radon-Nikodym theorem it follows that such a function exists and is determined up to an equivalence, that is, any two versions of $\mathbf{P}\{A \mid \mathscr{B}\}$ are equal almost everywhere; they can differ only on an ω-set of probability 0.

If $\xi = \xi(\omega)$ is a real and finite-valued random variable, then $\mathbf{P}\{A \mid \xi\}$ is defined as any one version of $\mathbf{P}\{A \mid \mathscr{B}\}$ where $\mathscr{B}$ is the σ-field generated by ξ, that is, $\mathscr{B}$ is the smallest σ-field which contains the sets $\{\xi(\omega) \leq x\}$. In this case $\mathbf{P}\{A \mid \xi\}$ is a Baire-function of ξ and we use the notation $\mathbf{P}\{A \mid \xi = x\} = \mathbf{P}\{A \mid \xi\}\,|_{\xi(\omega)=x}$.

The following formula

$$\mathbf{P}\{A\} = \int_{-\infty}^{\infty} \mathbf{P}\{A \mid \xi = x\}\, d\mathbf{P}\{\xi \leq x\} \tag{6}$$

is called the *theorem of total probability*.

Conditional Expectations. Let $(\Omega, \mathscr{A}, \mathbf{P})$ be a probability space, η a real and finite-valued random variable whose expectation exists, and $\mathscr{B}$ a σ-field of sets belonging to $\mathscr{A}$. The conditional expectation of η relative to $\mathscr{B}$, denoted by $\mathbf{E}\{\eta \mid \mathscr{B}\}$, is defined as any function of ω which is measurable with respect to $\mathscr{B}$ and which satisfies the equation

$$\int_B \mathbf{E}\{\eta \mid \mathscr{B}\}\, d\mathbf{P} = \int_B \eta\, d\mathbf{P} \tag{7}$$

for all $B \in \mathscr{B}$. By the Radon-Nikodym theorem it follows that such a function exists and is determined up to an equivalence, that is, any two versions of $\mathbf{E}\{\eta \mid \mathscr{B}\}$ are equal almost everywhere; they can differ only on an ω-set of probability 0.

If $\xi = \xi(\omega)$ is a real and finite-valued random variable, then $\mathbf{E}\{\eta \mid \xi\}$ is defined as any one version of $\mathbf{E}\{\eta \mid \mathscr{B}\}$ where $\mathscr{B}$ is the σ-field generated by ξ. In this case $\mathbf{E}\{\eta \mid \xi\}$ is a Baire-function of ξ and we use the notation $\mathbf{E}\{\eta \mid \xi = x\} = \mathbf{E}\{\eta \mid \xi\}\,|_{\xi(\omega)=x}$.

The following formula

$$\mathbf{E}\{\eta\} = \int_{-\infty}^{\infty} \mathbf{E}\{\eta \mid \xi = x\}\, d\mathbf{P}\{\xi \leq x\} \tag{8}$$

is called the *theorem of total expectation*.

Kolmogorov's Consistency Theorem. Let $(\Omega, \mathscr{A}, \mathbf{P})$ be a probability space, and $\xi_t(\omega)$, $t \in T$, any family of real-valued random variables. Then the probabilities

$$(9)\quad F_{t_1,t_2,\ldots,t_n}(x_1, x_2, \ldots, x_n) = \mathbf{P}\{\xi_{t_1} \leq x_1, \xi_{t_2} \leq x_2, \ldots, \xi_{t_n} \leq x_n\},$$

defined for all finite subsets $(t_1, t_2, \ldots, t_n)$ of the index set T, are called the finite dimensional distribution functions of the family of random variables ξ_t, $t \in T$. These multivariate distribution functions are mutually consistent, that is,

$$(10)\quad F_{t_{i_1},t_{i_2},\ldots,t_{i_n}}(x_{i_1}, x_{i_2}, \ldots, x_{i_n}) = F_{t_1,t_2,\ldots,t_n}(x_1, x_2, \ldots, x_n)$$

for any permutation $(i_1, i_2, \ldots, i_n)$ of $(1, 2, \ldots, n)$, and

$$(11)\quad F_{t_1,t_2,\ldots,t_n}(x_1, x_2, \ldots, x_n) = \lim_{\substack{x_j \to \infty \\ j=n+1,\ldots,m}} F_{t_1,t_2,\ldots,t_m}(x_1, x_2, \ldots, x_m)$$

for $m = n + 1, n + 2, \ldots$.

Kolmogorov proved that if the distribution functions $F_{t_1,t_2,\ldots,t_n}(x_1, x_2, \ldots, x_n)$ are given for all finite subsets $(t_1, t_2, \ldots, t_n)$ of an index set T and if they are consistent, then there exists a probability space $(\Omega, \mathscr{A}, \mathbf{P})$, and a family of random variables $\xi_t(\omega)$, $t \in T$, such that

$$(12)\quad \mathbf{P}\{\xi_{t_1} \leq x_1, \xi_{t_2} \leq x_2, \ldots, \xi_{t_n} \leq x_n\} = F_{t_1,t_2,\ldots,t_n}(x_1, x_2, \ldots, x_n)$$

for all finite sets $(t_1, t_2, \ldots, t_n) \subset T$.

REFERENCES

[1] Kolmogorov, A. N. *Foundations of the Theory of Probability*, Chelsea, New York, 1950.

[2] Loève, M. *Probability Theory*, 3rd edition, Van Nostrand, Princeton, New Jersey, 1963.

[3] Neveu, J. *Mathematical Foundations of the Calculus of Probability*, Holden-Day, San Francisco, California, 1965.

2. INDEPENDENT AND IDENTICALLY DISTRIBUTED RANDOM VARIABLES

We say that $\xi_1, \xi_2, \ldots, \xi_n, \ldots$ form a sequence of mutually independent random variables if

$$(1)\quad \mathbf{P}\{\xi_1 \leq x_1, \xi_2 \leq x_2, \ldots, \xi_n \leq x_n\} = \mathbf{P}\{\xi_1 \leq x_1\}\mathbf{P}\{\xi_2 \leq x_2\} \cdots \mathbf{P}\{\xi_n \leq x_n\}$$

holds for $n = 2, 3, \ldots$ and for all $x_1, x_2, \ldots, x_n$. If $\xi_1, \xi_2, \ldots, \xi_n, \ldots$ are identically distributed random variables, then $\mathbf{P}\{\xi_n \leq x\} = F(x)$ for $n = 1, 2, \ldots$.

We say that ξ_n is a lattice-variable, if there exists a d such that $\sum_{j=-\infty}^{\infty} \mathbf{P}\{\xi_n = jd\} = 1$. If d is the greatest positive number with this property, then ξ_n is said to be a d-lattice variable. If there is no such d, then ξ_n is said to be a nonlattice variable.

In what follows we shall suppose that $\xi_1, \xi_2, \ldots, \xi_n, \ldots$ is an infinite sequence of mutually independent and identically distributed random variables for which $\mathbf{P}\{\xi_n \leq x\} = F(x)$, $\mathbf{E}\{\xi_n\} = a$ and $\mathbf{Var}\,\{\xi_n\} = b^2$ if they exist. We shall use the notation $\zeta_n = \xi_1 + \xi_2 + \cdots + \xi_n$ for $n = 1, 2, \ldots$. Now we shall mention a few fundamental theorems for such random variables.

The Weak Law of Large Numbers. If $\mathbf{E}\{|\xi_n|\} < \infty$, *then for any* $\epsilon > 0$

$$\lim_{n\to\infty} \mathbf{P}\left\{\left|\frac{\zeta_n}{n} - a\right| < \epsilon\right\} = 1, \tag{2}$$

that is, ζ_n/n *converges in probability to* a.

This theorem has been proved by J. Bernoulli [2] for the case where $\mathbf{P}\{\xi_n = 0\} = q$, $\mathbf{P}\{\xi_n = 1\} = p$ $(p + q = 1)$. P. L. Tchebyshev [23] proved it for the case where $b^2 < \infty$. The above generalization has been proved by A. Y. Khintchine [17].

The Strong Law of Large Numbers. If $\mathbf{E}\{|\xi_n|\} < \infty$, *then we have*

$$\mathbf{P}\left\{\lim_{n\to\infty} \frac{\zeta_n}{n} = a\right\} = 1, \tag{3}$$

that is ζ_n/n *converges to* a *with probability* 1.

This theorem in the particular case $\mathbf{P}\{\xi_n = 0\} = \mathbf{P}\{\xi_n = 1\} = \frac{1}{2}$ has been proved by É. Borel [5], in the case $\mathbf{P}\{\xi_n = 0\} = q$, $\mathbf{P}\{\xi_n = 1\} = p$ $(p + q = 1)$, by F. P. Cantelli [6], and in the above general case, by A. N. Kolmogorov [18].

The Central Limit Theorem. If $\mathbf{E}\{\xi_n^2\} < \infty$, *then*

$$\lim_{n\to\infty} \mathbf{P}\left\{\frac{\zeta_n - na}{\sqrt{nb^2}} \leq x\right\} = \frac{1}{\sqrt{2\pi}} \int_{-\infty}^{x} e^{-u^2/2}\, du. \tag{4}$$

This theorem for the particular case $\mathbf{P}\{\xi_n = 0\} = q$, $\mathbf{P}\{\xi_n = 1\} = p$ $(p + q = 1)$ has been found by A. De Moivre [11] and P. S. Laplace [20] and for the above case by P. L. Tchebyshev [24].

A Stable Limit Theorem. If $F(0) = 0$ *and* $1 - F(x) = h(x)x^{-\alpha}$, *where* $0 < \alpha < 2$ *is a constant and* $\lim_{x\to\infty} \frac{h(cx)}{h(x)} = 1$ *for any positive constant* c, *then for* $\alpha < 1$

$$\lim_{n\to\infty} \mathbf{P}\left\{\frac{\zeta_n}{b_n} \leq x\right\} = G_\alpha(x) \tag{5}$$

and for $\alpha > 1$,

$$\lim_{n\to\infty} \mathbf{P}\left\{\frac{\zeta_n - na}{b_n} \le x\right\} = G_\alpha(x) \tag{6}$$

where b_n *is chosen such that* $\lim_{n\to\infty} n[1 - F(b_n)] = 1$, *and* $G_\alpha(x)$ *is the stable distribution function for which*

$$\int_{-\infty}^{\infty} e^{izx}\, dG_\alpha(x) = \exp\left\{-|z|^\alpha\left(\cos\frac{\pi\alpha}{2} - i\sin\frac{\pi\alpha}{2}\operatorname{sgn} z\right)\Gamma(1-\alpha)\right\}. \tag{7}$$

The above theorem has been found by W. Doeblin [13].

Finally, we mention three theorems concerning the recurrent properties of the sequence $\zeta_1, \zeta_2, \ldots, \zeta_n, \ldots$.

1. *If* $\mathbf{E}\{|\xi_n|\} < \infty$, *then*

$$\mathbf{P}\left\{\sup_{1\le n<\infty} \zeta_n = \infty\right\} = \begin{cases} 1 & \text{when } a \ge 0 \text{ and } \mathbf{P}\{\xi_n = 0\} \ne 1, \\ 0 & \text{when } a < 0 \text{ or } \mathbf{P}\{\xi_n = 0\} = 1. \end{cases} \tag{8}$$

If $a \ne 0$, then this theorem follows immediately from the strong law of large numbers. If $a = 0$ and $\mathbf{P}\{\xi_n = 0\} \ne 1$, then it follows from a theorem of K. L. Chung and W. H. J. Fuchs [8].

2. *If* $F(0) = 0$, *that is,* ξ_n, $n = 1, 2, \ldots$, *are nonnegative random variables, then*

$$\lim_{x\to\infty} \frac{1}{x}\sum_{n=1}^{\infty} \mathbf{P}\{\zeta_n \le x\} = \frac{1}{a}. \tag{9}$$

This theorem has been proved by S. Täcklind [21].

3. *If* ξ_n, $n = 1, 2, \ldots$, *are nonlattice variables and* $\mathbf{E}\{\xi_n\} = a > 0$ ($a = \infty$ *is possible*), *then*

$$\lim \sum_{n=1}^{\infty} \mathbf{P}\{x < \zeta_n \le x + h\} = \begin{cases} \dfrac{h}{a} & \text{when } x \to \infty, \\ 0 & \text{when } x \to -\infty. \end{cases} \tag{10}$$

If ξ_n, $n = 1, 2, \ldots$ *are d-lattice variables and* $\mathbf{E}\{\xi_n\} = a > 0$, *then*

$$\lim \sum_{n=1}^{\infty} \mathbf{P}\{\zeta_n = kd\} = \begin{cases} \dfrac{d}{a} & \text{when } k \to \infty, \\ 0 & \text{when } k \to -\infty. \end{cases} \tag{11}$$

The above general theorem has been proved by D. Blackwell [4]. Particular cases have been proved by A. N. Kolmogorov [19], P. Erdös, W. Feller, and H. Pollard [14], D. Blackwell [3], K. L. Chung and J. Wolfowitz [10] and K. L. Chung and H. Pollard [9].

REFERENCES

[1] Beneš, V. E. "A 'renewal' limit theorem for general stochastic processes," *Ann. Math. Statist.* **33** (1962), 98–113.

[2] Bernoulli, J. *Ars Conjectandi*, (Opus posth.) Basileae, 1713.

[3] Blackwell, D. "A renewal theorem," *Duke Math. J.* **15** (1948), 145–150.

[4] Blackwell, D. "Extension of a renewal theorem," *Pacific J. Math.* **3** (1953), 315–320.

[5] Borel, É. "Les probabilités dénombrables et leurs applications arithmétiques," *Rend. Circ. Math. Palermo* **27** (1909), 247–271.

[6] Cantelli, F. P. "Sulla probabilità come limite della frequenza," *Rend. R. Accad. Lincei, Ser.* 5, *Cl. Sci. Fis. Mat. Nat.* **26** (1) (1917), 39–45.

[7] Chung, K. L. "On the renewal theorem in higher dimensions," *Skand. Aktuarietids.* **35** (1952), 188–194.

[8] Chung, K. L. and W. H. J. Fuchs, "On the distribution of values of sums of random variables," Four papers on probability, *Mem. Amer. Math. Soc. No.* 6 (1951), 1–12.

[9] Chung, K. L. and H. Pollard, "An extension of renewal theory," *Proc. Amer. Math. Soc.* **3** (1952), 303–309.

[10] Chung, K. L. and J. Wolfowitz, "On a limit theorem in renewal theory," *Annals of Mathematics* **55** (1952), 1–6.

[11] De Moivre, A. *The Doctrine of Chances*, London, First edition 1717; Second edition 1738; Third edition 1756.

[12] De Moivre, A. *Miscellanea analytica de seriebus et quadraturis*, London, 1730.

[13] Doeblin, W. "Sur l'ensemble de puissances d'une loi de probabilité," *Studia Math.* **9** (1941), 71–96.

[14] Erdös, P., W. Feller and H. Pollard, "A theorem on power series," *Bull. Amer. Math. Soc.* **55** (1949), 201–204.

[15] Erdös, P. and M. Kac, "On certain limit theorems of the theory of probability," *Bull. Amer. Math. Soc.* **52** (1946), 292–302.

[16] Feller, W. "Fluctuation theory of recurrent events," *Trans. Amer. Math. Soc.* **67** (1949), 98–119.

[17] Khintchine, A. "Sur la loi des grands nombres," *C. R. Acad. Sci., Paris*, **188** (1929) 477–479.

[18] Kolmogorov, A. N. "Sur la loi forte des grands nombres," *C. R. Acad. Sci., Paris*, **191** (1930) 910–911.

[19] Kolmogoroff, A. "Anfangsgründe der Markoffschen Ketten mit unendlichen vielen möglichen Zuständen, *Rec. Math.* (*Mat. Sbornik*) *N.S.* **1** (1936), 607–610.

[20] Laplace, P. S. *Theorie Analytique des Probabilités*," Courcier, Paris, 1812 [*Ouvres complètes de Laplace*, VII, Gauthier-Villars, Paris, 1886.]

[21] Täcklind, S. "Elementare Behandlung vom Erneuerungsproblem," *Skand. Aktuarietids.* **27** (1944), 1–15.

[22] Täcklind, S. "Fourieranalytische Behandlung vom Erneuerungsproblem," *Skand. Aktuarietids.* **28** (1945), 68–105.

[23] Tchebyscheff, P. L. "Des valeurs moyennes" *Liouv. J. Math. Pures et Appl.* 2 *série* **12** (1867), 177–184 [Oeuvres I, St. Petersburg, 1907 pp. 687–694.]

[24] Tchebysheff, P. L. "Sur deux théorèmes relatifs aux probabilités" *Acta Math. Petr.* **14,** (1890–1891), 305–315 [Oeuvres II, St. Petersburg, 1907 pp. 481–491.]

3. STOCHASTIC PROCESSES WITH STATIONARY INDEPENDENT INCREMENTS

Let $\{\xi(u), 0 \leq u < \infty\}$ be a real-valued stochastic process with stationary independent increments, that is, for any $0 \leq t_0 < t_1 < \cdots < t_n$ the random variables $\xi(t_1) - \xi(t_0), \xi(t_2) - \xi(t_1), \ldots, \xi(t_n) - \xi(t_{n-1})$ are mutually independent and the distribution of $\xi(t) - \xi(u)$ depends only on $t - u$. Suppose that $\mathbf{P}\{\xi(0) = 0\} = 1$. For such processes

$$\mathbf{E}\{e^{i\omega\xi(u)}\} = e^{u\Psi(\omega)} \tag{1}$$

exists for all real ω and $u \geq 0$ and the most general form of $\Psi(\omega)$ is given by

$$\Psi(\omega) = i\omega c - \frac{\sigma^2\omega^2}{2} + \int_{-\infty}^{-0} \left(e^{i\omega x} - 1 - \frac{i\omega x}{1 + x^2}\right) dM(x) + \int_{+0}^{\infty} \left(e^{i\omega x} - 1 - \frac{i\omega x}{1 + x^2}\right) dN(x) \tag{2}$$

where c is a real constant, σ^2 is a nonnegative constant, and $M(x)$, $-\infty < x < 0$, and $N(x)$, $0 < x < \infty$ are nondecreasing functions of x for which $\lim_{x\to-\infty} M(x) = \lim_{x\to\infty} N(x) = 0$ and

$$\int_{-1}^{-0} x^2 \, dM(x) + \int_{+0}^{1} x^2 \, dN(x) < \infty. \tag{3}$$

The above general form of $\Psi(\omega)$ has been found by P. Lévy [18]. Particular cases have been found earlier by B. de Finetti [9, 10], and A. N. Kolmogorov [16, 17]. Another formula for $\Psi(\omega)$ has been given by A. Y. Khintchine [13, 14].

Conversely, if we choose any c, σ^2, $N(x)$, $0 < x < \infty$, and $M(x)$, $-\infty < x < 0$, satisfying the above mentioned conditions, then by Kolmogorov's consistency theorem we can conclude that there exists a stochastic process $\{\xi(u), 0 \leq u < \infty\}$ with stationary independent increments for which $\mathbf{P}\{\xi(0) = 0\} = 1$, and (1) holds.

According to a theorem of J. L. Doob [8], p. 57, we can always choose a separable version for $\{\xi(u), 0 \leq u < \infty\}$. The process $\{\xi(u), 0 \leq u < \infty\}$ is separable if there is a sequence $\{u_j\}$ of parameter values such that

$$\mathbf{P}\left\{\sup_{u\in I} \xi(u) = \sup_{u_j\in I} \xi(u_j)\right\} = 1 \tag{4}$$

and

$$\mathbf{P}\left\{\inf_{u\in I} \xi(u) = \inf_{u_j\in I} \xi(u_j)\right\} = 1 \tag{5}$$

hold for every open interval I of $[0, \infty)$. Separability implies that if I is an open interval, then $\sup_{u \in I} \xi(u)$ and $\inf_{u \in I} \xi(u)$ are (finite- or infinite-valued) random variables, that is, measurable functions.

We can always choose the process $\{\xi(u), 0 \leq u < \infty\}$ in such a way that it is also centered. Then $\mathbf{P}\{\xi(u - 0) = \xi(u) = \xi(u + 0)\} = 1$ holds for all $u > 0$, that is, with probability 1 the process $\{\xi(u), 0 \leq u < \infty\}$ has no fixed points of discontinuity. The sample functions of a separable centered process with stationary independent increments have simple continuity properties. (Cf. P. Lévy [19] and J. L. Doob [8].) Except possibly for a set of sample functions of probability 0, the sample functions are bounded on $[0, t]$ for any finite $t > 0$; they have finite left- (right-) hand limits at every $t > 0$; their discontinuities are jumps.

Now we should like to mention two simple examples for processes with stationary independent increments.

The Brownian Motion or Wiener Process. In this case it is supposed that $\xi(t) - \xi(u)$ is normally distributed, with $\mathbf{E}\{\xi(t) - \xi(u)\} = 0$ and $\mathbf{E}\{[\xi(t) - \xi(u)]^2\} = \sigma^2|t - u|$ where σ is a positive constant, that is,

$$\mathbf{P}\left\{\frac{\xi(t) - \xi(u)}{\sqrt{\sigma^2(t - u)}} \leq x\right\} = \frac{1}{\sqrt{2\pi}} \int_{-\infty}^{x} e^{-y^2/2}\, dy \tag{6}$$

for $t > u$. The parameter set is usually taken as $[0, \infty)$ and it is supposed that $\mathbf{P}\{\xi(0) = 0\} = 1$. This process was first discussed by L. Bachelier [1], and later more rigorously by N. Wiener [23]. In this case $\Psi(\omega) = -\sigma^2\omega^2/2$.

Almost all sample functions of a separable Brownian motion process are continuous.

The Poisson Process. In this case it is supposed that the increments $\xi(t) - \xi(u)$ have a Poisson distribution with $\mathbf{E}\{\xi(t) - \xi(u)\} = \lambda(t - u)$ where λ is a positive constant, that is,

$$\mathbf{P}\{\xi(t) - \xi(u) = k\} = e^{-\lambda(t-u)} \frac{[\lambda(t - u)]^k}{k!} \tag{7}$$

for $t > u$ and $k = 0, 1, 2, \ldots$. The parameter set is usually taken as $[0, \infty)$ and it is supposed that $\mathbf{P}\{\xi(0) = 0\} = 1$. This process was first discussed by H. Bateman [2, 3]. In this case $\Psi(\omega) = \lambda(e^{i\omega} - 1)$.

Almost all sample functions of a separable Poisson process are non-decreasing step functions which increase only in jumps of unit magnitude.

Now consider a centered separable process $\{\xi(u), 0 \leq u < \infty\}$ with stationary independent increments for which $\mathbf{P}\{\xi(0) = 0\} = 1$ and (1) holds with (2). With probability 1 the process $\{\xi(u); 0 \leq u < \infty\}$ has no fixed points of discontinuity. Let $\nu_a(t)$ denote the number of jumps of magnitude $> a\ (> 0)$ occurring in the interval $(0, t]$. We say that a jump of magnitude $> a$ occurs at u if $\xi(u + 0) - \xi(u - 0) > a$. The process $\{\nu_a(t), 0 \leq t \leq a\}$ is a Poisson process for which

(8) $$\mathbf{E}\{\nu_a(t)\} = t[N(\infty) - N(a + 0)] = -tN(a + 0).$$

Similarly if $\nu_a^*(t)$ denotes the number of jumps of magnitude $\leq a\ (< 0)$ occurring in the interval $(0, t]$, then $\{\nu_a^*(t), 0 \leq t < \infty\}$ is a Poisson process for which

(9) $$\mathbf{E}\{\nu_a^*(t)\} = tM(a + 0).$$

If $\{\xi(u), 0 \leq u < \infty\}$ has stationary independent increments and $\mathbf{P}\{\xi(0) = 0\} = 1$, then

(10) $$\mathbf{E}\{\xi(t)\} = \rho t$$

whenever the expectation exists. Here ρ is a constant (possibly $\pm\infty$).

Many theorems valid for sums of mutually independent and identically distributed random variables can be carried over to stochastic processes with stationary independent increments. Thus we have the following theorems.

The Weak Law of Large Numbers. If ρ is finite, then for any $\epsilon > 0$

(11) $$\lim_{t\to\infty} \mathbf{P}\left\{\left|\frac{\xi(t)}{t} - \rho\right| < \epsilon\right\} = 1,$$

that is $\xi(t)/t$ converges in probability to ρ.

The Strong Law of Large Numbers. If $\{\xi(u), 0 \leq u < \infty\}$ is separable and ρ is finite, then

(12) $$\mathbf{P}\left\{\lim_{t\to\infty} \frac{\xi(t)}{t} = \rho\right\} = 1,$$

that is, $\xi(t)/t$ converges to ρ with probability 1.

For the proof of (12) we refer to J. L. Doob [8], p. 364.

The Central Limit Theorem. If **Var** *$\{\xi(u)\} = \sigma^2 u$ exists and σ^2 is a finite positive number, then*

(13) $$\lim_{t\to\infty} \mathbf{P}\left\{\frac{\xi(t) - \rho t}{\sqrt{\sigma^2 t}} \leq x\right\} = \frac{1}{\sqrt{2\pi}} \int_{-\infty}^{x} e^{-y^2/2}\, dy.$$

If $\{\xi(u), 0 \leq u < \infty\}$ is separable and $\mathbf{E}\{\xi(u)\} = \rho u$ exists, then

(14) $$\mathbf{P}\left\{\sup_{0 \leq u < \infty} \xi(u) = \infty\right\} = \begin{cases} 1 & \text{if } \rho \geq 0 \text{ and } \mathbf{P}\{\xi(u) = 0\} \neq 1 \text{ for } u > 0, \\ 0 & \text{if } \rho < 0 \text{ or } \mathbf{P}\{\xi(u) = 0\} = 1 \text{ for } u \geq 0. \end{cases}$$

REFERENCES

[1] Bachelier, L. "Théorie de la speculation," *Ann. Sci. École Norm. Sup.* (**3**) (1900), 21–86.

[2] Bateman, H. "On the probability distribution of α-particles," *Phil. Mag. Sixth Ser.* **20** (1910), 704–707.

[3] Bateman, H. "Some problems in the theory of probability," *Phil. Mag. Sixth Ser.* **21** (1911), 745–752.

[4] Baxter, G. and J. M. Shapiro, "On bounded infinitely divisible random variables," *Sankhyā, Ser. A.* **22** (1960), 253–260.

[5] Blum, J. R. and M. Rosenblatt, "On the structure of infinitely divisible distributions," *Pacific J. Math.* **9** (1959), 1–7.

[6] Borovkov, A. A. "On the first passage time for one class of processes with independent increments," *Theory of Probability and its Applications* **10** (1965), 331–334.

[7] Chatterjee S. D. and R. P. Pakshirajan, "On the unboundedness of the infinitely divisible laws," *Sankhyā, Ser. A* **17** (1955), 349–350.

[8] Doob, J. L. *Stochastic Processes.* John Wiley, New York, 1953.

[9] de Finetti, B. "Sulle funzioni a incremento aleatorio," *Atti. R. Accad. Naz. Lincei Rend. Cl. Sci. Fis. Mat. Nat., Ser. 6*, **10** (1929), 163–168.

[10] de Finetti, B. "Le funzioni caratteristiche di legge istantanea," *Atti. R. Accad. Naz. Lincei Rend. Cl. Sci. Fis. Mat. Nat., Ser.* 6, **12** (1930), 278–282.

[11] Gendenko, B. V. and A. N. Kolmogorov, *Limit Distributions for Sums of Independent Random Variables*, Addison-Wesley, Cambridge, 1954.

[12] Hartmann, P. and A. Wintner, "On the infinitesimal generators of integral convolutions," *American Journal of Mathematics* **64** (1942), 273–298.

[13] Khintchine, A. Y. "Déduction nouvelle d'une formule de M. Paul Lévy," *Bull. Univ. d'Etat Moscou. Sèr. Internat. Sect. A. Math. et Mécan.* **1** *No.* 1 (1937), 1–5.

[14] Khintchine, A. Y. "Zur Theorie der unbeschränkt teilbaren Verteilungsgesetze," *Rec. Math.* (*Mat. Sbornik*) *N.S.* **2**, **44** (1937) 79–120.

[15] Kingman, J. F. C. "Recurrence properties of processes with stationary independent increments," *J. Austral. Math. Soc.* **4** (1964), 223–228.

[16] Kolmogoroff, A. "Sulla forma generale di un processo stochastico omogeneo, (Un problema di Bruno Finetti), *Atti. R. Accad. Naz. Lincei Rend. Cl. Sci. Fis. Mat. Nat., Ser.* 6, **15** (1932), 805–808.

[17] Kolmogoroff, A. "Ancora sulla forma generale di un processo stochastico omogeneo," *Atti. R. Accad. Naz. Lincei Rend. Cl. Sci. Fis. Mat. Nat., Ser.* 6, **15** (1932), 866–869.

[18] Lévy, P. "Sur les intégrales dont les éléments sont des variables aléatoires indépendantes," *Annali della R. Scuola Normale Superiore di Pisa, Ser.* 2, **3** (1934), 337–366. [Observation sur un précédent memoire de l'auteur, *Ibid* **4** (1935), 217–218.]

[19] Lévy, P. *Théorie de l'Addition des Variables Aléatoires, Monographies des Probabilités*, Gauthier-Villars, Paris, 1937.

[20] Linnik, Yu. V. *Decomposition of Probability Distributions*, Oliver and Boyd, Edinburgh, 1964.

[21] Loève, M. *Probability Theory*, 3rd edition, Van Nostrand, Princeton, New Jersey, 1963.

[22] Skorohod, A. V. *Random Processes with Independent Increments*, (Russian) Izd-vo "Nauka," Moscow, 1964.
[23] Wiener, N. "Differential space," *J. Math. Phys. M.I.T.* **2** (1923), 131–174.
[24] Zolotarev, V. M. "The first passage time of a level and the behavior at infinity for a class of processes with independent increments," *Theory of Probability and its Applications* **9** (1964), 653–662.

4. INTERCHANGEABLE RANDOM VARIABLES

We say that $\xi_1, \xi_2, \ldots, \xi_n$ are interchangeable random variables if all the $n!$ permutations of $(\xi_1, \xi_2, \ldots, \xi_n)$ have the same joint distribution, that is, if

$$(1)\quad \mathbf{P}\{\xi_{i_1} \le x_1, \xi_{i_2} \le x_2, \ldots, \xi_{i_n} \le x_n\} = \mathbf{P}\{\xi_1 \le x_1, \xi_2 \le x_2, \ldots, \xi_n \le x_n\}$$

for all the $n!$ permutations $(i_1, i_2, \ldots, i_n)$ of $(1, 2, \ldots, n)$ and for all $(x_1, x_2, \ldots, x_n)$.

We say that $\xi_1, \xi_2, \ldots, \xi_n, \ldots$ is an infinite sequence of interchangeable random variables, if for all $n = 2, 3, \ldots, \xi_1, \ldots, \xi_n$ are interchangeable random variables.

For an infinite sequence of interchangeable random variables B. de Finetti [5, 6, 7, 8] proved that the concept of interchangeability is equivalent to that of conditional independence with a common distribution.

Theorem 1. *If $(\Omega, \mathscr{A}, \mathbf{P})$ is a probability space and $\xi_n(\omega)$, $n = 1, 2, \ldots,$ is an infinite sequence of interchangeable random variables, then there exists a nontrivial σ-subalgebra $\mathscr{B}$ of $\mathscr{A}$ such that for all $n = 1, 2, \ldots$ and $x_1, x_2, \ldots, x_n$*

$$(2)\quad \mathbf{P}\{\xi_1(\omega) \le x_1, \ldots, \xi_n(\omega) \le x_n \mid \mathscr{B}\} = \prod_{r=1}^{n} \mathbf{P}\{\xi_1(\omega) \le x_r \mid \mathscr{B}\}$$

with probability 1.

For the proof of this theorem we refer to M. Loève [14]. E. B. Dynkin [3] proved that in the above theorem $\mathscr{B}$ can be chosen as the σ-algebra generated by a random variable $\theta(\omega)$. That is we have

$$(3)\quad \mathbf{P}\{\xi_1 \le x_1, \ldots, \xi_n \le x_n \mid \theta\} = \prod_{r=1}^{n} \mathbf{P}\{\xi_1 \le x_r \mid \theta\}$$

with probability 1.

If we use the notation $\mathbf{P}\{\xi_1 \le x_1, \ldots, \xi_n \le x_n\} = F(x_1, x_2, \ldots, x_n)$, $\mathbf{P}\{\xi_1 \le x \mid \theta = y\} = F(x \mid y)$ and $\mathbf{P}\{\theta \le x\} = H(x)$, then by (3) we have

$$(4)\quad F(x_1, x_2, \ldots, x_n) = \int_{-\infty}^{\infty} F(x_1 \mid y) F(x_2 \mid y) \cdots F(x_n \mid y)\, dH(y).$$

Accordingly, an infinite sequence of interchangeable random variables can be represented as a randomized sequence of mutually independent and identically distributed random variables.

Theorem 1 makes it possible to apply the weak law of large numbers, the strong law of large numbers, and the central limit theorem to interchangeable random variables.

The strong law of large numbers for interchangeable random variables is as follows.

Theorem 2. *If* $\mathbf{E}\{|\xi_1|\} < \infty$, *then*

$$\lim_{n\to\infty} \frac{1}{n} \sum_{r=1}^{n} \xi_r = \mathbf{E}\{\xi_1 \mid \mathscr{B}\} \tag{5}$$

with probability 1.

For the proof of this theorem we refer to M. Loève [14].

If $G(x)$ denotes the distribution function of the random variable $\mathbf{E}\{\xi_1 \mid \mathscr{B}\}$, then by (5)

$$\lim_{n\to\infty} \mathbf{P}\left\{\frac{1}{n} \sum_{r=1}^{n} \xi_r \le x\right\} = G(x). \tag{6}$$

Finally, we note that if we consider a finite number of interchangeable random variables $\xi_1, \xi_2, \ldots, \xi_n$, then, in general, their joint distribution function $F(x_1, x_2, \ldots, x_n)$ cannot be represented in the form (4).

REFERENCES

[1] Bühlmann, H. "Le problème limite central pour les variables alèatoires èchangeables," *C. R. Acad. Sci. Paris* **246** (1958), 534–536.

[2] Bühlmann, H. "Austauschbare stochastische Variabeln und ihre Grenzwertsaetze," *University of California Publications in Statistics* **3** (1960), 1–36.

[3] Dynkin, E. B. "Classes of equivalent random variables," (Russian) *Uspehi Mat. Nauk* (8), **54** (1953), 125–134.

[4] de Finetti, B. "Funzione caratteristica di un fenomeno aleatorio," *Atti. R. Accad. Naz. Lincei Rend. Cl. Sci. Fis. Mat. Nat. Ser.* 6, **14** (1931), 251–299.

[5] de Finetti, B. "Classi di numeri aleatori equivalenti," *Atti. R. Accad. Naz. Lincei Rend. Cl. Sci. Fis. Mat. Nat., Ser.* 6, **18** (1933), 107–110.

[6] de Finetti, B. "La legge dei grandi numeri nel casso dei numeri aleatori equivalenti," *Atti. R. Accad. Naz. Lincei Rend. Cl. Sci. Fis. Mat. Nat., Ser.* 6, **18** (1933), 203–207.

[7] de Finetti, B. "Sulla legge di distribuzione dei valori in una successione di numeri aleatori equivalenti," *Atti. R. Acad. Naz. Lincei Rend. Cl. Sci. Fis. Mat. Nat., Ser.* 6, **18** (1933), 279–284.

[8] de Finetti, B. "La prévision: ses lois logiques, ses sources subjectives," *Annales de l'Institut Henri Poincaré* **7** (1937), 1–68.

[9] Fréchet, M. *Les probabilités associées à un système d'événements compatibles et dépendants*, II, Actualités Scientifiques et Industrielles, No. 942, Hermann, Paris, 1943.

[10] Haag, J. "Sur un problème général de probabilités et ses diverses applications," *Proceedings of the International Congress of Mathematicians, Toronto*, 1924, Toronto, 1928, pp. 659–674.

[11] Hewitt, E. and L. J. Savage. "Symmetric measures on Cartesian products," *Trans. Amer. Math. Soc.* **80** (1955), 470–501.

[12] Khintchine, A. Y. "Sur les classes d'événements équivalents," *Mat. Sobrnik* **39** (1932), 40–43.

[13] Khintchine, A. Y. "On the classes of equivalent events," (Russian) *Dokl. Akad. Nauk SSSR* **85** (1952), 713–714.

[14] Loève, M. *Probability Theory*. 3rd edition. D. Van Nostrand, Princeton, New Jersey, 1963.

[15] Teicher, H. "On the mixture of distributions," *Ann. Math. Statist.* **31** (1960) 55–73.

5. STOCHASTIC PROCESSES WITH INTERCHANGEABLE INCREMENTS

A stochastic process $\{\xi(u), 0 \le u \le T\}$ is said to have interchangeable increments if for all $n = 2, 3, \ldots,$ and for all finite $t \in (0, T]$

$$\xi\left(\frac{rt}{n}\right) - \xi\left(\frac{rt - t}{n}\right), \qquad (r = 1, 2, \ldots, n) \tag{1}$$

are interchangeable random variables.

If the expectation of $\xi(u)$ exists, then

$$\mathbf{E}\{\xi(u)\} = \rho u \tag{2}$$

for $0 \le u \le T$, where ρ is a constant (possibly infinite).

H. Bühlmann [1] proved that a stochastic process $\{\xi(u), 0 \le u < \infty\}$ with interchangeable increments can be represented as a stochastic process with conditionally independent and stationary increments.

Theorem 1. *If* $(\Omega, \mathscr{A}, \mathbf{P})$ *is a probability space, and* $\{\xi(u), 0 \le u < \infty\}$ *is a stochastic process with interchangeable increments, then there is a nontrivial σ-subalgebra* $\mathscr{B}$ *of* $\mathscr{A}$ *such that* $\{\xi(u), 0 \le u < \infty\}$ *has stationary independent increments with respect to* $\mathscr{B}$.

This theorem implies the strong law of large numbers for $\{\xi(u), 0 \le u < \infty\}$.

Theorem 2. *If* $\{\xi(u), 0 \le u < \infty\}$ *is separable and* $\mathbf{E}\{|\xi(1)|\} < \infty$, *then*

$$\lim_{t\to\infty} \frac{\xi(t)}{t} = \mathbf{E}\{\xi(1) \mid \mathscr{B}\} \tag{3}$$

with probability 1.

If $G(x)$ denotes the distribution function of the random variable $\mathbf{E}\{\xi(1) \mid \mathscr{B}\}$, then by (3)

$$\lim_{t\to\infty} \mathbf{P}\left\{\frac{\xi(t)}{t} \le x\right\} = G(x). \tag{4}$$

REFERENCES

[1] Blum, J. R., H. Chernoff, M. Rosenblatt, and H. Teicher, "Central limit theorems for interchangeable processes," *Canadian J. Math.* **10** (1958), 222–229.

[2] Bühlmann, H. "Austauschbare stochastische Variabeln und ihre Grenzwertsaetze," *University of California Publications in Statistics* **3** (1960), 1–36.

6. ABELIAN AND TAUBERIAN THEOREMS FOR GENERATING FUNCTIONS

Let $a_0, a_1, \ldots, a_k, \ldots$ be an infinite sequence of complex numbers, z a complex number, and define

$$f(z) = \sum_{k=0}^{\infty} a_k z^k \tag{1}$$

as the generating function of the sequence $\{a_k\}$.

Abelian Theorems.

1. *If $f(z)$ is convergent for $|z| < 1$ and*

$$\lim_{k\to\infty} \frac{a_k}{k^\alpha} = \frac{A}{\Gamma(\alpha + 1)} \tag{2}$$

exists for some $\alpha \geq 0$, then

$$\lim_{z\to 1-0} (1 - z)^{\alpha+1} f(z) = A. \tag{3}$$

If $\alpha = 0$, we get Abel's original theorem. The case $\alpha > 0$ was discovered by P. Appell [2].

2. *If $f(z)$ is convergent for $|z| < 1$ and*

$$a_k \sim \frac{A}{\Gamma(\alpha + 1)} k^\alpha L(k) \tag{4}$$

for $k \to \infty$ where $L(x)$ is such that $\lim_{x\to\infty} L(cx)/L(x) = 1$ for every positive c, then

$$f(z) \sim \frac{A}{(1 - z)^{\alpha+1}} L\left(\frac{1}{1 - z}\right) \tag{5}$$

as $z \to 1 - 0$.

This theorem was found by G. H. Hardy and J. E. Littlewood [4].

Tauberian Theorems.

1. *If $f(z)$ is convergent for $|z| < 1$, if*

$$\lim_{z\to 1-0} (1 - z)^{\alpha+1} f(z) = A \tag{6}$$

exists for some $\alpha \geq 0$, *and if* $k(a_k - a_{k-1}) > -K$, $k = 1, 2, \ldots$, *where* K *is a positive constant, then*

$$\lim_{k\to\infty} \frac{a_k}{k^\alpha} = \frac{A}{\Gamma(\alpha + 1)}. \tag{7}$$

If $\lim_{k\to\infty} k(a_k - a_{k-1}) = 0$, we get Tauber's original theorem. The above theorem was found by G. H. Hardy and J. E. Littlewood [4, 5]. See also J. Karamata [6].

2. *Let* $f(z)$ *be convergent for* $|z| < 1$ *and let*

$$f(z) \sim \frac{A}{(1 - z)^{\alpha+1}} L\left(\frac{1}{1 - z}\right) \tag{8}$$

for $z \to 1 - 0$ *where* $\alpha \geq 0$ *and* $L(x)$ *is such that* $\lim_{x\to\infty} L(cx)/L(x) = 1$ *for every positive* c. *If either* $a_0 \leq a_1 \leq \cdots \leq a_k \leq \cdots$ *or* $\alpha > 0$ *and* $k(a_k - a_{k-1}) > -Kk^\alpha L(k)$ *where* K *is a positive constant, then*

$$a_k \sim \frac{A}{\Gamma(\alpha + 1)} k^\alpha L(k) \tag{9}$$

as $k \to \infty$.

For the proof of this theorem we refer to G. H. Hardy and J. E. Littlewood [5].

REFERENCES

[1] Abel, N. H. "Unterscuhungen über die Reihe $1 + \frac{m}{1}x + \frac{m(m-1)}{1 \cdot 2}x^2 + \cdots$" *Journal für die reine und angewandte Mathematik* **1** (1826), 311–339.

[2] Appell, P. "Sur certaines séries ordonnés par rapport aux puissances d'une variable" *Comptes Rendus Acad. Sci. Paris* **87** (1878), 689–692.

[3] Hardy, G. H. *Divergent Series*, Oxford University Press, Oxford, 1949.

[4] Hardy, G. H. and J. E. Littlewood, "Tauberian theorems concerning power series and Dirichlet's series whose coefficients are positive," *Proc. London Math. Soc. Sec. Ser.* **13** (1914), 174–192.

[5] Hardy, G. H. and J. E. Littlewood, "Notes on the theory of series (XI): On Tauberian theorems," *Proc. London Math. Soc. Sec. Ser.* **30** (1929), 23–37.

[6] Karamata, J. "Über die Hardy-Littlewoodschen Umkehrungen des Abelschen Stetigkeitssatzes," *Math. Zeitschrift* **32** (1930), 319–320.

[7] Kronecker, L. "Quelques remarques sur la détermination des valeurs moyennes," *Comptes Rendus Acad. Sci. Paris* **103** (1886), 980–987.

[8] Littlewood, J. E. "The converse of Abel's theorem," *Proc. London Math. Soc. Sec. Ser.* **9** (1911), 434–448.

[9] Tauber, A. "Ein Satz aus der Theorie der unendlichen Reihen," *Monatschefte für Mathematik und Physik* **8** (1897), 273–277.

7. ABELIAN AND TAUBERIAN THEOREMS FOR LAPLACE-STIELTJES TRANSFORMS

If $\alpha(x)$, $0 \leq x < \infty$, is of bounded variation in every finite interval, then the integral

(1) $$\phi(s) = \int_0^\infty e^{-sx}\, d\alpha(x) = \alpha(0) + \int_{+0}^\infty e^{-sx}\, d\alpha(x)$$

is called the Laplace-Stieltjes transform of $\alpha(x)$.

Abelian Theorems.

1. *If $\phi(s)$ is convergent for* $\operatorname{Re}(s) > 0$ *and*

(2) $$\lim_{x\to\infty} \frac{\alpha(x)}{x^c} = \frac{A}{\Gamma(c+1)}$$

exists for some $c \geq 0$, then

(3) $$\lim_{s\to+0} s^c \phi(s) = A.$$

For the proof of this theorem we refer to D. V. Widder [6], p. 182.

2. *If $\phi(s)$ is convergent for* $\operatorname{Re}(s) > 0$ *and*

(4) $$\alpha(x) \sim \frac{Ax^c}{\Gamma(c+1)} L(x)$$

for $x \to \infty$ where $L(x)$ is such that $\lim_{x\to\infty} \dfrac{L(ax)}{L(x)} = 1$ *for every positive a, then*

(5) $$\phi(s) \sim \frac{A}{s^c} L\left(\frac{1}{s}\right)$$

for $s \to +0$.

See G. H. Hardy and J. E. Littlewood [3].

Tauberian Theorems.

1. *If $\alpha(x)$, $0 \leq x < \infty$, is a nonnegative and nondecreasing function of x, if $\phi(s)$ is convergent for* $\operatorname{Re}(s) > 0$, *and if for some $c \geq 0$*

(6) $$\lim_{s\to+0} s^c \phi(s) = A,$$

then

(7) $$\lim_{x\to\infty} \frac{\alpha(x)}{x^c} = \frac{A}{\Gamma(c+1)}.$$

For the proof of this theorem we refer to D. V. Widder [6], p. 192.

2. *If* $\alpha(x)$, $0 \leq x < \infty$, *is a nonnegative and nondecreasing function of* x, *if* $\phi(s)$ *is convergent for* $\mathrm{Re}(s) > 0$, *and if*

$$\phi(s) \sim \frac{A}{s^c} L\left(\frac{1}{s}\right) \tag{8}$$

as $s \to +0$ *where* $c \geq 0$ *and* $L(x)$ *is such that* $\lim_{x\to\infty} \frac{L(ax)}{L(x)} = 1$ *for every positive* a, *then*

$$\alpha(x) \sim \frac{Ax^c}{\Gamma(c+1)} L(x) \tag{9}$$

as $x \to \infty$.

See G. H. Hardy [2], p. 166.

3. *If* $\alpha(x)$, $0 \leq x < \infty$, *is a nonnegative and nondecreasing function of* x, *if* $\phi(s)$ *is convergent for* $\mathrm{Re}(s) > 1$ *and if there exists a constant* A *such that the difference*

$$\phi(s) - \frac{A}{s-1} \tag{10}$$

approaches a finite limit uniformly in every finite interval of the line $\mathrm{Re}(s) = 1$ *as* $\mathrm{Re}(s) \to 1 + 0$, *then*

$$\lim_{x\to\infty} \frac{\alpha(x)}{e^x} = A. \tag{11}$$

This theorem was found by S. Ikehara [4, 5]. See also N. I. Achieser [1], p. 238.

REFERENCES

[1] Achieser, N. I. *Theory of Approximation*, F. Ungar, New York, 1956.

[2] Hardy, G. H. *Divergent Series*, Oxford University Press, Oxford, 1949.

[3] Hardy, G. H. and J. E. Littlewood, "Notes on the theory of series (XI): On Tauberian theorems," *Proc. London Math. Soc. Sec. Ser.* **30** (1929), 23–37.

[4] Ikehara, S. "An extension of Landau's theorem in the analytical theory of numbers," *J. Math. Phys. M.I.T.* **10** (1930–31), 1–12.

[5] Ikehara, S. "On Tauberian theorems of Hardy and Littlewood and a note on Wintner's paper," *J. Math. Phys. M.I.T.* **10** (1930–31), 75–83.

[6] Widder, D. V. *The Laplace Transform*, Princeton University Press, Princeton, New Jersey, 1946.

[7] Wiener, N. *The Fourier Integral and Certain of its Applications*, Cambridge University Press, 1933.

8. CONTINUITY THEOREMS FOR DISTRIBUTION FUNCTIONS AND FOR THEIR TRANSFORMS

Let ξ_n, $n = 1, 2, \ldots$, be an infinite sequence of real-valued random variables. Let $F_n(x) = \mathbf{P}\{\xi_n \leq x\}$ and $R_n = \{x : F_n(x + \epsilon) - F_n(x - \epsilon) > 0 \text{ for all } \epsilon > 0\}$. Define $R = \limsup_{n\to\infty} R_n$.

Helly-Bray Theorem. Suppose that there exists a distribution function $F(x)$ *such that* $\lim_{n\to\infty} F_n(x) = F(x)$ *for every finite* x *which is a continuity point of* $F(x)$. *If* $g(x)$ *is bounded and continuous on* R, *then*

$$\lim_{n\to\infty} \int_{-\infty}^{\infty} g(x)\, dF_n(x) = \int_{-\infty}^{\infty} g(x)\, dF(x). \tag{1}$$

For the proof we refer to M. Loève [4].

If $\lim_{x\to\infty} g(x) = \lim_{x\to-\infty} g(x) = 0$, then (1) is valid also if $F(x)$ is not necessarily a proper distribution function.

If $R_n \subset \{0, 1, 2, \ldots\}$ and $g(x) = z^x$ where $|z| \leq 1$, then we obtain the continuity theorem for generating functions. If $|z| < 1$, then (1) is valid also for improper $F(x)$.

If $R_n \subset [0, \infty)$ and $g(x) = e^{-sx}$ where $\text{Re}(s) \geq 0$, then we obtain the continuity theorem for Laplace-Stieltjes transforms. If $\text{Re}(s) > 0$, then (1) is valid also for improper $F(x)$.

If $R_n \subset (-\infty, \infty)$ and $g(x) = e^{i\omega x}$ where $-\infty < \omega < \infty$, then we obtain the continuity theorem for characteristic functions.

Now we shall mention some theorems which are the converse of Helly-Bray theorem. We shall consider generating functions, Laplace-Stieltjes transforms, and characteristic functions.

Generating Functions. Suppose that ξ_n, $n = 1, 2, \ldots$, takes on only nonnegative integers and let

$$U_n(z) = \mathbf{E}\{z^{\xi_n}\} \tag{2}$$

for $|z| \leq 1$. If $\lim_{n\to\infty} U_n(z) = U(z)$ for $z \in D$ where $z = 1$ is an accumulation point of the set D, and if $\lim_{z\to 1} U(z) = 1$, then $\lim_{n\to\infty} \mathbf{P}\{\xi_n = k\} = P_k$, $k = 0, 1, 2, \ldots$, is a probability distribution and

$$\sum_{k=0}^{\infty} P_k z^k = U(z) \tag{3}$$

for $|z| \leq 1$. $U(z)$ is uniquely determined for $|z| \leq 1$ by analytical continuation and by continuity. (See W. Feller [2], p. 262.)

Laplace-Stieltjes Transforms. Suppose that ξ_n, $n = 1, 2, \ldots$, takes on only nonnegative real numbers and let

$$\phi_n(s) = \mathbf{E}\{e^{-s\xi_n}\} \tag{4}$$

for $\text{Re}(s) \geq 0$. If $\lim_{n\to\infty} \phi_n(s) = \phi(s)$ for $s \in D$ where $s = 0$ is an accumulation point of the set D, and if $\lim_{s\to 0} \phi(s) = 1$, then there is a distribution function $F(x)$ such that $\lim_{n\to\infty} \mathbf{P}\{\xi_n \leq x\} = F(x)$ for every continuity point of $F(x)$, and

$$\int_0^\infty e^{-sx}\, dF(x) = \phi(s) \tag{5}$$

for $\operatorname{Re}(s) \geq 0$. $\phi(s)$ is uniquely determined for $\operatorname{Re}(s) \geq 0$ by analytical continuation and by continuity. (See Z. Zygmund [5] and W. Feller [3], p. 408.)

Characteristic Functions. Suppose that ξ_n, $n = 1, 2, \ldots$, are real-valued random variables and let

$$\psi_n(\omega) = \mathbf{E}\{e^{i\omega\xi_n}\} \tag{6}$$

for real ω values. If $\lim_{n\to\infty} \psi_n(\omega) = \psi(\omega)$ for all finite ω and $\lim_{\omega\to 0} \psi(\omega) = 1$, then there is a distribution function $F(x)$ such that $\lim_{n\to\infty} \mathbf{P}\{\xi_n \leq x\} = F(x)$ for every continuity point of $F(x)$ and

$$\int_{-\infty}^\infty e^{i\omega x}\, dF(x) = \psi(\omega). \tag{7}$$

(See H. Cramér [1].)

REFERENCES

[1] Cramér, H. *Random Variables and Probability Distributions*, Cambridge Tracts in Mathematics, No. 36, Cambridge University Press, 1937.

[2] Feller, W. *An Introduction to Probability Theory and its Applications*, I, 2nd edition, John Wiley and Sons, New York, 1957.

[3] Feller, W. *An Introduction to Probability Theory and its Applications*, II, John Wiley and Sons, New York, 1966.

[4] Loève, M. *Probability Theory*, 3rd edition, D. Van Nostrand, Princeton, New Jersey, 1963.

[5] Zygmund, A. "A remark on characteristic functions," *Proceedings of the Second Berkeley Symposium on Mathematical Statistics and Probability*, University of California Press, Berkeley and Los Angeles (1951), 369–372.

9. SOME THEOREMS ON FUNCTIONS OF A COMPLEX VARIABLE

Hadamard-Liouville Theorem. If $f(z)$ is regular for all finite values of z and $\lim_{|z|\to\infty} \dfrac{f(z)}{z^k} = 0$, then $f(z)$ is a polynomial of degree $<k$.

See E. C. Titchmarsh [5], p. 85.

Rouché's Theorem. If $f(z)$ and $g(z)$ are regular in a domain D (open connected set) and $|g(z)| < |f(z)|$ on the boundary of D, then $f(z)$ and $f(z) \pm g(z)$ have the same number of zeros in D.
See E. C. Titchmarsh [5], p. 116.

Lagrange's Expansion. Let $g(z)$ be regular in a domain D and let a be a point of D. Let w be such that the inequality

$$|wg(z)| < |z - a| \tag{1}$$

is satisfied on the boundary of D. Then the equation

$$\zeta = a + wg(\zeta), \tag{2}$$

regarded as an equation in ζ, has exactly one root in D. If $f(z)$ is regular in D, then

$$f(\zeta) = f(a) + \sum_{n=1}^{\infty} \frac{w^n}{n!} \frac{d^{n-1}\{f'(a)[g(a)]^n\}}{da^{n-1}}. \tag{3}$$

See E. T. Whittaker and G. N. Watson [7], p. 132.

Bürmann's Theorem. If the first n derivatives of $f(z)$ and the first $n - 1$ derivatives of $g(z)$ exist at $z = 0$ and if $w = u/g(u)$ and $g(0) \neq 0$, then

$$f(u) = f(0) + \sum_{k=1}^{n} \frac{w^k}{k!}\left(\frac{d^{k-1}f'(a)[g(a)]^k}{da^{k-1}}\right)_{a=0} + o(w^n). \tag{4}$$

See E. T. Whittaker and G. N. Watson [7], p. 128.

Faa di Bruno's Formula. If $z = f(y)$ and $y = g(x)$, then the nth derivative of $z = f(g(x))$ with respect to x at $x = 0$ is given by

$$\left(\frac{d^n f(g(x))}{dx^n}\right)_{x=0} = \sum_{r=1}^{n} Y_{n,r}\left(\frac{d^r f(y)}{dy^r}\right)_{y=g(0)} \tag{5}$$

where

$$Y_{n,r} = \sum_{\substack{j_1+j_2+\cdots+j_n=r \\ j_1+2j_2+\cdots+nj_n=n}} \frac{n!}{j_1!j_2!\cdots j_n!}\left(\frac{g^{(1)}(0)}{1!}\right)^{j_1}\left(\frac{g^{(2)}(0)}{2!}\right)^{j_2}\cdots\left(\frac{g^{(n)}(0)}{n!}\right)^{j_n}, \tag{6}$$

provided that the derivatives in question exist.
See Faa di Bruno [1] and Ch. Jordan [3], p. 33.

Finally we mention briefly that the method of Hopf and Wiener for solving the integral equation

$$f(x) = \begin{cases} \int_0^{\infty} k(x - y)f(y)\,dy & \text{if } x > 0, \\ 0 & \text{if } x \leq 0 \end{cases} \tag{7}$$

is discussed by E. C. Titchmarsh [5], pp. 339–342.

REFERENCES

[1] de Bruno, Faà. "Note sur une nouvelle formule de calcul différentiel," *Quarterly Journal of Pure and Applied Mathematics* **1** (1857), 359–360.

[2] Hopf, E. *Mathematical Problems of Radiative Equilibrium*, Cambridge Tracts in Mathematics and Mathematical Physics, No. 31, Cambridge University Prress, 1934.

[3] Jordan, Ch. *Calculus of Finite Differences*, Budapest, 1939, Chelsea, New York, 1947.

[4] Muskhelishvili, N. I. *Singular Integral Equations*, P. Noordhoff, Groningen, Holland, 1953.

[5] Titchmarsh, E. C. *The Theory of Functions*, 2nd edition, Oxford University Press, Oxford, 1939.

[6] Titchmarsh, E. C. *Introduction to the Theory of Fourier Integrals*, 2nd edition, Oxford University Press, Oxford, 1948.

[7] Whittaker, E. T. and G. N. Watson, *A Course of Modern Analysis*, 4th edition, Cambridge University Press, Cambridge, 1927.

[8] Wiener, N. and E. Hopf, "Über eine Klasse singulärer Integralgleichungen," *Sitz. Ber. Preuss. Akad. Wiss., Phys. Math. Klasse, Berlin*, XXXI (1931), 696–706.

[9] Wiener, N. and R. E. A. C. Paley., *Fourier Transforms in the Complex Domain*, *Amer. Math. Soc. Coll. Publ.* **19,** New York (1934).

Solutions

Chapter 1

1. Denote by $N(a, b)$ the number of favorable voting records. The total number of possible voting records is $\binom{a+b}{a}$. Thus $P(a, b) = N(a, b) \Big/ \binom{a+b}{a}$. If $a \leq b\mu$, then evidently $N(a, b) = 0$. If $a > b\mu$, then we have

$$(1) \qquad N(a, b) = N(a-1, b) + N(a, b-1).$$

This equation reflects the fact that the last vote counted may be either a vote for A or a vote for B. Now $N(a, b)$ can be obtained successively by (1) if we start from $N(a, 0) = 1$ for $a \geq 1$. The general solution of (1) which satisfies the condition $N(a, 0) = 1$ for $a \geq 1$ is

$$(2) \qquad N(a, b) = \sum_{j=0}^{b} C_j \binom{a+b-1-j}{b-j}$$

where the constants C_j, $j = 0, 1, 2, \ldots$, are independent of a and b. We have $C_0 = 1$, and C_j, $j = 1, 2, \ldots$, are determined by the requirements

$$(3) \qquad N([b\mu], b) = \sum_{j=0}^{b} C_j \binom{[b\mu]+b-1-j}{b-j} = 0$$

for $b = 1, 2, \ldots$. Here $[b\mu]$ denotes the greatest integer $\leq b\mu$. Thus we get

$$(4) \qquad P(a, b) = \sum_{j=0}^{b} C_j \frac{\binom{a+b-1-j}{b-j}}{\binom{a+b}{a}} = \frac{a}{a+b} \sum_{j=0}^{b} C_j \frac{\binom{b}{j}}{\binom{a+b-1}{j}}$$

if $a > b\mu$ and $P(a, b) = 0$ if $a \leq b\mu$.

If, in particular, μ is a nonnegative integer, then by (3) we get $C_j = -\mu$, $j = 1, 2, \ldots$, and hence by (4)

$$P(a, b) = \frac{a - b\mu}{a+b}$$

for $a \geq b\mu$. This is in agreement with (1) of Section 2.

2. Let us add one more vote for A to the $a + b$ votes. Then the probability that A leads throughout the counting by a majority of more than μ:1 is

$$P(a+1, b) = \frac{a+1-\mu b}{a+1+b}.$$

On the other hand,

$$P(a + 1, b) = \frac{a + 1}{a + 1 + b}\, Q(a, b).$$

For A leads throughout by a majority of more than $\mu:1$, if and only if, the first vote is for A and apart from this vote, throughout the counting his majority is at least $\mu:1$. Comparing the above two formulas, we obtain

$$Q(a, b) = \frac{a + 1 - \mu b}{a + 1}$$

which is in agreement with (2) of Section 2.

3. Suppose that a particle performs a random walk on the x axis. Starting from the origin the particle moves a unit distance to the right if a vote is registered for A and a unit distance to the left if a vote is registered for B. In $a + b$ steps there are $\binom{a+b}{a}$ possible paths. We want to find the number of paths which do not touch the point $x = -c$. The number of paths which consist of a steps in the positive direction and b steps in the negative direction and touch the point $x = -c$ is $\binom{a+b}{a+c}$. This can be seen by using the reflection principle. Consider a voting record for which the corresponding path touches the point $x = -c$. When the path touches $x = -c$ for the first time, let us change all the subsequent votes into their opposites. Thus we obtain a voting record which consists of $b - c$ votes for A and $a + c$ votes for B. Conversely, to each such voting record corresponds a voting record for which the associated path touches $x = -c$. In this way we established a one-to-one correspondence between these two sets of voting records. The number of such voting records is $\binom{a+b}{a+c}$. Thus the probability we seek for is

$$Q_c(a, b) = \frac{\binom{a+b}{a} - \binom{a+b}{a+c}}{\binom{a+b}{a}} = 1 - \frac{\binom{b}{c}}{\binom{a+c}{c}}.$$

If, in particular, $c = 1$, then $Q_1(a, b) = (a + 1 - b)/(a + 1)$ which is in agreement with (2) of Section 2 in the case where $\mu = 1$.

4. Denote by S_0 the set of all voting records which contain a votes for A and b votes for B. The number of these voting records is

$$N(S_0) = \binom{a+b}{a}.$$

In general, $N(S)$ stands for the number of elements of a set S. Let S be the set of all voting records which contain $a - kd$ votes for A and $b + kd$ votes for B where $k = 0, \pm 1, \pm 2, \ldots$. Then

$$N(S) = \sum_k \binom{a+b}{a-kd}.$$

Denote by S^* the set of voting records containing $b - c - kd$ votes for A and $a + c + kd$ votes for B where $k = 0, \pm 1, \pm 2, \ldots$. Then

$$N(S^*) = \sum_k \binom{a+b}{a+c+kd}.$$

The set of all voting records which contain $a + b$ votes can be divided into two disjoint subsets: C contains all the voting records for which $c - d < \beta_r - \alpha_r < c$ holds for $r = 1, 2, \ldots, a + b$, and $\bar{C}$ contains all the voting records for which at least one of the above inequalities does not hold. The probability we seek for is evidently

$$(1) \qquad P = \frac{N(S_0C)}{N(S_0)} = \frac{N(SC)}{N(S_0)} = \frac{N(S) - N(S\bar{C})}{N(S_0)}.$$

Now we shall prove that $N(S\bar{C}) = N(S^*)$. If a voting record belongs to the set $S\bar{C}$, then there is a smallest r $(r = 1, 2, \ldots, a + b)$ for which either $\beta_r - \alpha_r = c$ or $\beta_r - \alpha_r = c - d$. If this smallest subscript is $r = j$, then let us change all the $j + 1$st, $j + 2$nd, $\ldots$, $a + b$th votes into their opposites. Thus we obtain a voting record belonging to S^*. Conversely, if a voting record belongs to S^*, then there is a smallest r such that either $\beta_r - \alpha_r = c$ or $\beta_r - \alpha_r = c - d$. If this smallest subscript is $r = j$, then let us change all the $j + 1$st, $j + 2$nd, $\ldots$, $a + b$th votes into their opposites. Thus we obtain a voting record belonging to $S\bar{C}$. In this way we have established a one-to-one correspondence between the elements of the two sets $S\bar{C}$ and S^*. Hence $N(S\bar{C}) = N(S^*)$ and (1) reduces to

$$(2) \qquad P = \frac{N(S) - N(S^*)}{N(S_0)} = \frac{1}{\binom{a+b}{a}} \sum_k \left[\binom{a+b}{a-kd} - \binom{a+b}{a+c+kd}\right].$$

5. Let $N_r = \nu_1 + \cdots + \nu_r$ for $r = 1, \ldots, n$. We want to prove that

$$(1) \qquad \mathbf{P}\{N_r < r \quad \text{for} \quad r = 1, \ldots, n\} = 1 - \frac{k}{n}$$

if $k = 0, 1, \ldots, n$. If $n = 1$, then (1) is evidently true. Suppose that it is true for $n - 1$. We shall prove that it is true for n. Hence the theorem follows by induction for $n \geq 1$. If $k = n$, then (1) holds. Let $k < n$. By assumption

$$(2) \qquad \mathbf{P}\{N_r < r \quad \text{for} \quad r = 1, \ldots, n-1 \mid N_{n-1} = j\} = 1 - \frac{j}{n-1}$$

if $j = 0, 1, \ldots, n-1$ where the conditional probability is defined up to an equivalence. Thus by the theorem of total probability

$$(3)\qquad \mathbf{P}\{N_r < r \quad \text{for} \quad r = 1, \ldots, n\} = \sum_{j=0}^{n-1}\left(1 - \frac{j}{n-1}\right)\mathbf{P}\{N_{n-1} = j\}$$
$$= 1 - \frac{1}{n-1}\mathbf{E}\{N_{n-1}\}$$
$$= 1 - \frac{1}{(n-1)}\frac{(n-1)k}{n} = 1 - \frac{k}{n}.$$

Here we used that each ν_i $(i = 1, 2, \ldots, n)$ has the same expectation. Since $\nu_1 + \cdots + \nu_n = k$, we have $\mathbf{E}\{\nu_i\} = k/n$ for $i = 1, 2, \ldots, n$.

6. The case $\phi(t) > t$ is trivial. Suppose that $\phi(t) \le t$. If $\psi(u) = \inf\{v - \phi(v)$ for $v \ge u\}$, then $\psi(u)$ is a continuous and nondecreasing function of u and $\psi(t) - \psi(0) = t - \phi(t)$. Since $\phi(u)$ contains only a finite number of jumps in the interval $(0, t)$, the interval $(0, t)$ can be divided into a finite number of disjoint intervals such that in these intervals alternately $\delta(u) = 1$ and $\delta(u) = 0$. If $\delta(u) = 1$ in an interval (α, β), then $\psi(u) = u - \phi(u)$ for $\alpha < u < \beta$. Hence $\phi(u)$ cannot have a jump in (α, β), that is, $\phi(u)$ is constant in (α, β), and consequently $\psi(\beta) - \psi(\alpha) = \beta - \alpha$. If $\delta(u) = 0$ in an interval (α, β), then necessarily $\psi(\beta) - \psi(\alpha) = 0$. Accordingly in the interval $(0, t)$, $\delta(u) = 1$ on a set of measure $\psi(t) - \psi(0) = t - \phi(t)$.

7. (a) We can ask equivalently: If in a ballot candidates A and B both score n votes, what is the probability that throughout the counting the number of votes registered for A is greater than or equal to the number of votes registered for B. If $a = n$, $b = n$ and $\mu = 1$ in (2) of Section 2, then we get $Q = 1/(n+1)$ for the probability in question.

(b) The probability that there never go over the bridge more men than women is $1/(n+1)$, and the probability that no man goes over before his wife is $1/2^n$. Thus the conditional probability we seek for is $(n+1)/2^n$.

(c) Denote by α_r and by β_r the number of games lost and won respectively among the first r games. Then $\alpha_1 + \cdots + \alpha_{3n+2} = n + 1$ and $\beta_1 + \cdots + \beta_{3n+2} = 2n + 1$ and the probability we seek for is $P = \mathbf{P}\{0 \le \beta_r - \alpha_r \le n$ for $r = 1, 2, \ldots, 3n+2\}$. This is given by (2) of Problem 4 if $a = n+1$, $b = 2n+1$, $c = n+1$, $d = n+2$ in it. Accordingly,

$$P = \frac{1}{\binom{3n+2}{n+1}}\left[\binom{3n+2}{n+1} + \binom{3n+2}{2n+3} - \binom{3n+2}{2n+2} - \binom{3n+2}{n}\right]$$
$$= \frac{n}{4n+6}.$$

8. We have

$$\mathbf{P}\{\alpha_1^{(r)} \ge \alpha_2^{(r)} \ge \cdots \ge \alpha_n^{(r)} \text{ for } r = 1, 2, \ldots, a_1 + \cdots + a_n\}$$
$$= \prod_{j=1}^{n-1}\prod_{i=j+1}^{n}\left(\frac{a_j - a_i + i - j}{a_j + i - j}\right).$$

Chapter 2

1. Define the random variables ν_r, $r = 1, 2, \ldots, a + b$, as follows: $\nu_r = 0$ if the rth vote is cast for A and $\nu_r = \mu + 1$ if the rth vote is cast for B. In this case $\nu_1, \nu_2, \ldots, \nu_{a+b}$ are interchangeable random variables taking on non-negative integral values for which $\nu_1 + \nu_2 + \cdots + \nu_{a+b} = b(\mu + 1)$. Set $N_r = \nu_1 + \cdots + \nu_r$, $r = 1, 2, \ldots, a + b$. Since $N_r = \beta_r(\mu + 1)$ and $r = \alpha_r + \beta_r$, the inequality $\mu\beta_r < \alpha_r + c$ holds if and only if $N_r < r + c$. Now by (1) of Section 6

$$P = \mathbf{P}\{N_r < r + c \text{ for } r = 1, \ldots, a + b\}$$

$$= 1 - \sum_{j=1}^{b(\mu+1)-c} \left(\frac{a + c - b\mu}{a + b - j}\right) \mathbf{P}\{N_j = j + c\}$$

and obviously

$$\mathbf{P}\{N_j = s(\mu + 1)\} = \frac{\binom{a}{j - s}\binom{b}{s}}{\binom{a + b}{j}}$$

for $s = 0, 1, \ldots, \min(b, j)$. Thus we get

$$P = 1 - \frac{(a + c - b\mu)}{(a + b)} \sum_{\frac{c+1}{\mu+1} \leq s \leq b} \frac{\binom{a}{s\mu - c}\binom{b}{s}}{\binom{a + b - 1}{s\mu + s - c}}.$$

2. Define ν_r $(r = 1, 2, \ldots)$ as 1 plus the gain of A in the rth game. Then $\nu_1, \nu_2, \ldots, \nu_r, \ldots$ are mutually independent and identically distributed random variables for which $\mathbf{P}\{\nu_r = 0\} = q$ and $\mathbf{P}\{\nu_r = 2\} = p$. By Theorem 2 of Section 7 we have $P_A = Q_b/Q_{a+b}$ where $Q_0 = qQ_1$ and $Q_k = qQ_{k+1} + pQ_{k-1}$ for $k = 1, 2, \ldots$. The solution of these equations is given by

$$Q_k = \frac{Q_0}{q}\left(\frac{1 - (p/q)^k}{1 - p/q}\right) \quad \text{if} \quad p \neq q \quad \text{and} \quad k \geq 1,$$

and

$$Q_k = 2Q_0 k \qquad \text{if} \quad p = q \quad \text{and} \quad k \geq 1.$$

3. Let $N_r = \nu_1 + \cdots + \nu_r$, $r = 1, 2, \ldots$, where $\{\nu_r\}$ is defined as in Problem 2. By (16) of Section 8

$$\mathbf{P}\{\rho(a) = n\} = \frac{a}{n}\mathbf{P}\{N_n = n - a\} = \frac{a}{n}\binom{n}{\frac{1}{2}(n - a)} p^{(n-a)/2} q^{(n+a)/2}$$

if $n = a, a + 2, a + 4, \ldots$. If $p \leq q$, then $\mathbf{P}\{\rho(a) < \infty\} = 1$ and $\mathbf{E}\{\rho(a)\} = a/(1 - 2p)$ for $p < q$; $\mathbf{E}\{\rho(a)\} = \infty$ if $p = q$. If $p > q$, then $\mathbf{P}\{\rho(a) = \infty\} = (q/p)^a$.

4. Define ν_r $(r = 1, 2, \ldots)$ as 1 plus the gain of A in the rth game. Then $\nu_1, \nu_2, \ldots, \nu_r, \ldots$ are mutually independent and identically distributed random variables for which $\mathbf{P}\{\nu_r = j\} = pq^j, j = 0, 1, 2, \ldots$. By Theorem 2 of Section 7 we have $P_A = Q_b/Q_{a+b}$ and by (8) of Section 7

$$\sum_{k=0}^{\infty} Q_k z^k = \frac{Q_0 p}{(1-z)(p-qz)}$$

whence

$$Q_k = Q_0 \sum_{j=0}^{k} \left(\frac{q}{p}\right)^j = \begin{cases} Q_0 \left(\dfrac{1-(q/p)^{k+1}}{1-q/p}\right) & \text{if } p \neq q, \\ Q_0(k+1) & \text{if } p = q. \end{cases}$$

5. Let $N_r = \nu_1 + \cdots + \nu_r$, $r = 1, 2, \ldots$, where $\{\nu_r\}$ is defined as in Problem 4. By (16) of Section 8

$$\mathbf{P}\{\rho(a) = n\} = \frac{a}{n} \mathbf{P}\{N_n = n - a\} = \frac{a}{n} \binom{2n-a-1}{n-a} p^n q^{n-a}$$

if $n = a, a + 1, \ldots$. If $q \leq p$, then $\mathbf{P}\{\rho(a) < \infty\} = 1$ and $\mathbf{E}\{\rho(a)\} = ap/(2p-1)$ for $q < p$; $\mathbf{E}\{\rho(a)\} = \infty$ if $q = p$. If $q > p$, then $\mathbf{P}\{\rho(a) = \infty\} = (p/q)^a$.

6. Now $\gamma = \mathbf{E}\{\nu_r\} = 2p$. If $2p < 1$, then by Theorem 3 of Section 6

$$\mathbf{P}\left\{\sup_{1 \leq r < \infty} (N_r - r) < k\right\} = 1 - (1 - 2p) \sum_{r \geq \max(0, (k+1)/2)} \binom{2r-k}{r} p^r q^{r-k}$$

for all k and by Theorem 4 of Section 6

$$\mathbf{P}\left\{\sup_{1 \leq r < \infty} (N_r - r) < k\right\} = 1 - \left(\frac{p}{q}\right)^k$$

if $k \geq 1$ and $\mathbf{P}\left\{\sup_{1 \leq r < \infty} (N_r - r) < 0\right\} = 1 - 2p$. If $2p \geq 1$, then

$$\mathbf{P}\left\{\sup_{1 \leq r < \infty} (N_r - r) = \infty\right\} = 1.$$

By (6) of Section 8 we have

$$\mathbf{P}\left\{\sup_{1 \leq r < \infty} (r - N_r) < k\right\} = 1 - \sum_{r=0}^{\infty} \frac{k}{k+2r} \binom{k+2r}{r} p^r q^{k+r}$$

for $k > 0$. By (7) of Section 8 we have

$$\mathbf{P}\left\{\sup_{1 \leq r < \infty} (r - N_r) < k\right\} = 1 - \delta^k$$

for $k > 0$ where $\delta = q/p$ if $2p > 1$ and $\delta = 1$ if $2p \leq 1$.

7. In this case the random variables $\nu_1, \nu_2, \ldots, \nu_r, \ldots$ can be represented as in Example 4 of Section 10 provided that $h = 2$. We use similar notation here as in Section 10. By using the results of Problem 6 we obtain

$$\mathbf{P}\left\{\sup_{1 \leq r < \infty} (N_r - r) < k \mid \theta = x\right\} = \begin{cases} 1 - \left(\dfrac{x}{1-x}\right)^k & \text{if } 0 \leq x \leq \frac{1}{2}, \\ 0 & \text{if } \frac{1}{2} \leq x \leq 1, \end{cases}$$

and $k = 1, 2, \ldots,$ and

$$\mathbf{P}\left\{\sup_{1\le r<\infty} (N_r - r) < 0 \mid \theta = x\right\} = \begin{cases} 1 - 2x & \text{if } 0 \le x \le \frac{1}{2}, \\ 0 & \text{if } \frac{1}{2} \le x \le 1. \end{cases}$$

The distribution of θ is given by (15) of Section 10,

$$\mathbf{P}\{\theta \le x\} = \frac{\Gamma(\alpha+\beta)}{\Gamma(\alpha)\Gamma(\beta)} \int_0^x y^{\alpha-1}(1-y)^{\beta-1}\, dy$$

for $0 \le x \le 1$ where $\alpha = a/c$ and $\beta = b/c$. Hence

$$\mathbf{P}\left\{\sup_{1\le r<\infty} (N_r - r) < k\right\} = \frac{\Gamma(\alpha+\beta)}{\Gamma(\alpha)\Gamma(\beta)} \int_0^{1/2} [x^{\alpha-1}(1-x)^{\beta-1} - x^{\alpha+k-1}(1-x)^{\beta-k-1}]\, dx$$

for $k = 1, 2, \ldots$ and

$$\mathbf{P}\left\{\sup_{1\le r<\infty} (N_r - r) < 0\right\} = \frac{\Gamma(\alpha+\beta)}{\Gamma(\alpha)\Gamma(\beta)} \int_0^{1/2} [x^{\alpha-1}(1-x)^{\beta} - x^{\alpha}(1-x)^{\beta-1}]\, dx.$$

By the results of Problem 6 we have

$$\mathbf{P}\left\{\sup_{1\le r<\infty} (r - N_r) < k \mid \theta = x\right\} = \begin{cases} 1 - \left(\dfrac{1-x}{x}\right)^k & \text{if } \frac{1}{2} \le x \le 1, \\ 0 & \text{if } 0 \le x \le \frac{1}{2}, \end{cases}$$

and $k = 1, 2, \ldots.$ Hence unconditionally

$$\mathbf{P}\left\{\sup_{1\le r<\infty} (r - N_r) < k\right\} = \frac{\Gamma(\alpha+\beta)}{\Gamma(\alpha)\Gamma(\beta)} \int_{1/2}^{1} [x^{\alpha-1}(1-x)^{\beta-1} - x^{\alpha-k-1}(1-x)^{\beta+k-1}]\, dx$$

for $k = 1, 2, \ldots.$ By (21) of Section 10 we can also write

$$\mathbf{P}\left\{\sup_{1\le r<\infty} (r - N_r) < k\right\} = 1 - \sum_{r=0}^{\infty} \frac{k}{(k+2r)} \frac{\dbinom{\alpha+r-1}{r}\dbinom{\beta+k+r-1}{k+r}}{\dbinom{\alpha+\beta+k+2r-1}{k+2r}}$$

for $k = 1, 2, \ldots.$

8. By (26) of Section 6 for $a < 1$ we have

$$\sum_{j=-k}^{\infty} e^{-aj} \frac{(aj)^{j+k}}{(j+k)!} = \frac{1}{1-a}$$

if $k < 0$,

$$\sum_{j=1}^{\infty} e^{-aj} \frac{(aj)^j}{j!} = \frac{a}{1-a},$$

and

$$\sum_{j=1}^{\infty} e^{-aj} \frac{(aj)^{j+k}}{(j+k)!} = \frac{1-Q_k}{1-a}$$

if $k \geq 0$ where by (12) of Section 10

$$Q_k = (1 - a)\sum_{j=0}^{k}(-1)^j e^{a(k-j)} \frac{[a(k-j)]^j}{j!}.$$

By (21) of Section 8

$$\sum_{j=k}^{\infty} \frac{k}{j} e^{-aj} \frac{(aj)^{j-k}}{(j-k)!} = \delta^k$$

if $k = 1, 2, \ldots$ where $\delta = 1$ if $a \leq 1$ and δ is the only root of $e^{-a(1-\delta)} = \delta$ in the interval $(0, 1)$ if $a > 1$.

9. Suppose that $n - 1$ random points are distributed independently and uniformly on the interval $(0, 1)$. Denote by ν_r the number of points in the interval $((r-1)/n, r/n)$. Then $\nu_1, \nu_2, \ldots, \nu_n$, are interchangeable random variables taking on nonnegative integers. If $N_r = \nu_1 + \cdots + \nu_r$ for $r = 1, 2, \ldots, n$, then

$$\mathbf{P}\{N_r = j\} = \binom{n-1}{j}\left(\frac{r}{n}\right)^j\left(1 - \frac{r}{n}\right)^{n-1-j}$$

for $r = 1, 2, \ldots, n - 1$ and $\mathbf{P}\{N_n = n - 1\} = 1$. If $k = 1$ in (1) of Section 8, then we get

$$\sum_{j=1}^{n} \frac{1}{j} \mathbf{P}\{N_j = j - 1\} = 1$$

which was to be proved.

10. In this case $\phi(s) = \mathbf{E}\{e^{-s\xi_r}\} = \lambda e^{-\alpha s}/(\lambda - s)$ for $\text{Re}(s) > -\lambda$. If $0 \leq w < 1$, then we can write

$$1 - w\phi(s) = \frac{\lambda - s - \lambda w e^{-\alpha s}}{\lambda - s} = \frac{\Phi^+(s, w)}{\Phi^-(s, w)}$$

for $\text{Re}(s) > -\lambda$ where $\Phi^+(s, w) = [\lambda - s - \lambda w e^{-\alpha s}]/[s - \delta(w)]$ and $\Phi^-(s, w) = (\lambda - s)/(s - \delta(w))$ and $s = \delta(w)$ is the only root of

$$\lambda w e^{-\alpha s} = \lambda - s \tag{1}$$

in the domain $\text{Re}(s) > 0$. If $|\lambda - s| \geq \lambda$ and $\text{Re}(s) \geq 0$, then $|\lambda w e^{-\alpha s}| < \lambda$ and so (1) cannot have a root in this domain. If $|\lambda - s| = \lambda$, then $|\lambda w e^{-\alpha s}| < \lambda$ and by Rouché's theorem it follows that (1) has the same number of roots in $|\lambda - s| < \lambda$ as $\lambda - s = 0$, that is (1) has exactly one root $s = \delta(w)$ in the domain $|\lambda - s| < \lambda$.

$\Phi^+(s, w)$ is a regular function of s and free from zeros in the domain $\text{Re}(s) \geq 0$ and $\Phi^-(s, w)$ is a regular function of s and free from zeros in the domain $\text{Re}(s) \leq 0$.

Let $\Phi_n(s) = \mathbf{E}\{e^{-s\eta_n}\}$ for $\text{Re}(s) \geq 0$. By (20) of Section 11

$$(1 - w)\sum_{n=0}^{\infty} \Phi_n(s) w^n = \frac{\Phi^+(0, w)}{\Phi^+(s, w)} = \left(1 - \frac{s}{\delta(w)}\right)\frac{\lambda(1 - w)}{\lambda - s - \lambda w e^{-\alpha s}},$$

and by Lagrange's expansion we obtain that

$$\frac{1}{\delta(w)} = \frac{1}{\lambda} + \frac{1}{\lambda}\sum_{n=1}^{\infty} \frac{e^{-\lambda\alpha n}w^n}{n} \sum_{j=0}^{n-1} \frac{(j+1)(\lambda\alpha n)^{n-1-j}}{(n-1-j)!}$$

for $|w| < 1$. Accordingly we can easily obtain $\Phi_n(s)$, $n = 1, 2, \ldots$, and by inversion $\mathbf{P}\{\eta_n \le x\}$, $n = 1, 2, \ldots$, can be calculated explicitly.

Chapter 3

1. In this case

$$\mathbf{P}\{\chi(u) = j\} = e^{-\lambda u}\frac{(\lambda u)^j}{j!}$$

for $u \ge 0$ and $j = 0, 1, 2, \ldots$. By Theorem 1 of Section 15

$$\mathbf{P}\left\{\sup_{0\le u\le t}[\chi(u) - u] \le x\right\} = \mathbf{P}\{\chi(t) \le t + x\}$$

$$- \sum_{x<j\le k\le t+x} \left(\frac{t+x-k}{t+x-j}\right) \mathbf{P}\{\chi(j-x) = j\}\mathbf{P}\{\chi(t+x-j) = k-j\}$$

$$= \mathbf{P}\{\chi(t) \le t + x\} - \sum_{x<j\le t+x} \mathbf{P}\{\chi(j-x) = j\}$$

$$\cdot [\mathbf{P}\{\chi(t+x-j) \le t+x-j\} - \lambda\mathbf{P}\{\chi(t+x-j) \le t+x-j-1\}]$$

for all x.

Here we used that

$$j\mathbf{P}\{\chi(u) = j\} = \lambda u\mathbf{P}\{\chi(u) = j-1\}$$

for $j = 1, 2, \ldots$ and $u \ge 0$.

If, in particular, $x = 0$, then by (3) of Section 15

$$\mathbf{P}\left\{\sup_{0\le u\le t}[\chi(u) - u] \le 0\right\} = \sum_{0\le j\le t}\left(1 - \frac{j}{t}\right)\mathbf{P}\{\chi(t) = j\}$$

$$= \mathbf{P}\{\chi(t) \le t\} - \lambda\mathbf{P}\{\chi(t) \le t - 1\}.$$

By Theorem 1 of Section 17

$$\mathbf{P}\left\{\sup_{0\le u\le t}[u - \chi(u)] \le x\right\} = 1 - \sum_{0\le j\le t} \frac{x}{x+j}\mathbf{P}\{\chi(x+j) = j\}.$$

2. In this case $\mathbf{E}\{\chi(u)\} = \lambda u$ for $u \ge 0$, that is, $\rho = \lambda$. By Theorem 1 of Section 14,

$$\mathbf{P}\{\chi(u) \le u \text{ for } 0 \le u < \infty\} = \begin{cases} 1 - \lambda & \text{if } \lambda \le 1, \\ 0 & \text{if } \lambda \ge 1. \end{cases}$$

3. If $x > 0$, then $\mathbf{E}\{\chi(u)/x\} = \lambda\alpha u/x$ for $u \ge 0$. The process $\{\chi(u)/x, 0 \le u < \infty\}$ satisfies the conditions of Theorem 1 of Section 14 and $\rho = \lambda\alpha/x$.

Accordingly if $x > 0$, we have

$$\mathbf{P}\{\chi(u) \le xu \text{ for } 0 \le u < \infty\} = \begin{cases} 1 - \dfrac{\lambda\alpha}{x} & \text{for } \lambda\alpha \le x, \\ 0 & \text{for } \lambda\alpha > x. \end{cases}$$

4. If $\lambda < 1$, then by (37) of Section 15

$$\sum_{j>x} \mathbf{P}\{\chi(j-x) = j\} = \sum_{j>\max(0,x)} e^{-\lambda(j-x)} \frac{[\lambda(j-x)]^j}{j!} = \frac{1 - W(x)}{1 - \lambda}$$

where $W(x) = 0$ for $x < 0$, $W(0) = 1 - \lambda$ and by (20) of Section 19

$$W(x) = (1 - \lambda) \sum_{j=0}^{[x]} (-1)^j e^{\lambda(x-j)} \frac{[\lambda(x-j)]^j}{j!}$$

for $x > 0$.

By (20) of Section 17 for $x > 0$ we have

$$\sum_{j=0}^{\infty} \frac{x}{x+j} \mathbf{P}\{\chi(x+j) = j\} = \sum_{j=0}^{\infty} \frac{x}{x+j} e^{-\lambda(x+j)} \frac{[\lambda(x+j)]^j}{j!} = e^{-\omega x}$$

where $\omega = 0$ if $\lambda \le 1$ and ω is the only positive real root of $\omega = \lambda(1 - e^{-\omega})$ if $\lambda > 1$.

5. If $\lambda\alpha < 1$, then by Problem 4, $F_{\lambda\alpha}(x/\alpha) = 1/(1 - \lambda\alpha)$ for $x > 0$. If $\lambda\alpha > 1$, then there is a λ^* for which $\lambda\alpha^* < 1$ and $e^{-\lambda\alpha}\lambda\alpha = e^{-\lambda^*\alpha}\lambda^*\alpha$. Since

$$e^{-\lambda\alpha x} F_{\lambda\alpha}(x/\alpha) = e^{-\lambda^*\alpha x} F_{\lambda^*\alpha}(x/\alpha)$$

and $F_{\lambda^*\alpha}(x/\alpha) = 1/(1 - \lambda^*\alpha)$ for $x > 0$, we have $F_{\lambda\alpha}(x/\alpha) = e^{(\lambda-\lambda^*)\alpha x}/(1 - \lambda^*\alpha)$ for $x > 0$ and $\lambda\alpha > 1$. The above two cases can be combined into a single formula. We have

$$F_{\lambda\alpha}(x/\alpha) = \frac{e^{\omega\alpha x}}{1 - (\lambda - \omega)\alpha}$$

for $x > 0$ where ω is the smallest nonnegative real root of $\lambda(1 - e^{-\alpha\omega}) = \omega$. If $\lambda\alpha < 1$, then $\omega = 0$, whereas if $\lambda\alpha > 1$, then $\omega > 0$. If $\lambda\alpha = 1$, then $F_{\lambda\alpha}(x/\alpha) = \infty$ for $x > 0$.

6. First we prove Abel's identity for $x > 0$ and $t > x + n$. Suppose that n random points are distributed independently and uniformly on the interval $(0, t)$. Denote by $\chi(u)$, $0 \le u \le t$, the number of points in the interval $(0, u)$. Then $\{\chi(u), 0 \le u \le t\}$ is a stochastic process having nonnegative interchangeable increments for which

$$\mathbf{P}\{\chi(u) = k\} = \binom{n}{k}\left(\frac{u}{t}\right)^k\left(1 - \frac{u}{t}\right)^{n-k}$$

if $k = 0, 1, \ldots, n$ and $0 \le u \le t$ and $\mathbf{P}\{\chi(t) = n\} = 1$. If $0 < x < t - n$, then by (1) of Section 17

$$\sum_{x \le y \le t} \frac{x}{y} \mathbf{P}\{\chi(y) = y - x\} = 1,$$

or equivalently

$$\sum_{0\le k\le t-x} \frac{x}{x+k} \mathbf{P}\{\chi(x+k)=k\}$$
$$= \sum_{k=0}^{n} \frac{x}{x+k} \binom{n}{k} \left(\frac{x+k}{t}\right)^k \left(1-\frac{x+k}{t}\right)^{n-k} = 1.$$

Hence

$$\sum_{k=0}^{n} x \binom{n}{k} (x+k)^{k-1}(t-x-k)^{n-k} = t^n$$

for $0 < x < t - n$. If t is fixed, the left-hand side of this equation is a polynomial of x and constant for $0 < x < t - n$. Consequently it is constant for every x (real or complex). Similarly if x is fixed, the left-hand side is a polynomial of t and equal to t^n for $t > n + x$. Consequently it is equal to t^n for all t (real or complex). Accordingly the above identity holds for all x and t.

7. Suppose that $0 < x < t - n$. Let $\{\nu(u), 0 \le u < \infty\}$ be a Poisson process of unity density. Then

$$\mathbf{P}\{\nu(u) = k\} = e^{-u} \frac{u^k}{k!}$$

for $k = 0, 1, 2, \ldots$ and $u > 0$, and the identity to be proved can be expressed as follows

$$\sum_{k=0}^{n} \mathbf{P}\{\nu(x+k)=k\}\mathbf{P}\{\nu(t-x-k)=n-k\} = \mathbf{P}\{\nu(t)\le n\}.$$

If $0 < x < t - n$, then by (2) of Section 15 we have

$$\mathbf{P}\{\nu(u) \le u - x \text{ for } 0 \le u \le t \text{ and } \nu(t) \le n\} = \mathbf{P}\{\nu(t) \le n\}$$
$$- \sum_{0<k\le l\le n}\sum \left(1 - \frac{l-k}{t-k}\right) \mathbf{P}\{\nu(x+k)=k\}\mathbf{P}\{\nu(t-x-k)=l-k\}.$$

Here the left-hand side is evidently 0 and if we take into consideration that

$$\mathbf{P}\{\nu(t-x-k)=l-k\} = \frac{(t-k)}{(l-k)} \mathbf{P}\{\nu(t-x-k)=l-k-1\}$$

for $l = k+1, k+2, \ldots$, then we obtain

$$\mathbf{P}\{\nu(t)\le n\} = \sum_{k=0}^{n} \mathbf{P}\{\nu(x+k)=k\}[\mathbf{P}\{\nu(t-x-k)\le n-k\}$$
$$- \mathbf{P}\{\nu(t-x-k)\le n-k-1\}]$$

which was to be proved. Since the left-hand side of the identity to be proved is a polynomial in both variables x and t, we can conclude that it is valid for all x and t.

8. In this case

$$\mathbf{P}\{\nu(u) = j\} = e^{-\lambda u}\frac{(\lambda u)^j}{j!}$$

for $j = 0, 1, 2, \ldots$ and $u \geq 0$. By Theorem 1 of Section 15

$$\mathbf{P}\Big\{\sup_{0\leq u\leq t}[\nu(u) - cu] \leq x\Big\} = \mathbf{P}\{\nu(t) \leq ct + x\}$$

$$- \sum_{x<j\leq k\leq ct+x}\sum\left(\frac{ct + x - k}{ct + x - j}\right)\mathbf{P}\left\{\nu\left(\frac{j - x}{c}\right) = j\right\}\mathbf{P}\left\{\nu\left(t - \frac{j - x}{c}\right) = k - j\right\}$$

$$= \mathbf{P}\{\nu(t) \leq ct + x\} - \sum_{x<j\leq ct+x}\mathbf{P}\left\{\nu\left(\frac{j - x}{c}\right) = j\right\}\Bigg[\mathbf{P}\left\{\nu\left(t - \frac{j - x}{c}\right)\right.$$

$$\left.\leq ct + x - j\right\} - \frac{\lambda}{c}\mathbf{P}\left\{\nu\left(t - \frac{j - x}{c}\right) \leq ct + x - j - 1\right\}\Bigg]$$

for all x, and by (3) of Section 15

$$\mathbf{P}\Big\{\sup_{0\leq u\leq t}[\nu(u) - cu] \leq 0\Big\}$$

$$= \sum_{0\leq j\leq ct}\left(1 - \frac{j}{ct}\right)\mathbf{P}\{\nu(t) = j\} = \mathbf{P}\{\nu(t) \leq ct\} - \frac{\lambda}{c}\mathbf{P}\{\nu(t) \leq ct - 1\}.$$

By Theorem 3 of Section 15 we have for $\lambda < c$ that

$$\mathbf{P}\Big\{\sup_{0\leq u<\infty}[\nu(u) - cu] \leq x\Big\} = 1 - \left(1 - \frac{\lambda}{c}\right)\sum_{j>x}\mathbf{P}\left\{\nu\left(\frac{j - x}{c}\right) = j\right\}$$

and $\mathbf{P}\Big\{\sup_{0\leq u<\infty}[\nu(u) - cu] \leq x\Big\} = 0$ if $\lambda \geqq c$.

By Theorem 1 of Section 17 we have

$$\mathbf{P}\Big\{\sup_{0\leq u\leq t}[cu - \nu(u)] \leq x\Big\} = 1 - \sum_{0\leq j\leq ct-x}\frac{cx}{x + j}\mathbf{P}\left\{\nu\left(\frac{x + j}{c}\right) = j\right\}$$

for $x > 0$ and by (6) of Section 17

$$\mathbf{P}\Big\{\sup_{0\leq u<\infty}[cu - \nu(u)] \leq x\Big\} = 1 - \sum_{j=0}^{\infty}\frac{cx}{x + j}\mathbf{P}\left\{\nu\left(\frac{x + j}{c}\right) = j\right\}$$

for $x > 0$, where the right-hand side is 0 if $\lambda \leq c$.

9. If $t < n\alpha$, then $P_n(t) = 0$. Suppose that $t \geq n\alpha$. Denote by $\nu(u), 0 \leq u \leq t$, the number of collisions of an electron with gas molecules in the interval $(0, u)$. Then $\{\nu(u), 0 \leq u \leq t\}$ is a Poisson process of density λ for which

$$\mathbf{P}\{\nu(u) = j\} = e^{-\lambda u}\frac{(\lambda u)^j}{j!}$$

for $j = 0, 1, 2, \ldots$ and $u \geq 0$. Let $\chi(u) = \alpha\nu(u)$ for $0 \leq u \leq t$. The probability that in the interval $(0, t)$ an electron has exactly $n + k$ collisions with gas molecules, and at least n among them lead to ionization is

$$\mathbf{P}\{\chi(u) \leq u + k\alpha \text{ for } 0 \leq u \leq t \text{ and } \chi(t) = (n + k)\alpha\}$$

if $t \geq n\alpha$. By Theorem 1 of Section 15 this probability is equal to

$$\mathbf{P}\{\chi(t) = (n + k)\alpha\} - \sum_{0<y\leq n\alpha} \left(\frac{t - n\alpha}{t - y}\right) \mathbf{P}\{\chi(y) = y + k\alpha, \chi(t) = (n + k)\alpha\}$$

and $\mathbf{P}\{\chi(y) = y + k\alpha\} = 0$ except if $y = j\alpha$ and $j \geq -k$. Thus the above probability reduces to

$$\mathbf{P}\{\nu(t) = n + k\} - \sum_{j=1}^{n} \left(\frac{t - n\alpha}{t - j\alpha}\right) \mathbf{P}\{\nu(j\alpha) = j + k, \nu(t) = n + k\}.$$

If we add these probabilities for $k = 0, 1, 2, \ldots$, then we get

$$P_n(t) = \mathbf{P}\{\nu(t) \geq n\} - \sum_{j=1}^{n} \left(\frac{t - n\alpha}{t - j\alpha}\right) \mathbf{P}\{\nu(j\alpha) \geq j\}\mathbf{P}\{\nu(t - j\alpha) = n - j\}$$

for $t \geq n\alpha$.

10. If we take into consideration that the first event in the underlying Poisson process occurs at time y $(0 < y < \infty)$ and the magnitude of the first jump is z $(0 < z < \infty)$, then we obtain that

$$W(x) = \int_0^\infty \int_0^{x+y} W(x + y - z)e^{-\lambda y}\lambda \, dy \, dH(z).$$

Let

$$\Omega(s) = \int_0^\infty e^{-sx} \, dW(x)$$

and

$$\psi(s) = \int_0^\infty e^{-sx} \, dH(x)$$

for $\text{Re}(s) \geq 0$, and denote by a the expectation of $H(x)$.

If we form the Laplace transform of the integral equation mentioned above, then we get

$$\Omega(s) = \lambda s \int_0^\infty \int_0^\infty \int_0^{u+z} e^{-su-sz-\lambda y+sy} W(u) \, du \, dH(z) \, dy.$$

If $s \neq \lambda$, then

$$\Omega(s) = \frac{\lambda s}{\lambda - s} \int_0^\infty \int_0^\infty [e^{-s(u+z)} - e^{-\lambda(u+z)}] W(u) \, du \, dH(z)$$

$$= \frac{\lambda s}{\lambda - s}\left[\frac{\Omega(s)}{s}\psi(\lambda) - \frac{\Omega(\lambda)}{\lambda}\psi(s)\right],$$

whence

$$\Omega(s) = \frac{s\Omega(\lambda)\psi(\lambda)}{s - \lambda[1 - \psi(s)]}$$

for $\text{Re}(s) > 0$.

If $\lambda a < 1$, then by the strong law of large numbers $\lim_{x \to \infty} W(x) = 1$, or equivalently, $\lim_{s \to +0} \Omega(s) = 1$. This yields that $\Omega(\lambda)\psi(\lambda) = 1 - \lambda a$ and therefore

$$\Omega(s) = \frac{1 - \lambda a}{1 - \lambda \dfrac{[1 - \psi(s)]}{s}}$$

for $\text{Re}(s) > 0$. If $\lambda a \geq 1$, then $W(x) = 0$ for all x. $W(x)$ can be obtained explicitly by inversion. See formulas (13), (14) and (17) in Section 19.

NOTE. If we take into consideration that the probability that exactly one event occurs in the underlying Poisson process in the interval $(0, u)$ is $\lambda u + o(u)$, and the probability that more than one event occurs in $(0, u)$ is $o(u)$, then we can write

$$W(x) = (1 - \lambda u)W(x + u) + \lambda u \int_0^{x+u} W(x + u - y)\, dH(y) + o(u).$$

Hence by the limiting procedure $u \to 0$ we get

$$W'(x) = \lambda W(x) - \lambda \int_0^x W(x - y)\, dH(y)$$

for $x > 0$. If we form the Laplace-transform of this equation, we get

$$s[\Omega(s) - W(0)] = \lambda\Omega(s) - \lambda\Omega(s)\psi(s)$$

for $\text{Re}(s) \geq 0$, whence

$$\Omega(s) = \frac{sW(0)}{s - \lambda[1 - \psi(s)]}$$

for $\text{Re}(s) > 0$. If $\lambda a < 1$, then $\lim_{s \to +0} \Omega(s) = 1$ and this yields that $W(0) = 1 - \lambda a$. If $\lambda \alpha \geq 1$, then $\Omega(s) \equiv 0$.

Chapter 4

1. In this case the arrivals form a Poisson process of density λ. The departures can be characterized in the following way. We consider a Poisson process of density μ which is independent of the arrival process. A departure occurs only when an event occurs in the Poisson process of density μ and there is at least one customer in the system when the event occurs. Accordingly, $\zeta(t)$, the queue size at time t, can be expressed in the following way. Let $\{\nu_1(u), 0 \leqq u < \infty\}$ and $\{\nu_2(u), 0 \leq u < \infty\}$ be independent Poisson processes of densities λ and μ respectively. Let $\xi(u) = \nu_1(u) - \nu_2(u)$ for $u \geq 0$. Then

$$\zeta(t) = \sup\{\zeta(0) + \xi(t) \text{ and } \xi(t) - \xi(u) \text{ for } 0 \leq u \leq t\}.$$

The process $\{\xi(u), 0 \leq u < \infty\}$ is a random walk process considered in Section 22. By (3) of Section 22 we have

$$\mathbf{P}\{\xi(t) = k\} = e^{-(\lambda+\mu)t}\left(\frac{\lambda}{\mu}\right)^{k/2} I_k(2\lambda^{1/2}\mu^{1/2}t)$$

for $k = 0, \pm 1, \pm 2, \ldots$.

If we replace $\xi(t) - \xi(u)$ by $\xi(t-u)$ for $0 \le u \le t$ in the expression of $\zeta(t)$, then we obtain a new random variable

$$\tilde{\zeta}(t) = \sup\{\zeta(0) + \xi(t) \text{ and } \xi(u) \text{ for } 0 \le u \le t\}$$

which has exactly the same distribution as $\zeta(t)$. Thus

$$P_{ik}(t) = \mathbf{P}\left\{\sup_{0\le u\le t} \xi(u) \le k \text{ and } \xi(t) \le k - i\right\}.$$

By (13) of Section 22

$$\mathbf{P}\left\{\sup_{0\le u\le t} \xi(u) \le k \text{ and } \xi(t) = j\right\} = \mathbf{P}\{\xi(t) = j\} - \left(\frac{\lambda}{\mu}\right)^{k+1} \mathbf{P}\{\xi(t) = j - 2k - 2\}$$

for $j \le k$. If we add this probabilities for $j \leqq k - i$, then we get

$$P_{ik}(t) = \mathbf{P}\{\xi(t) \le k - i\} - \left(\frac{\lambda}{\mu}\right)^{k+1} \mathbf{P}\{\xi(t) \le -k - i - 2\}.$$

If $\lambda < \mu$, then

$$\lim_{t\to\infty} P_{ik}(t) = 1 - \left(\frac{\lambda}{\mu}\right)^{k+1}.$$

2. If $\{\xi(u), 0 \le u < \infty\}$ is defined in the same way as in Problem 1, then $\theta(i)$ can be interpreted as the time when $\xi(u) = -i$ for the first time. By (14) of Section 22

$$\mathbf{P}\{\theta(i) \le t\} = 1 - \mathbf{P}\left\{\sup_{0\le u\le t} \xi^*(u) < i\right\}$$

where $\xi^*(u) = -\xi(u)$ for $u \ge 0$. Hence by (9) of Section 22

$$\mathbf{P}\{\theta(i) \le t\} = \mathbf{P}\{\xi(t) \le -i\} + \left(\frac{\mu}{\lambda}\right)^i \mathbf{P}\{\xi(t) > i\}.$$

3. First, we suppose that $\{\xi(u), 0 \le u < \infty\}$ is the random walk process discussed in Section 22, and we shall find the probability $\mathbf{P}\{-b < \xi(u) < a$ for $0 \le u \le t\}$. Then we put

$$p = \frac{1}{2} + \frac{\alpha}{2\sigma\lambda^{1/2}}, \qquad q = \frac{1}{2} - \frac{\alpha}{2\sigma\lambda^{1/2}}$$

$a = [x\lambda^{1/2}/\sigma]$, $b = [y\lambda^{1/2}/\sigma]$ in it and let $\lambda \to \infty$. Thus we obtain $\mathbf{P}\{-y \le \zeta(u) \le x$ for $0 \le u \le t\}$.

By using the solution of Problem 4 of Chapter 1 we obtain

$$\mathbf{P}\{-b < \xi(u) < a \text{ for } 0 \le u \le t \text{ and } \xi(t) = j \mid \nu(t) = n\}$$

$$= \mathbf{P}\{-b < N_r - r < a \text{ for } r = 0, 1, \ldots, n \text{ and } N_n - n = j\}$$

$$= \left[\sum_k \binom{n}{\frac{1}{2}(n-j) - k(a+b)} - \sum_k \binom{n}{\frac{1}{2}(n-j) + a + k(a+b)}\right] p^{(n+j)/2} q^{(n-j)/2}$$

if $-b < j < a$. For $\{N_r - r,\ r = 0, 1, 2, \ldots, n\}$ describes the path of the random walk during the first n steps. If $N_n - n = j$, then each path has probability $p^{(n+j)/2}q^{(n-j)/2}$ and the number of favorable paths is given in the solution of Problem 4 of Chapter 1 if $a = (n - j)/2$, $b = (n + j)/2$, $c = a$ and $d = a + b$ there. Thus

$$\mathbf{P}\{-b < \xi(u) < a \text{ for } 0 \le u \le t \text{ and } \xi(t) = j\}$$
$$= \sum_k \left(\frac{p}{q}\right)^{-k(a+b)} \mathbf{P}\{\xi(t) = j + 2(a + b)k\}$$
$$- \sum_k \left(\frac{p}{q}\right)^{k(a+b)+a} \mathbf{P}\{\xi(t) = j - 2a - 2k(a + b)\}.$$

If we add these probabilities for $-b < j < a$, then we get

$$\mathbf{P}\{-b < \xi(u) < a \text{ for } 0 \le u \le t\}$$
$$= \sum_k \left(\frac{p}{q}\right)^{-k(a+b)} \mathbf{P}\{2(a + b)k - b < \xi(t) < 2(a + b)k + a\}$$
$$- \sum_k \left(\frac{p}{q}\right)^{k(a+b)+a} \mathbf{P}\{-2(a + b)(k + 1) + b < \xi(t) < -2(a + b)k - a\}.$$

If we use the mentioned limiting procedure and take into consideration that

$$\lim_{\lambda\to\infty} \left(\frac{p}{q}\right)^{\sqrt{\lambda}} = e^{2\alpha/\sigma}$$

and

$$\lim_{\lambda\to\infty} \mathbf{P}\left\{\frac{y\sqrt{\lambda}}{\sigma} < \xi(t) < \frac{x\sqrt{\lambda}}{\sigma}\right\} = \Phi\left(\frac{x - \alpha t}{\sigma\sqrt{t}}\right) - \Phi\left(\frac{y - \alpha t}{\sigma\sqrt{t}}\right)$$

where

$$\Phi(x) = \frac{1}{\sqrt{2\pi}} \int_{-\infty}^{x} e^{-u^2/2}\, du,$$

then, finally, we obtain

$$\mathbf{P}\{-y \le \zeta(u) \le x \text{ for } 0 \le u \le t\}$$
$$= \sum_k \exp\left(\frac{-2k\alpha(x + y)}{\sigma^2}\right) \left[\Phi\left(\frac{2k(x + y) + x - \alpha t}{\sigma\sqrt{t}}\right)\right.$$
$$\left. - \Phi\left(\frac{2k(x + y) - y - \alpha t}{\sigma\sqrt{t}}\right)\right]$$
$$- \sum_k \exp\left[\frac{2k\alpha(x + y) + 2\alpha x}{\sigma^2}\right] \left[\Phi\left(\frac{-2k(x + y) - x - \alpha t}{\sigma\sqrt{t}}\right)\right.$$
$$\left. - \Phi\left(\frac{-2(k + 1)(x + y) + y - \alpha t}{\sigma\sqrt{t}}\right)\right].$$

4. For the process $\{\zeta(u), 0 \leq u < \infty\}$, (3) and (4) of Section 23 hold. Now we shall apply the method described in Section 25. In this case (7) of Section 25 has the following form. If $0 < w < \infty$ and $\text{Re}(s) = 0$, then

$$1 - \frac{\Psi(z)}{w} = \frac{w + az - \frac{1}{2}\sigma^2 z^2}{w} = \Psi^+(z, w)\Psi^-(z, w)$$

where

$$\Psi^+(z, w) = z - \frac{a - \sqrt{a^2 + 2w\sigma^2}}{\sigma^2}$$

is regular and free from zeros in the domain $\text{Re}(z) \geq 0$, and $\Psi^-(z, w)$ is regular and free from zeros in the domain $\text{Re}(z) \leq 0$. If $\eta(t) = \sup_{0 \leq u \leq t} \zeta(u)$, then by (9) of Section 25

$$w \int_0^\infty e^{-wt} \mathbf{E}\{e^{-s\eta(t)}\}\, dt = \frac{\Psi^+(0, w)}{\Psi^+(s, w)} = \frac{\sqrt{a^2 + 2w\sigma^2} - a}{\sigma^2 s + \sqrt{a^2 + 2w\sigma^2} - a}.$$

Hence by inversion we get

$$\mathbf{P}\{\eta(t) \leq x\} = 1 - \frac{x}{\sqrt{2\pi}\sigma} \int_0^t \exp\left[-\frac{(x - au)^2}{2\sigma^2 u}\right] \frac{du}{u^{3/2}}$$

for $x \geq 0$.

We note that if $a = 0$, then $\mathbf{P}\{\eta(t) \leq x\} = \mathbf{P}\{\eta(1) \leq x/\sqrt{t}\}$.

5. If we use the following relations for the Bessel function $I_k(t)$:

$$\frac{2kI_k(t)}{t} = I_{k-1}(t) - I_{k+1}(t)$$

and

$$2I_k'(t) = I_{k-1}(t) + I_{k+1}(t),$$

then we obtain that

$$\frac{k}{t}\mathbf{P}\{\xi(t) = k\} = \lambda p \mathbf{P}\{\xi(t) = k - 1\} - \lambda q \mathbf{P}\{\xi(t) = k + 1\}$$

and

$$\frac{d\mathbf{P}\{\xi(t) \leq k\}}{dt} = \lambda q \mathbf{P}\{\xi(t) = k + 1\} - \lambda p \mathbf{P}\{\xi(t) = k\}.$$

The latter relation can also be proved in a probabilistic way by considering that

$$\mathbf{P}\{\xi(t + \Delta t) \leq k\} = \mathbf{P}\{\xi(t) \leq k\} + \mathbf{P}\{\xi(t) = k + 1\}\lambda q\, \Delta t - \mathbf{P}\{\xi(t) = k\}\lambda p\, \Delta t + o(\Delta t).$$

Since $\mathbf{P}\{\xi(t) = k\} = (p/q)^k \mathbf{P}\{\xi(t) = -k\}$, it follows that

$$\frac{d[\mathbf{P}\{\xi(t) < k\} - (p/q)^k \mathbf{P}\{\xi(t) < -k\}]}{dt} = \lambda q \mathbf{P}\{\xi(t) = k\} - \lambda p \mathbf{P}\{\xi(t) = k - 1\}$$
$$- \left(\frac{p}{q}\right)^k \lambda q \mathbf{P}\{\xi(t) = -k\} + \left(\frac{p}{q}\right)^k \lambda p \mathbf{P}\{\xi(t) = -k - 1\} = \lambda q \mathbf{P}\{\xi(t) = k + 1\}$$
$$- \lambda p \mathbf{P}\{\xi(t) = k - 1\} = -\frac{k}{t}\mathbf{P}\{\xi(t) = k\}.$$

If we integrate the last equation from 0 to t, then we get the identity to be proved.

6. By Theorem 5 of Section 24 we have

$$\mathbf{P}\left\{\sup_{0\le u\le\theta(c)} \zeta(u) \le x - c\right\} = \frac{W(x-c)}{W(x)}$$

for $0 < c < x$ and

$$\int_0^\infty e^{-sx} W(x)\, dx = \frac{1}{\Psi(s)}$$

for Re $(s) > \omega$ where

$$\Psi(s) = as - \int_0^\infty \left(1 - e^{-sx} - \frac{sx}{1+x^2}\right)\frac{dx}{x^2} = (a + \gamma - 1)s + s\log s,$$

$\gamma = 0.5772157 \cdots$ is Euler's constant, and $\omega = e^{1-a-\gamma}$ is the largest nonnegative real root of $\Psi(\omega) = 0$. Thus

$$\int_0^\infty e^{-sx} W(x)\, dx = \frac{1}{s\log(s/\omega)}$$

for Re$(s) > \omega$, and by inversion we get

$$W(x) = \frac{1}{\omega}\int_0^\infty \frac{(\omega x)^{u+1}}{\Gamma(u+2)}\, du$$

for $x \ge 0$.

7. Let $\eta(t) = \sup_{0\le u\le t} \zeta(u)$. If Re$(s) \ge 0$ and $0 < w < \infty$, then

$$w\int_0^\infty e^{-wt}\mathbf{E}\{e^{-s\eta(t)}\}\, dt = \exp\left[-\mathbf{A}\left\{\log\left(1 - \frac{\Psi(s)}{w}\right)\right\}\right]$$

where now $\Psi(s) = -|s|$ for Re$(s) = 0$. We can easily see that $\mathbf{P}\{\eta(t) \le x\} = F(x/t)$ for $t > 0$ where the distribution function $F(x)$ has a density function $f(x) = F'(x)$ for $x > 0$. Thus

$$w\int_0^\infty e^{-wt}\mathbf{E}\{e^{-s\eta(t)}\}\, dt = w\int_0^\infty e^{-wt}\int_0^\infty e^{-sx} f\left(\frac{x}{t}\right)\frac{dx}{t}\, dt = w\int_0^\infty \frac{f(x)}{w + sx}\, dx.$$

On the other hand we have

$$\mathbf{A}\left\{\log\left(1 + \frac{|s|}{w}\right)\right\} = \frac{1}{2\pi}\int_{-\infty}^\infty \frac{s}{s^2 + y^2}\log\left(1 + \frac{|y|}{w}\right) dy$$

$$= \frac{1}{\pi}\int_0^\infty \frac{s}{s^2 + y^2}\log\left(1 + \frac{y}{w}\right) dy.$$

If $\sigma = w/s$, then we get the following Stieltjes' integral equation

$$\sigma^{1/2}\int_0^\infty \frac{f(x)}{x + \sigma}\, dx = \exp\left[-\frac{1}{\pi}\int_0^\infty \frac{\log(u + \sigma)}{1 + u^2}\, du\right]$$

whose solution is given by

$$f(x) = \frac{1}{\pi x^{1/2}(1 + x^2)^{3/4}} \exp\left\{-\frac{1}{\pi}\int_0^x \frac{\log v}{1 + v^2}\,dv\right\}$$

for $x > 0$.

8. Since

$$\sup_{0\leq u\leq t+h} \zeta(u) = \max\left\{\sup_{0\leq u\leq h} \zeta(u) \text{ and } \zeta(h) + \sup_{h\leq u\leq t+h} (\zeta(u) - \zeta(h))\right\}$$

we have

$$\mathbf{P}\{\eta(t + h) \leq x\} = \mathbf{P}\{\max(\eta(h) \text{ and } \zeta(h) + \eta^*(t)) \leq x\}$$

where $\eta^*(t)$ has the same distribution as $\eta(t)$ and independent of $\{\zeta(u), 0 \leq u \leq h\}$. If $x > 0$, then it can be proved that

$$\mathbf{P}\{\eta(t + h) \leq x\} = \mathbf{P}\{\max(0 \text{ and } \zeta(h) + \eta^*(t)) \leq x\} + o(h).$$

Hence

$$\mathbf{E}\{e^{-s\eta(t+h)}\} = \mathbf{A}\{e^{h\Psi(s)}\mathbf{E}\{e^{-s\eta(t)}\}\} + o(h).$$

If we subtract $\mathbf{E}\{e^{-s\eta(t)}\}$ from both sides of this equation, if we divide it by h and if we let $h \to 0$, then we obtain

$$\frac{\partial\mathbf{E}\{e^{-s\eta(t)}\}}{\partial t} = \mathbf{A}\{\Psi(s)\mathbf{E}\{e^{-s\eta(t)}\}\}.$$

If

$$\Omega(s, w) = \int_0^\infty e^{-wt}\mathbf{E}\{e^{-s\eta(t)}\}\,dt$$

for $\mathrm{Re}(w) > 0$ and $\mathrm{Re}(s) \geq 0$, then we get

$$w\Omega(s, w) = \mathbf{A}\{\Psi(s)\Omega(s, w)\},$$

and the solution of this equation is given by

$$\Omega(s, w) = \exp(-\mathbf{A}\{\log[w - \Psi(s)]\}).$$

Chapter 5

1. Consider a busy period which starts at the arrival of a customer. Denote by $\chi_1, \chi_2, \ldots, \chi_n, \ldots$ the lengths of the successive service times, and $\nu_1, \nu_2, \ldots, \nu_n, \ldots$ the number of arrivals during the 1st, 2nd, ..., nth, ... service time respectively. Then we have

$$G_n(x) = \mathbf{P}\{\chi_1 + \cdots + \chi_n \leq x, \nu_1 \geq 1, \nu_1 + \nu_2 \geq 2, \ldots, \nu_1 + \cdots + \nu_{n-1} \geq n - 1 \text{ and } \nu_1 + \cdots + \nu_n = n - 1\}.$$

Since $\nu_1, \nu_2, \ldots, \nu_n$ are mutually independent and identically distributed random variables, we can replace $\nu_1, \nu_2, \ldots, \nu_n$ by $\nu_n, \nu_{n-1}, \ldots, \nu_1$ respectively without a change in the probability. Thus we get

$$G_n(x) = \mathbf{P}\{\chi_1 + \cdots + \chi_n \leqq x, \nu_1 < 1, \nu_1 + \nu_2 < 2, \ldots, \nu_1 + \cdots + \nu_{n-1} < n - 1 \text{ and } \nu_1 + \cdots + \nu_n = n - 1\}.$$

Now by Theorem 1 of Section 4

$$\mathbf{P}\{\nu_1 < 1, \nu_1 + \nu_2 < 2, \ldots, \nu_1 + \cdots + \nu_{n-1} < n - 1 \mid \nu_1 + \cdots + \nu_n = n - 1, \chi_1 + \cdots + \chi_n = u\} = 1/n,$$

further

$$\mathbf{P}\{\nu_1 + \cdots + \nu_n = n - 1 \mid \chi_1 + \cdots + \chi_n = u\} = e^{-\lambda u} \frac{(\lambda u)^{n-1}}{(n-1)!}$$

and

$$\mathbf{P}\{\chi_1 + \cdots + \chi_n \leq x\} = H_n(x)$$

where $H_n(x)$ denotes the nth iterated convolution of $H(x)$ with itself. Thus finally

$$G_n(x) = \frac{1}{n} \int_0^x e^{-\lambda u} \frac{(\lambda u)^{n-1}}{(n-1)!} \, dH_n(u)$$

for $n = 1, 2, \ldots$ and $x \geq 0$. The probability that the busy period has length $\leq x$ is given by

$$G(x) = \sum_{n=1}^{\infty} \frac{1}{n} \int_0^x e^{-\lambda u} \frac{(\lambda u)^{n-1}}{(n-1)!} \, dH_n(u).$$

2. Denote by $\chi_1, \chi_2, \ldots, \chi_n$ the lengths of the first n service times and $\nu_1, \nu_2, \ldots, \nu_n$ the number of arrivals during the 1st, 2nd, ... nth service time respectively. If we use Theorem 1 of Section 4, then we obtain that

$$\begin{aligned} G_n^{(i)}(x) &= \mathbf{P}\{\chi_1 + \cdots + \chi_n \leq x, \nu_1 + \cdots + \nu_r > r - i \text{ for } r = i, \ldots, n-1 \\ &\qquad \text{and } \nu_1 + \cdots + \nu_n = n - i\} \\ &= \mathbf{P}\{\chi_1 + \cdots + \chi_n \leq x, \nu_1 + \cdots + \nu_r < r \text{ for } r = 1, \ldots, n - i \\ &\qquad \text{and } \nu_1 + \cdots + \nu_n = n - i\} \\ &= \frac{i}{n} \mathbf{P}\{\nu_1 + \cdots + \nu_n = n - i \text{ and } \chi_1 + \cdots + \chi_n \leq x\} \\ &= \frac{i}{n} \int_0^x e^{-\lambda u} \frac{(\lambda u)^{n-i}}{(n-i)!} \, dH_n(u). \end{aligned}$$

Evidently $G_n^{(1)}(x) = G_n(x)$ found in Problem 1. The probability that the initial busy period has length $\leq x$ is given by

$$G^{(i)}(x) = \sum_{n=i}^{\infty} \frac{i}{n} \int_0^x e^{-\lambda u} \frac{(\lambda u)^{n-i}}{(n-i)!} \, dH_n(u).$$

Evidently $G^{(i)}(x)$ is the ith iterated convolution of $G^{(1)}(x) = G(x)$ with itself.

3. We have

$$G_n(x \mid c) = \frac{\lambda^n c e^{-\lambda c}}{n!} \int_0^{x-c} e^{-\lambda u} (u + c)^{n-1} \, dH_n(u)$$

for $x \geq c$ and $G_n(x \mid c) = 0$ if $x < c$. If $n = 0$, then this is trivially true. Let $n \geq 1$. Denote by $\chi_1, \chi_2, \ldots, \chi_n$ the lengths of the first n services following the initial occupation time of the server. Denote by ν_0 the number of arrivals in the interval $(0, c)$ and by $\nu_1, \nu_2, \ldots, \nu_n$ the number of arrivals during the 1st, 2nd, ..., nth service time following the initial occupation time of the server. Then

$$G_n(x \mid c) = \mathbf{P}\{\chi_1 + \cdots + \chi_n \le x - c, \nu_0 \ge 1, \nu_0 + \nu_1 \ge 2, \ldots, \nu_0 + \cdots + \nu_{n-1} \ge n, \nu_0 + \cdots + \nu_n = n\}.$$

Hence

$$G_n(x \mid c) = \sum_{j=1}^{n} \mathbf{P}\{\nu_0 = j\}\mathbf{P}\{\chi_1 + \cdots + \chi_n \le x - c, \nu_1 + \cdots + \nu_j \ge 1, \ldots, \nu_1 + \cdots + \nu_{n-1} \ge n - j, \nu_1 + \cdots + \nu_n = n - j\}.$$

By Theorem 1 of Section 4

$$\mathbf{P}\{\nu_1 + \cdots + \nu_j \ge 1, \ldots, \nu_1 + \cdots + \nu_{n-1} \ge n - j \mid \nu_1 + \cdots + \nu_n = n - j, \chi_1 + \cdots + \chi_n = u\}$$
$$= \mathbf{P}\{\nu_1 < 1, \nu_1 + \nu_2 < 2, \ldots, \nu_1 + \cdots + \nu_{n-j} < n - j \mid \nu_1 + \cdots + \nu_n = n - j, \chi_1 + \cdots + \chi_n = u\} = \frac{j}{n}$$

for $j = 1, 2, \ldots, n$. Further $\mathbf{P}\{\nu_0 = j\} = e^{-\lambda c}(\lambda c)^j/j!$,

$$\mathbf{P}\{\nu_1 + \cdots + \nu_n = n - j \mid \chi_1 + \cdots + \chi_n = u\} = e^{-\lambda u}\frac{(\lambda u)^{n-j}}{(n-j)!},$$

and

$$\mathbf{P}\{\chi_1 + \cdots + \chi_n \le x\} = H_n(x).$$

Thus for $x \ge c$

$$G_n(x \mid c) = \sum_{j=1}^{n} e^{-\lambda c}\frac{(\lambda c)^j}{j!}\frac{j}{n}\int_0^{x-c} e^{-\lambda u}\frac{(\lambda u)^{n-j}}{(n-j)!}\,dH_n(u)$$
$$= \frac{\lambda c}{n}\int_0^{x-c} e^{-\lambda(u+c)}\frac{[\lambda(u+c)]^{n-1}}{(n-1)!}\,dH_n(u).$$

4. Let

$$a_r = \int_0^\infty x^r\,dH(x)$$

for $r = 1, 2, \ldots$ and $a = a_1$. If $\lambda a \le 1$, then $G(\infty) = 1$ and we can define

$$\Gamma_r = \int_0^\infty x^r\,dG(x)$$

for $r = 0, 1, 2, \ldots$. (Possibly $\Gamma_r = \infty$.) Now by using the solution of Problem 1 we obtain that

$$\Gamma_r = \sum_{n=1}^{\infty}\frac{\lambda^{n-1}}{n!}\int_0^\infty e^{-\lambda x}x^{n-1+r}\,dH_n(x).$$

If $\lambda a < 1$ and $a_{r+1} < \infty$, then $\Gamma_r < \infty$. If $\lambda a = 1$, or $a_{r+1} = \infty$, then $\Gamma_r = \infty$.
Let

$$\psi(s) = \int_0^\infty e^{-sx}\,dH(x).$$

The moments of $G(x)$ can also be obtained in another way. We shall show that if $\mathrm{Re}(s) > 0$, then

$$\gamma(s) = \int_0^\infty e^{-sx}\, dG(x)$$

is the only root in z of the equation

$$z = \psi(s + \lambda - \lambda z)$$

in the domain $|z| < 1$.

If we take into consideration that during the first service in the busy period the number of arrivals may be $j = 0, 1, 2, \ldots$, then we get

$$\begin{aligned}\gamma(s) &= \sum_{j=0}^{\infty} [\gamma(s)]^j \int_0^\infty e^{-(s+\lambda)u} \frac{(\lambda u)^j}{j!}\, dH(u) = \int_0^\infty e^{-[s+\lambda-\lambda\gamma(s)]u}\, dH(u)\\ &= \psi(s + \lambda - \lambda\gamma(s))\end{aligned}$$

for $\mathrm{Re}(s) \geq 0$. If $\mathrm{Re}(s) > 0$, then by Rouché's theorem it follows that $z = \psi(s + \lambda - \lambda z)$ has exactly one root in the domain $|z| < 1$ and therefore this root is the required $\gamma(s)$. If $\lambda a < 1$, then $\gamma(+0) = 1$ and $\Gamma_r = \gamma^{(r)}(+0)$. We can calculate $\gamma^{(r)}(+0)$ easily by using Bürmann's theorem (see Appendix).

Let $u = s + \lambda[1 - \gamma(s)]$. Then $s = u - \lambda[1 - \psi(u)]$. Hence

$$\Gamma_1 = \frac{1}{\lambda}\left[\left(\frac{du}{ds}\right)_{s=0} - 1\right] = \frac{a_1}{1 - \lambda a}$$

if $\lambda a < 1$. Further

$$\begin{aligned}\Gamma_{r+1} = \frac{(-1)^r}{\lambda}\left(\frac{d^{r+1}u}{ds^{r+1}}\right)_{s=0} &= \frac{(-1)^r}{\lambda}\left[\frac{d^r}{du^r}\left(\frac{u}{s}\right)^{r+1}\right]_{u=0}\\ &= \frac{(-1)^r}{\lambda}\left[\frac{d^r}{du^r}\left(\frac{1}{1 - \lambda\dfrac{1 - \psi(u)}{u}}\right)^{r+1}\right]_{u=0}\end{aligned}$$

for $r = 1, 2, \ldots$ and the derivative on the right-hand side can be calculated by using Faa di Bruno's formula (see Appendix).

Thus if $\lambda a < 1$, we get

$$\Gamma_{r+1} = \sum_{\nu=1}^{r} \frac{(r + \nu)!\, \lambda^{\nu-1}}{r!\,(1 - \lambda a)^{r+\nu+1}} Y_{r,\nu}$$

for $r = 1, 2, \ldots$ where

$$Y_{r,\nu} = \sum_{\substack{j_1+j_2+\cdots+j_r=\nu\\ j_1+2j_2+\cdots+rj_r=r}} \frac{r!}{j_1!\, j_2! \cdots j_r!}\left(\frac{a_2}{2!}\right)^{j_1}\left(\frac{a_3}{3!}\right)^{j_2}\cdots\left(\frac{a_{r+1}}{(r + 1)!}\right)^{j_r}.$$

In particular, we have

$$\Gamma_2 = \frac{a_2}{(1 - \lambda a)^3}, \qquad \Gamma_3 = \frac{a_3}{(1 - \lambda a)^4} + \frac{3\lambda a_2^{\,2}}{(1 - \lambda a)^5},$$

and

$$\Gamma_4 = \frac{a_4}{(1 - \lambda a)^5} + \frac{10\lambda a_2 a_3}{(1 - \lambda a)^6} + \frac{15\lambda^2 a_2^{\,3}}{(1 - \lambda a)^7}.$$

NOTE. If we consider the case $H(x) = 1 - e^{-x/a}$ for $x \geq 0$, then $a_r = r!\, a^r$ and

$$Y_{r,\nu} = a^{r+\nu} \sum_{\substack{j_1+j_2+\cdots+j_r=\nu \\ j_1+2j_2+\cdots+rj_r=r}} \frac{r!}{j_1!\,j_2!\cdots j_r!} = \frac{r!}{\nu!}\binom{r-1}{\nu-1} a^{r+\nu}.$$

5. Let

$$a = \int_0^\infty x\, dH(x)$$

and

$$\psi(s) = \int_0^\infty e^{-sx}\, dH(x).$$

If $\lambda a < 1$, then the process $\{\eta(t),\ 0 \leq t < \infty\}$ has a stationary distribution $\mathbf{P}\{\eta(t) \leq x\} = W(x)$ and its Laplace-Stieltjes transform is given by

$$\Omega(s) = \frac{1 - \lambda a}{1 - \lambda \dfrac{1 - \psi(s)}{s}}$$

for $\mathrm{Re}(s) > 0$. (See formulas (25) and (50) of Section 29.) $W(x)$ can be expressed explicitly by (13), (14) and (17) of Section 19. Let

$$W_r = \int_0^\infty x^r\, dW(x)$$

for $r = 0, 1, \ldots$. We have

$$W_r = (-1)^r \left(\frac{d^r \Omega(s)}{ds^r}\right)_{s=+0}$$

and the right-hand side can be calculated by using Faa di Bruno's formula (see Appendix). Thus we get

$$W_r = \sum_{\nu=1}^{r} \frac{\lambda^\nu \nu!}{(1 - \lambda a)^\nu} Y_{r,\nu}$$

for $r = 1, 2, \ldots$ where $Y_{r,\nu}$ is defined in the solution of Problem 4. In particular,

$$W_1 = \frac{\lambda a_2}{2(1 - \lambda a)}, \qquad W_2 = \frac{\lambda a_3}{3(1 - \lambda a)} + \frac{\lambda^2 a_2^2}{2(1 - \lambda a)^2},$$

and

$$W_3 = \frac{\lambda a_4}{4(1 - \lambda a)} + \frac{\lambda^2 a_2 a_3}{(1 - \lambda a)^2} + \frac{3\lambda^3 a_2^3}{4(1 - \lambda a)^3}.$$

6. By Theorem 2 of Section 28 it follows that if $\lambda a < 1$, then the limiting distribution $\lim_{n\to\infty} \mathbf{P}\{\xi_n = k\} = \lim_{n\to\infty} \mathbf{P}\{\zeta_n = k\} = P_k$, $k = 0, 1, 2, \ldots$, exists and is independent of the initial distribution and $\{P_k\}$ is the unique stationary distribution of $\{\xi_n\}$ and $\{\zeta_n\}$. We have

$$P(z) = \sum_{k=0}^{\infty} P_k z^k = \frac{(1 - \lambda a)(1 - z)\psi(\lambda(1 - z))}{\psi(\lambda(1 - z)) - z}$$

for $|z| < 1$ where $\psi(s)$ is the Laplace-Stieltjes transform of $H(x)$. If $\lambda a \geq 1$, then $\lim_{n\to\infty} \mathbf{P}\{\xi_n = k\} = \lim_{n\to\infty} \mathbf{P}\{\zeta_n = k\} = 0$, and $\{\xi_n\}$ and $\{\zeta_n\}$ have no stationary distributions.

Since

$$P(z) = \Omega(\lambda(1 - z))\psi(\lambda(1 - z)) = (1 - \lambda a)(1 - z) + z\Omega(\lambda(1 - z)),$$

where $\Omega(s)$ is given in the solution of Problem 5, we obtain easily that

$$B_1 = \sum_{k=0}^{\infty} kP_k = \lambda(W_1 + a)$$

and

$$B_r = \sum_{k=r}^{\infty} \binom{k}{r} P_k = \frac{\lambda^r W_r}{r!} + \frac{\lambda^{r-1} W_{r-1}}{(r - 1)!}$$

for $r = 2, 3, \ldots$ where $W_1, W_2, \ldots$ are defined in the solution of Problem 5.

7. If a denotes the expectation of the service times and $\lambda a < 1$, then $\{\xi(t), 0 \leq t < \infty\}$ has a stationary distribution $\mathbf{P}\{\xi(t) = k\} = P_k^*$, $k = 0, 1, \ldots,$ and $P_k^* = P_k$ where $\{P_k\}$ is defined in the solution of Problem 6. If $\lambda a \geq 1$, then $\{\xi(t), 0 \leq t < \infty\}$ has no stationary distribution.

Now the state space of the process $\{\xi(t), 0 \leq t < \infty\}$ is $I = \{0, 1, 2, \ldots\}$. If the process is stationary, then the expected number of transitions $k \to k + 1$ occurring in the interval $(0, t)$ is $\lambda P_k^* t$ and the expected number of transitions $k + 1 \to k$ in $(0, t)$ is $\lambda P_k t$ for all $k = 0, 1, 2, \ldots$. Since these expectations are equal for a stationary process, we obtain that $P_k^* = P_k$ for $k = 0, 1, 2, \ldots$.

8. If $\chi(u)$, $0 \leq u < \infty$, denotes the total service times of all those customers who arrive in the interval $(0, u]$, then $\{\chi(u), 0 \leq u < \infty\}$ is a compound Poisson process for which

$$\mathbf{P}\{\chi(u) \leq x\} = \sum_{n=0}^{\infty} e^{-\lambda u} \frac{(\lambda u)^n}{n!} H_n(x)$$

where $H_n(x)$ denotes the nth iterated convolution $H(x)$ with itself. By Theorem 1 of Section 29 we obtain that

$$\mathbf{P}\{\eta(t) \leq x \mid \eta(0) = c\} = \sum_{n=0}^{\infty} e^{-\lambda t} \frac{(\lambda t)^n}{n!} \Bigg[H_n(t + x - c)$$

$$- \sum_{j=1}^{n} \binom{n}{j} \iint_{0 \leq y \leq z \leq t-c} \left(\frac{t - z}{t - y}\right) \left(\frac{y}{t}\right)^j \left(1 - \frac{y}{t}\right)^{n-j} d_y H_j(y + x)\, d_z H_{n-j}(z - y) \Bigg]$$

for all x, $c \geq 0$ and $t > 0$.

9. Denote by η_n the waiting time and χ_n the service time of the nth arriving customer. Let $\mathbf{P}\{\eta_n \leq x\} = W_n(x)$, $\mathbf{P}\{\chi_n \leq x\} = H(x)$, $\mathbf{E}\{e^{-s\eta_n}\} = \Omega_n(s)$ and $\mathbf{E}\{e^{-s\chi_n}\} = \psi(s)$. Denote by ζ_n the queue size immediately after the nth departure.

If the initial queue size is 0, then the queue size immediately after the nth departure is equal to the number of customers joining the queue during the time spent in the system by the nth customer, that is, during a time interval of length $\eta_n + \chi_n$. Accordingly

$$\mathbf{P}\{\zeta_n = j\} = \int_0^\infty e^{-\lambda x} \frac{(\lambda x)^j}{j!} d_x[W_n(x) * H(x)].$$

Hence for $|z| \leq 1$

$$\mathbf{E}\{z^{\zeta_n}\} = \Omega_n(\lambda(1 - z))\psi(\lambda(1 - z)).$$

If $\lambda a < 1$, where a is the expected service time, then $\lim_{n\to\infty} \mathbf{E}\{z^{\zeta_n}\} = P(z)$ exists for $|z| \leq 1$ and $P(z)$ is given in the solution of Problem 6. Accordingly

$$\lim_{n\to\infty} \Omega_n(s) = \Omega(s)$$

exists for $|s - \lambda| \leq \lambda$ and

$$\Omega(s) = \frac{P\left(1 - \dfrac{s}{\lambda}\right)}{\psi(s)} = \frac{1 - \lambda a}{1 - \lambda\left(\dfrac{1 - \psi(s)}{s}\right)}.$$

By using the continuity theorem for Laplace-Stieltjes transforms (see Appendix) we can conclude that if $\lambda a < 1$, then $\lim_{n\to\infty} W_n(x) = W(x)$ exists, $W(x)$ is a distribution function and its Laplace-Stieltjes transform is given by $\Omega(s)$ for $\text{Re}(s) > 0$. If we consider an arbitrary initial state, then we obtain the same result.

If $\lambda a \geq 1$, then $\lim_{n\to\infty} \mathbf{P}\{\eta_n \leq x\} = 0$ for all x.

10. If $\chi(u)$, $0 \leq u \leq T$, denotes the total service time of all those customers who arrive in the time interval $(0, u]$, then $\{\chi(u), 0 \leq u \leq T\}$ is a stochastic process with interchangeable increments. By Theorem 1 of Section 29

$$\mathbf{P}\{\eta(t) \leq x\} = \mathbf{P}\{\chi(t) \leq t + x\} - \iint\limits_{0<y\leq z\leq t} \left(\frac{t - z}{t - y}\right) d_y\, d_z \mathbf{P}\{\chi(y) \leq y + x, \chi(t) \leq z + x\}$$

for all x and $0 < t \leq T$. Now

$$\mathbf{P}\{\chi(u) \leq x\} = \sum_{j=0}^{n} \binom{n}{j} \left(\frac{u}{T}\right)^j \left(1 - \frac{u}{T}\right)^{n-j} H_j(x)$$

for $0 \leq u \leq T$ and

$$\mathbf{P}\{\chi(u) \leq x, \chi(v) \leq y\}$$
$$= \sum\sum_{0\leq j\leq k\leq n} \frac{n!}{j!\,(k - j)!\,(n - k)!} \left(\frac{u}{T}\right)^j \left(\frac{v - u}{T}\right)^{k-j} \left(1 - \frac{v}{T}\right)^{n-k} \int_0^x H_{k-j}(y - z)\, dH_j(z)$$

for $0 \leq u \leq v \leq T$ and $H_j(x)$ denotes the jth iterated convolution of $H(x)$ with itself.

11. If we denote by Q' the queuing process in question, then Q' is the inverse process of Q defined in the Example following Theorem 11 of Section 28. In this case $\zeta_0 = 1$. If ρ_0' denotes the number of customers served in the initial busy period, then by Theorem 10 of Section 28

$$\mathbf{P}\{\rho_0' \le n \mid \zeta_0 = 1\} = 1 - \sum_{j=0}^{n} \left(1 - \frac{j}{n}\right) \mathbf{P}\{N_n = j\}$$

where by (68) of Section 28

$$\mathbf{P}\{N_n = j\} = \int_0^\infty e^{-\mu x} \frac{(\mu x)^j}{j!} \, dF_n(x)$$

and $F_n(x)$ denotes the nth iterated convolution of $F(x)$ with itself.

If we denote by W' the queuing process in question, then W' is the inverse process of W defined in the Example following Theorem 11 of Section 29. In this case $\eta(0) = 0$. If θ_0' denotes the length of the initial busy period, then by Theorem 10 of Section 29

$$\mathbf{P}\{\theta_0' \le t \mid \eta(0) = 0\} = 1 - \int_0^t \left(1 - \frac{y}{t}\right) d_y \mathbf{P}\{\chi(t) \le y\}$$

and by (80) of Section 29

$$\mathbf{P}\{\chi(t) \le y\} = \sum_{n=0}^{\infty} e^{-\mu t} \frac{(\mu t)^n}{n!} F_n(y).$$

Hence

$$\mathbf{P}\{\theta_0' \le t \mid \eta(0) = 0\} = \mu \sum_{n=1}^{\infty} e^{-\mu t} \frac{(\mu t)^n}{n!} \int_0^t [1 - F_n(y)] \, dy.$$

NOTE. The probability that the initial busy period consists of n services and has length $\le t$ is given by

$$\mathbf{P}\{\rho_0' = n, \theta_0' \le t\} = \frac{\mu^n}{(n-1)!} \iint\limits_{\substack{u+v \le t \\ 0 \le u, 0 \le v}} e^{-\mu(u+v)} v(u+v)^{n-2} [1 - F(v)] \, dF_{n-1}(u) \, dv.$$

(See reference [76].)

12. We have

$$\mathbf{P}\{\theta_0' \le x \mid \zeta_0 = i\} = \sum_{n=i+1}^{\infty} e^{-\mu x} \frac{(\mu x)^n}{n!} \sum_{j=1}^{n-i} \binom{n}{i+j} \iint\limits_{\substack{u+v \le x \\ 0 \le u, 0 \le v}} \left(1 - \frac{v}{x-u}\right) \left(\frac{u}{x}\right)^{i+j} \cdot \left(1 - \frac{u}{x}\right)^{n-i-j} dF_j(u) \, dF_{n-i-j}(v)$$

where $F_n(x)$ denotes the nth iterated convolution of $F(x)$ with itself. For a direct proof of this result we refer to Theorem 8 of [88].

$\mathbf{P}\{\theta_0' \le x \mid \zeta_0 = i\}$ can also be obtained by Theorem 10 of Section 29. For $\mathbf{P}\{\theta_0' \le x \mid \zeta_0 = i\} = \mathbf{E}\{\mathbf{P}\{\theta_0' \le x \mid \eta(0)\}\}$ where $\mathbf{P}\{\eta(0) \le x\} = F_i(x)$ and $\mathbf{P}\{\theta_0' \le x \mid \eta(0) = c\}$ is given by (72) of Section 29.

Chapter 6

1. In this case

$$\mathbf{P}\{\chi(t) \leq x\} = \frac{1}{\Gamma(t)} \int_0^{\mu x} e^{-y} y^{t-1}\, dy$$

for $x \geq 0$ and $t > 0$. Further $\mathbf{E}\{\chi(t)\} = t/\mu$, that is, $\rho = 1/\mu$. By (2) of Section 15 we obtain that

$$\mathbf{P}\{\eta(t) \leq x \mid \eta(0) = c\}$$

$$= \mathbf{P}\left\{\sup_{0 \leq u \leq t} [\chi(u) - u] \leq x \text{ and } \chi(t) \leq t + x - c\right\} = \frac{1}{\Gamma(t)} \int_0^{\mu(t+x-c)} e^{-y} y^{t-1}\, dy$$

$$- \mu^t e^{-\mu x} \iint_{0 \leq y \leq z \leq t-c} \left(\frac{t-z}{t-y}\right) \frac{e^{-\mu z}(x+y)^{y-1}(z-y)^{t-y-1}}{\Gamma(y)\Gamma(t-y)}\, dy\, dz$$

for $x \geq 0$ and $0 \leq c \leq t$. By Theorem 3 of Section 15 we have

$$\lim_{t\to\infty} \mathbf{P}\{\eta(t) < x\} = \mathbf{P}\left\{\sup_{0 \leq u < \infty} [\chi(u) - u] \leq x\right\}$$

$$= 1 - (\mu - 1)\, e^{-\mu x} \int_0^{\infty} \frac{e^{-\mu y}[\mu(x+y)]^{y-1}}{\Gamma(y)}\, dy$$

for $x \geq 0$ whenever $\mu > 1$. By Theorem 1 of Section 17

$$\mathbf{P}\{\alpha(t) \leq x - c \mid \eta(0) = c\} = \mathbf{P}\{u - \chi(u) \leq x \text{ for } 0 \leq u \leq t\}$$

$$= 1 - x e^{\mu x} \int_x^t \frac{e^{-\mu y} \mu^y (y - x)^{y-1}}{\Gamma(y+1)}\, dy$$

for $0 \leq c \leq x < t$. Since $\mathbf{E}\{\chi(t)\} = t/\mu$ and $\mathbf{Var}\,\{\chi(t)\} = t/\mu^2$ by Theorem 4 of Section 29 we obtain that

$$\lim_{t\to\infty} \mathbf{P}\left\{\frac{\alpha(t) - \dfrac{(\mu-1)t}{\mu}}{\sqrt{t/\mu}} \leq x\right\} = \frac{1}{\sqrt{2\pi}} \int_{-\infty}^{x} e^{-u^2/2}\, du$$

whenever $\mu > 1$ and by Theorem 3 of Section 17

$$\lim_{t\to\infty} \mathbf{P}\{\alpha(t) \leq x - c \mid \eta(0) = c\} = 1 - e^{-\omega x}$$

for $0 \leq c \leq x$ where ω is the largest real root of the equation $\mu e^{\omega} = \mu + \omega$. If $\mu < 1$, then $\omega > 0$, whereas if $\mu \geq 1$, then $\omega = 0$. We have

$$\omega = \mu\left(\sum_{j=1}^{\infty} e^{-\mu j} \frac{(\mu j)^{j-1}}{j!} - 1\right)$$

which can be obtained by Lagrange's expansion. (See Appendix.)

2. In this case

$$\mathbf{P}\{\chi^*(t) \le x\} = \frac{1}{\Gamma(x)} \int_{\mu t}^{\infty} e^{-y} y^{x-1}\, dy$$

for $x \ge 0$, $\mathbf{E}\{\chi^*(t)\} = \mu t$ and $\mathbf{Var}\,\{\chi^*(t)\} = \mu t$.
By (77) of Section 29 we have

$$\mathbf{P}\{\theta_0^* \le t + c \mid \eta(0) = c\} = 1 - \mathbf{P}\{\eta(t) \le c \mid \eta(0) = 0\}$$

where the right-hand side is given in the solution of Problem 1.
By (65) of Section 29 we have

$$\mathbf{P}\{\beta^*(t) \le x + c \mid \eta(0) = c\} = \mathbf{P}\{\eta(x) \le t - x \mid \eta(0) = 0\}$$

where the right-hand side is given in the solution of Problem 1.
If $\mu > 1$ and $0 \le c$, $0 \le t$, then

$$\lim_{t\to\infty} \mathbf{P}\{\theta_0^* \le t + c \mid \eta(0) = c\} = 1 - \lim_{t\to\infty} \mathbf{P}\{\eta(t) \le c\}$$

and the right-hand side is given in the solution of Problem 1.
If $\mu < 1$, then by (66) of Section 29

$$\lim_{t\to\infty} \mathbf{P}\left\{\frac{\beta^*(t) - \mu t}{\sqrt{\mu t}} \le x\right\} = \frac{1}{\sqrt{2\pi}} \int_{-\infty}^{x} e^{-u^2/2}\, du.$$

3. If $\{\eta(t), 0 \le t < \infty\}$ is a stationary process, then by Theorem 4 of Section 33 we have

$$\mathbf{P}\{\eta(t) \le x\} = \frac{W(x)}{W(m)}$$

for $0 \le x \le m$ where $W(x)$, $0 \le x < \infty$, is defined by

$$\Omega(s) = \int_0^{\infty} e^{-sx}\, dW(x) = \frac{W(0)s}{s - \Phi(s)}$$

for $\mathrm{Re}(s) > \omega$ and ω is the largest real root of $\Phi(s) = s$.
In this case

$$\Phi(s) = \frac{1}{\sqrt{4\pi}} \int_0^{\infty} (1 - e^{-sx}) e^{-\mu y} \frac{dy}{y^{3/2}} = (s + \mu)^{1/2} - \mu^{1/2},$$

$\rho = \Phi'(+0) = 1/2\sqrt{\mu}$ and $\omega = 0$ if $\mu \ge \frac{1}{4}$ and $\omega = 1 - 2\sqrt{\mu}$ if $\mu < \frac{1}{4}$. Further we have

$$\frac{\partial \mathbf{P}\{\chi(t) \le x\}}{\partial x} = \frac{t}{\sqrt{4\pi x^3}} \exp\left[-\frac{\mu}{x}\left(x - \frac{t}{2\sqrt{\mu}}\right)^2\right]$$

for $x > 0$.

By (54) of Section 19 we obtain that

$$W(x) = W(0)\left\{\frac{e^{\omega x}}{1-\Phi'(\omega)} - \frac{e^{-\mu x}}{\sqrt{4\pi}} \int_{\max(0,-x)}^{\infty} \exp\left[(\sqrt{\mu}-\mu)y - \frac{y^2}{4(x+y)}\right]\frac{dy}{(x+y)^{3/2}}\right\}$$

if $\mu \neq \frac{1}{4}$ and here $\Phi'(\omega) = 1/2(\omega + \sqrt{\mu})$.

If $\mu = \frac{1}{4}$, then $W(x)$ can be obtained in the following way. Now

$$\frac{dH^*(x)}{dx} = \sqrt{\frac{\mu}{\pi}} \int_x^\infty e^{-\mu y} \frac{dy}{y^{3/2}}$$

for $x > 0$ and

$$\psi^*(s) = \int_0^\infty e^{-sx}\, dH^*(x) = \frac{\Phi(s)}{\rho s} = \frac{2[\sqrt{\mu^2+\mu s} - \mu]}{s}$$

for $\mathrm{Re}(s) \geq 0$. If $\rho = 1$, that is, $\mu = \frac{1}{4}$, then

$$\Omega(s) = \frac{W(0)}{1-\psi^*(s)} = W(0)\left[1 + \frac{1}{s} + \psi^*(s)\right],$$

whence by inversion we get

$$W(x) = W(0)[1 + x + H^*(x)].$$

NOTE. We can write also that

$$\Omega(s) = \frac{W(0)s}{s + \mu^{1/2} - (s+\mu)^{1/2}} = W(0)\left\{\frac{s + 2\mu^{1/2}}{s + 2\mu^{1/2} - 1} + \frac{s/2\mu^{1/2}}{s + 2\mu^{1/2} - 1}\psi^*(s)\right\}$$

whence by inversion

$$W(x) = W(0)\left\{\frac{1 - \rho e^{-(1-\rho)x/\rho}}{1-\rho} + \rho\int_0^x e^{-(1-\rho)(x-y)/\rho}\, dH^*(y)\right\}$$

if $\rho < 1$, and

$$W(x) = W(0)\left\{\frac{\rho e^{(\rho-1)x/\rho} - 1}{\rho - 1} + \rho\int_0^x e^{(\rho-1)(x-y)/\rho}\, dH^*(y)\right\}$$

if $\rho > 1$.

4. For a stationary process $\{\eta(t), 0 \leq t < \infty\}$ by Theorem 4 of Section 33 we have

$$\mathbf{P}\{\eta(t) \leq x\} = \frac{W(x)}{W(m)}$$

for $0 \leq x \leq m$, and $W(x)$, $0 \leq x < \infty$, is defined by

$$\Omega(s) = \int_0^\infty e^{-sx}\, dW(x) = \frac{W(0)s}{s - \Phi(s)}$$

for $\mathrm{Re}(s) > \omega$ where ω is the largest real root of $\Phi(s) = s$.

In this case

$$\Phi(s) = \int_0^\infty (1 - e^{-sx})e^{-\mu x}\,\frac{dx}{x} = \log\left(1 + \frac{s}{\mu}\right),$$

and

$$\mathbf{P}\{\chi(t) \le x\} = \frac{1}{\Gamma(t)}\int_0^{\mu x} e^{-y}y^{t-1}\,dy$$

for $x \ge 0$ and $t > 0$. Further $\lambda = \Phi(\infty) = \infty$, and $\rho = \Phi'(+0) = 1/\mu$. If $\rho \le 1$, then $\omega = 0$. If $\rho > 1$, then ω is the largest nonnegative real root of $\mu e^{\omega} = \mu + \omega$. We have $\Phi'(\omega) = 1/(\mu + \omega)$.

If $\rho \ne 1$, then by (62) of Section 19

$$W(x) = W(0)\left\{\frac{e^{\omega x}}{1 - \Phi'(\omega)} - e^{-\mu x}\int_{\max(0,-x)}^{\infty} \frac{(e^{-\mu}\mu)^y(x + y)^{y-1}}{\Gamma(y)}\,dy\right\}.$$

$W(x)$ can also be obtained in the following way. Now

$$H^*(x) = \mu\int_0^x\left(\int_{\mu u}^\infty \frac{e^{-y}}{y}\,dy\right)du = \frac{1 - e^{-\mu x}}{\mu} + x\int_{\mu x}^\infty \frac{e^{-y}}{y}\,dy$$

and by (61) of Section 19

$$W(x) = W(0)\sum_{n=0}^\infty \left(\frac{1}{\mu}\right)^n H_n^*(x)$$

where $H_n^*(x)$ denotes the nth iterated convolution of $H^*(x)$ with itself.

5. If $\{\eta(t), 0 \le t < \infty\}$ is a stationary process, then by Theorem 4 of Section 33 we have

$$\mathbf{P}\{\eta(t) \le x\} = \frac{W(x)}{W(m)}$$

for $0 \le x \le m$ and $W(x)$, $0 \le x < \infty$, is defined by

$$\Omega(s) = \int_0^\infty e^{-sx}\,dW(x) = \frac{W(0)s}{s - \Phi(s)}$$

for $\mathrm{Re}(s) > \omega$ where ω is the largest nonnegative real root of $\Phi(s) = s$.

In this case

$$\Phi(s) = \frac{1}{\sqrt{4\pi}}\int_0^\infty (1 - e^{-sx})\,\frac{dx}{x^{3/2}} = s^{1/2}$$

and

$$\frac{\partial \mathbf{P}\{\chi(t) \le x\}}{\partial x} = \frac{t}{\sqrt{4\pi x^3}}\,e^{-t^2/4x}$$

for $x > 0$. Further, $\lambda = \Phi(\infty) = \infty$, $\rho = \Phi'(+0) = \infty$, $\omega = 1$, $\Phi'(\omega) = \frac{1}{2}$.

Now by (46) of Section 19

$$W(x) = W(0) \sum_{n=0}^{\infty} \frac{x^{n/2}}{\Gamma(\frac{1}{2}n + 1)}$$

for $x \geq 0$, or by (49) of Section 19

$$W(x) = W(0)\left[2e^{x} - \frac{1}{\sqrt{4\pi}} \int_{\max(0,-x)}^{\infty} e^{-y^2/4(x+y)} \frac{dy}{(x + y)^{3/2}}\right]$$

for all x.

6. If $\{\eta(t), 0 \leq t < \infty\}$ is a stationary process, then by Theorem 5 of Section 33 we have

$$\mathbf{P}\{\eta(t) \leq x\} = \frac{W(x)}{W(m)}$$

for $0 \leq x \leq m$ and $W(x)$, $0 \leq x < \infty$, is defined by

$$\int_0^{\infty} e^{-sx}\, W(x)\, dx = \frac{C}{\Psi(s)}$$

for $\text{Re}(s) > \omega$ where ω is the largest nonnegative real root of $\Psi(s) = 0$ and C is a non-null constant. In this case

$$\Psi(s) = -as + \tfrac{1}{2}\, \sigma^2 s^2$$

and $\omega = 0$ if $a \leq 0$ and $\omega = 2a/\sigma^2$ if $a \geq 0$. Hence

$$\int_0^{\infty} e^{-sx}\, W(x)\, dx = \frac{2C}{\sigma^2 s^2 - 2as} = \frac{C}{a}\left[\frac{\sigma^2}{\sigma^2 s - 2a} - \frac{1}{s}\right]$$

for $\text{Re}(s) > \omega$ and by inversion

$$W(x) = \frac{C}{a}\,(e^{2ax/\sigma^2} - 1)$$

if $a \neq 0$ and $W(x) = 2Cx/\sigma^2$ if $a = 0$.

7. If $\{\eta(t), 0 \leq t < \infty\}$ is a stationary process, then by Theorem 5 of Section 33

$$\mathbf{P}\{\eta(t) \leq x\} = \frac{W(x)}{W(m)}$$

for $0 \leq x \leq m$ and

$$\int_0^{\infty} e^{-sx}\, W(x)\, dx = \frac{C}{\Psi(s)} = \frac{C}{s \log (s/\omega)}$$

for $\text{Re}(s) > \omega$ where C is a non-null constant, $\omega = e^{1-a-\gamma}$ and $\gamma = 0.5772157\ldots$ is Euler's constant. By inversion we get

$$W(x) = \frac{C}{\omega} \int_0^{\infty} \frac{(\omega x)^{u+1}}{\Gamma(u + 2)}\, du.$$

Chapter 7

1. By (21) of Section 35 we have

$$\int_0^\infty e^{-wt}\,\Omega(t,s)\,dt = \frac{1}{w-s+\lambda[1-\psi(s)]}\left(1-\frac{s}{\omega(w)}\right)$$

for $\mathrm{Re}(s) \geq 0$ and $\mathrm{Re}(w) > 0$ where now $\psi(s) = \mu/(\mu+s)$ and $s = \omega(w)$ is the only root of $\lambda[1-\psi(s)] = s - w$ in the domain $\mathrm{Re}(s) \geq 0$. We have

$$\omega(w) = \frac{\lambda + w - \mu + \sqrt{(\lambda+w+\mu)^2 - 4\lambda\mu}}{2}$$

and thus

$$\int_0^\infty e^{-wt}\Omega(t,s)\,dt = \frac{2(\mu+s)}{2w\mu + s(\lambda+w-\mu) + s\sqrt{(\lambda+w+\mu)^2-4\lambda\mu}}$$

for $\mathrm{Re}\,(s) \geq 0$ and $\mathrm{Re}\,(w) > 0$.

2. Let $\phi_0(z) \equiv 1$ and

(1) $$\phi_k(z) = \sum_{j_1+j_2+\cdots=k} z^{j_1}\frac{j_1^{j_2} j_2^{j_3}\cdots}{j_1!\,j_2!\cdots}$$

for $k = 1, 2, \ldots$ where $j_1, j_2, \ldots$ are positive integers. It can easily be seen that

(2) $$\phi_k(z) = \sum_{j=1}^{k} \frac{z^j}{j!}\,\phi_{k-j}(j)$$

for $k = 1, 2, \ldots$. Now we shall prove by mathematical induction that

(3) $$\phi_k(z) = \frac{(k+z)^{k-1}z}{k!}.$$

This is true for $k = 1$. If we suppose that this is true for $k = 1, 2, \ldots, n-1$, then by using the above recurrence formula we can see immediately that it is true for $k = n$. Consequently (3) is valid for all $k = 1, 2, \ldots$.

3. By (39) of Section 35 we have

$$\mathbf{E}\{e^{-z\theta_x}\} = e^{-x\omega(z)}$$

for $\mathrm{Re}(z) > 0$ where $s = \omega(z)$ is the only root of the equation

$$s = z + \lambda[1-\psi(s)]$$

in the domain $\mathrm{Re}(s) \geq 0$. If $\rho = \lambda a \leq 1$, then $\mathbf{P}\{\theta_x < \infty\} = \omega(+0) = 1$ and $\mathbf{E}\{\theta_x\} = x\omega'(+0) = x/(1-\rho)$ for $\rho < 1$ and $\mathbf{E}\{\theta_x\} = x\omega'(+0) = \infty$ for $\rho = 1$. If $\rho < 1$, then $\mathbf{Var}\,\{\theta_x\} = -x\omega''(+0) = \sigma^2 x/(1-\rho)^3$ where $\sigma^2 = \lambda(a^2 + \sigma_a{}^2)$. Since $\{\theta_x, 0 \leq x < \infty\}$ is a stochastic process with stationary independent increments, we can conclude that if $\rho < 1$ and $\sigma^2 < \infty$, then

$$\lim_{x\to\infty}\mathbf{P}\left\{\frac{\theta_x - \mathbf{E}\{\theta_x\}}{\sqrt{\mathbf{Var}\,\{\theta_x\}}} \leq z\right\} = \frac{1}{\sqrt{2\pi}}\int_{-\infty}^{z} e^{-y^2/2}\,dy.$$

4. Now
$$W(t, x) = \mathbf{P}\{\tilde{\chi}(u) \leq cu + x \text{ for } 0 \leq u \leq t\}.$$

If we take into consideration that in the underlying Poisson process in the interval $(0, \Delta t)$ one event occurs with probability $\lambda\Delta t + o(\Delta t)$, and more than one event occurs with probability $o(\Delta t)$, then we can write

$$W(t + \Delta t, x) = (1 - \lambda\Delta t)\, W(t, x + c\Delta t) + \lambda\Delta t \int_{-\infty}^{x+c\Delta t} W(t, x - y + c\Delta t)\, dH(y) + o(\Delta t).$$

If we subtract $W(t, x)$ from both sides of this equation, if we divide both sides by Δt and if we let $\Delta t \to 0$, then we obtain that

$$\frac{\partial W(t,x)}{\partial t} = c\,\frac{\partial W(t,x)}{\partial x} - \lambda W(t, x) + \lambda \int_{-\infty}^{x} W(t, x - y)\, dH(y)$$

holds for almost all $t \geq 0$ and $x \geq 0$.

5. Now $W(x) = \mathbf{P}\{\sup_{0<u<\infty} [\chi(u) - cu] \leq x\}$ where

$$\mathbf{E}\{e^{-s\chi(u)}\} = e^{-\lambda s/(1+s)}.$$

If $c > 0$ and $\lambda < c$, then by (23) of Section 35, we obtain that

$$\int_0^\infty e^{-sx}\, dW(x) = \frac{1 - \dfrac{\lambda}{c}}{1 - \dfrac{\lambda}{c(1+s)}},$$

whence by inversion

$$W(x) = 1 - \frac{\lambda}{c} \exp\left[-\left(1 - \frac{\lambda}{c}\right)x\right]$$

for $x \geq 0$.

6. Now $W(x) = \mathbf{P}\left\{\sup_{0\leq u<\infty} [\chi(u) - cu] \leq x\right\}$ where

$$\mathbf{E}\{e^{-s\chi(u)}\} = \exp\left\{-\lambda\left[1 - \left(\frac{1}{1+s}\right)^2\right]\right\}.$$

If $c \geq 0$ and $\lambda < c/2$, then by (23) of Section 35, we obtain that

$$\int_0^\infty e^{-sx}\, dW(x) = \frac{1 - \dfrac{2\lambda}{c}}{1 - \dfrac{\lambda(2+s)}{c(1+s)^2}}$$

or

$$\int_0^\infty e^{-sx}\, dW(x) = \left(1 - \frac{2\lambda}{c}\right) - \frac{A_1\gamma_1}{(s+\gamma_1)} + \frac{A_2\gamma_2}{(s+\gamma_2)}$$

where

$$\gamma_1 = 1 - \frac{\lambda}{2c} + \frac{\sqrt{\lambda^2 + 4\lambda c}}{2c},$$

$$\gamma_2 = 1 - \frac{\lambda}{2c} - \frac{\sqrt{\lambda^2 + 4\lambda c}}{2c},$$

$$A_1 = \lambda \frac{c + \lambda - \sqrt{\lambda^2 + 4\lambda c}}{c\sqrt{\lambda^2 + 4\lambda c}},$$

$$A_2 = \lambda \frac{c + \lambda + \sqrt{\lambda^2 + 4\lambda c}}{c\sqrt{\lambda^2 + 4\lambda c}}.$$

Hence by inversion we get

$$W(x) = 1 + A_1 e^{-\gamma_1 x} - A_2 e^{-\gamma_2 x}$$

for $x \geq 0$.

7. Let $\zeta(u) = \tilde{\chi}(u) - cu$ for $u \geq 0$. Then

$$\mathbf{E}\{e^{-s\zeta(u)}\} = e^{u\Psi(s)}$$

exists for $-1 < \operatorname{Re}(s) < 1$ and

$$\Psi(s) = cs + \lambda s \frac{s + 1 - 2\alpha}{(1 + s)(1 - s)},$$

or

$$\Psi(s) = -\frac{cs(s - \gamma_1)(s - \gamma_2)}{(1 + s)(1 - s)}$$

where

$$\gamma_1 = \frac{\lambda + \sqrt{\lambda^2 + 4c[c + \lambda(1 - 2\alpha)]}}{2c}$$

and

$$\gamma_2 = \frac{\lambda - \sqrt{\lambda^2 + 4c[c + \lambda(1 - 2\alpha)]}}{2c}.$$

If $c > 0$ and $c + \lambda(1 - 2\alpha) > 0$, then $\gamma_1 > 0$ and $\gamma_2 < 0$. In this case $\mathbf{P}\{\sup_{0 \leq u < \infty} \zeta(u) \leq x\} = W(x)$ is a proper distribution function and its Laplace-Stieltjes transform is given by

$$\int_0^\infty e^{-sx}\, dW(x) = \frac{(1 + s)\gamma_2}{\gamma_2 - s}$$

which can be obtained by using the method of factorization. Hence by inversion we get

$$W(x) = 1 - (1 + \gamma_2)e^{\gamma_2 x}$$

for $x \geq 0$.

If $c < 0$ and $c + \lambda(1 - 2\alpha) > 0$, then $\gamma_1 < 0$ and $\gamma_2 < 0$. In this case $\mathbf{P}\{\sup_{0 \leq u < \infty} \zeta(u) \leq x\} = W(x)$ is a proper distribution function and its Laplace-Stieltjes transform is given by

$$\int_0^\infty e^{-sx}\, dW(x) = \frac{(1 + s)\gamma_1\gamma_2}{(\gamma_1 - s)(\gamma_2 - s)}$$

which can be obtained by the method of factorization. Hence by inversion we get

$$W(x) = 1 - \frac{(1+\gamma_1)\gamma_2}{\gamma_2 - \gamma_1} e^{\gamma_1 x} - \frac{(1+\gamma_2)\gamma_1}{\gamma_1 - \gamma_2} e^{\gamma_2 x}$$

for $x \geq 0$.

8. By (5) of Section 25 we have

$$w \int_0^\infty e^{-wt}\, \Omega(t, s)\, dt = \exp\left[-\mathbf{A}\left\{\log\left(1 - \frac{cs - \lambda[1 - \psi(s)]}{w}\right)\right\}\right]$$

for $0 < w < \infty$ and $\mathrm{Re}(s) \geq 0$ where the operator **A** is defined in Section 11. Since

$$\mathbf{A}\left\{\log\left(1 - \frac{cs - \lambda[1 - \psi(s)]}{w}\right)\right\}$$

$$= \mathbf{A}\left\{\log\left(\frac{\lambda + w - cs}{w}\right)\right\} - \sum_{n=1}^{\infty} \frac{1}{n}\left(\frac{\lambda}{\lambda + w}\right)^n \mathbf{A}\left\{\left(\frac{\lambda + w}{\lambda + w - cs}\right)^n (\psi(s))^n\right\}$$

we obtain the result to be proved.

Chapter 8

1. Since $(a, b) = 1$, we can choose two positive integers p and q such that $aq - bp = 1$. Define the random variables $\gamma_1, \gamma_2, \ldots, \gamma_{a+b}$ as follows: $\gamma_r = q$ if the rth vote is cast for A, and $\gamma_r = -p$ if the rth vote is cast for B. Then $\gamma_1, \gamma_2, \ldots, \gamma_{a+b}$ are interchangeable random variables taking on integral values for which $\gamma_1 + \cdots + \gamma_{a+b} = 1$. Now $\alpha_r \geq a\beta_r/b$ holds if and only if $\alpha_r > p\beta_r/q$, or equivalently, $\gamma_1 + \cdots + \gamma_r > 0$. Accordingly $Q_j(a, b) = \mathbf{P}\{\gamma_1 + \cdots + \gamma_r > 0 \text{ for } j \text{ subscripts } r = 1, 2, \ldots, a + b\} = 1/(a + b)$ which follows from Theorem 2 of Section 37.

2. Let $\nu_1, \nu_2, \ldots, \nu_n$ be interchangeable random variables taking on non-negative integers. Set $N_r = \nu_1 + \cdots + \nu_r$ for $r = 1, \ldots, n$. Then

$$\mathbf{P}\{N_r \leq r \text{ holds for } j \text{ indices } r = 1, 2, \ldots, n \mid N_n = n\}$$

$$= \mathbf{P}\{N_n - N_r < n - r \text{ holds for } n - j \text{ indices } r = 1, 2, \ldots, n \mid N_n = n\}$$

$$= \mathbf{P}\{N_r < r \text{ holds for } n - j \text{ indices } r = 1, 2, \ldots, n \mid N_n = n\}$$

$$= \begin{cases} \displaystyle\sum_{i=1}^{j} \frac{1}{i(n-i)} \mathbf{P}\{N_i = i - 1 \mid N_n = n\} & \text{if } j = 1, 2, \ldots, n-1, \\ \displaystyle 1 - \sum_{i=1}^{n-1} \frac{1}{i} \mathbf{P}\{N_i = i - 1 \mid N_n = n\} & \text{if } j = n, \end{cases}$$

where the last equality follows from Theorem 3 of Section 37.

Define the random variables $\nu_1, \nu_2, \ldots, \nu_{2a}$ as follows: $\nu_r = 0$ if the rth vote is cast for A and $\nu_r = 2$ if the rth vote is cast for B. Then $\nu_1, \nu_2, \ldots, \nu_{2a}$ are interchangeable random variables with sum $\nu_1 + \nu_2 + \cdots + \nu_{2a} = 2a$. Let

$N_r = \nu_1 + \cdots + \nu_r$ for $r = 1, 2, \ldots, 2a$. Then $Q_j(a, a) = \mathbf{P}\{N_r \le r$ holds for j indices $r = 1, 2, \ldots, 2a\}$ and

$$\mathbf{P}\{N_r = 2s\} = \frac{\binom{r}{s}\binom{2a-r}{a-s}}{\binom{2a}{a}}.$$

Hence we get

$$Q_j(a, a) = \frac{1}{\binom{2a}{a}} \sum_{s=0}^{[(j-1)/2]} \frac{\binom{2s}{s}\binom{2a-2s-2}{a-s-1}}{(s+1)(a-s)}$$

for $j = 1, 2, \ldots, 2a - 1$ and

$$Q_{2a}(a, a) = 1 - \frac{1}{\binom{2a}{a}} \sum_{s=0}^{a-1} \frac{1}{(s+1)} \binom{2s}{s}\binom{2a-2s-1}{a-s} = \frac{1}{a+1}.$$

3. Let $\nu_1, \nu_2, \ldots, \nu_n$ be interchangeable random variables taking on non-negative integers. Set $N_r = \nu_1 + \cdots + \nu_r$ for $r = 1, 2, \ldots, n$. Then we have

$$\mathbf{P}\{N_r < r + 1 \text{ for } j \text{ indices } r = 1, \ldots, n \mid N_n = k\}$$
$$= \sum_{i=n-j}^{k-1} \frac{(n+1-k)}{i(n-i)} \mathbf{P}\{N_i = i + 1 \mid N_n = k\}$$

for $j = n - k + 1, \ldots, n - 1$, and $k = 1, 2, \ldots, n$. This formula can be proved in a similar way as (3) of Section 37, if we take into consideration that there exists an r such that $N_r = r + 1$ and $r = i$ $(i = n - j, \ldots, k - 1)$ is the greatest r with this property. By Theorem 1 of Section 6 we have

$$\mathbf{P}\{N_r < r + 1 \text{ for all } r = 1, \ldots, n \mid N_n = k\}$$
$$= 1 - \sum_{i=1}^{k-1} \frac{(n+1-k)}{(n-i)} \mathbf{P}\{N_i = i + 1 \mid N_n = k\}$$

for $k = 1, 2, \ldots, n$.

Define the random variables $\nu_1, \nu_2, \ldots, \nu_{a+b}$ as follows: $\nu_r = 0$ if the rth vote is cast for A and $\nu_r = (\mu + 1)$ if the rth vote is cast for B. Then $\nu_1, \nu_2, \ldots, \nu_{a+b}$ are interchangeable random variables with sum $\nu_1 + \nu_2 + \cdots + \nu_{a+b} = b(\mu+1)$. Let $N_r = \nu_1 + \cdots + \nu_r$ for $r = 1, 2, \ldots, a + b$. Now we have

$$Q_j(a, b) = \mathbf{P}\{N_r < r + 1 \text{ holds for } j \text{ indices } r = 1, 2, \ldots, a + b\}$$

and

$$\mathbf{P}\{N_i = i + 1\} = \frac{\binom{a}{s\mu - 1}\binom{b}{s}}{\binom{a+b}{s\mu + s - 1}}$$

for $i = s(\mu + 1) - 1$, $s = 0, 1, \ldots, b$. Thus

$$Q_j(a, b) = \sum_{\frac{a+b+1-j}{\mu+1} \le s \le b} \frac{(a + 1 - b\mu)}{(s\mu + s - 1)(a + b + 1 - s\mu - s)} \frac{\binom{a}{s\mu - 1}\binom{b}{s}}{\binom{a + b}{s\mu + s - 1}}$$

for $0 \le a - b\mu < j < a + b$ and $Q_{a+b}(a, b) = (a + 1 - b\mu)/(a + b)$.

4. Let $\nu_1, \nu_2, \ldots, \nu_n$ be interchangeable random variables taking on non-negative integers. Set $N_r = \nu_1 + \cdots + \nu_r$ for $r = 1, 2, \ldots, n$ and $N_0 = 0$. By Theorem 6 of Section 37 we have

$$\begin{aligned}
&\mathbf{P}\{N_r < r + 1 \text{ for } j \text{ indices } r = 1, 2, \ldots, n\} \\
&\quad = \mathbf{P}\{N_j - N_i \le j - i \text{ for } i = 0, 1, \ldots, j - 1 \text{ and } N_j - N_i < j - i \text{ for } \\
&\qquad\qquad i = j + 1, \ldots, n\} \\
&\quad = \sum_{l=0}^{j} \mathbf{P}\{N_j - N_i \le j - i \text{ for } i = 0, 1, \ldots, j - 1 \text{ and } N_j = l\} \\
&\qquad\qquad \cdot \mathbf{P}\{N_j - N_i < j - i \text{ for } i = j + 1, \ldots, n \mid N_j = l\}.
\end{aligned}$$

Here by Theorem 1 of Section 6

$$\begin{aligned}
&\mathbf{P}\{N_j - N_i \le j - i \text{ for } i = 0, 1, \ldots, j - 1 \text{ and } N_j = l\} \\
&\quad = \mathbf{P}\{N_r < r + 1 \text{ for } r = 1, 2, \ldots, j \text{ and } N_j = l\} \\
&\quad = \mathbf{P}\{N_j = l\} - \sum_{i=1}^{j-1} \frac{(j + 1 - l)}{(j - i)} \mathbf{P}\{N_i = i + 1 \text{ and } N_j = l\}
\end{aligned}$$

and

$$\begin{aligned}
&\mathbf{P}\{N_j - N_i < j - i \text{ for } i = j + 1, \ldots, n \mid N_j = l\} \\
&\quad = \mathbf{P}\{N_{j+1} - N_j > 1 \mid N_j = l\} - \sum_{r=j+2}^{n} \frac{1}{(r - j - 1)} \mathbf{P}\{N_r - N_j = r - j, \\
&\qquad\qquad N_{j+1} - N_j = 0 \mid N_j = l\}
\end{aligned}$$

which can be obtained by using the following general formula

$$\mathbf{P}\{N_r > r \text{ for } r = 1, \ldots, n\} = \mathbf{P}\{N_1 > 1\} - \sum_{r=2}^{n} \frac{1}{(r - 1)} \mathbf{P}\{N_r = r, N_1 = 0\}.$$

Thus finally we get

$$\begin{aligned}
&\mathbf{P}\{N_r < r + 1 \text{ for } j \text{ indices } r = 1, 2, \ldots, n\} \\
&\quad = \sum_{l=0}^{j} \Bigg[\mathbf{P}\{N_j = l, N_{j+1} > l + 1\} - \sum_{i=1}^{j-1} \frac{(j + 1 - l)}{(j - i)} \mathbf{P}\{N_i = i + 1, N_j = l, \\
&\qquad\qquad N_{j+1} > l + 1\} \Bigg] \\
&\quad - \sum_{l=0}^{j} \sum_{r=j+2}^{n} \Bigg[\frac{1}{(r - j - 1)} \mathbf{P}\{N_j = l, N_{j+1} = l, N_r = l + r - j\} \\
&\quad - \sum_{i=1}^{j-1} \frac{(j + 1 - l)}{(j - i)(r - j - 1)} \mathbf{P}\{N_i = i + 1, N_j = l, N_{j+1} = l, N_r = l + r - j\} \Bigg].
\end{aligned}$$

If we define the random variables $\nu_1, \nu_2, \ldots, \nu_{a+b}$ in the same way as in Problem 3, then

$$Q_j(a, b) = \mathbf{P}\{N_r < r + 1 \text{ for } j \text{ indices } r = 1, 2, \ldots, a + b\}$$

is given by the above formula, where now

$$\mathbf{P}\{N_i = r(\mu + 1)\} = \frac{\binom{i}{r}\binom{a+b-i}{b-r}}{\binom{a+b}{b}},$$

$$\mathbf{P}\{N_i = r(\mu + 1), N_j = s(\mu + 1)\} = \frac{\binom{i}{r}\binom{j-i}{s-r}\binom{a+b-j}{b-s}}{\binom{a+b}{b}}$$

for $1 \le i \le j \le a + b$, and

$$\mathbf{P}\{N_i = r(\mu + 1), N_j = s(\mu + 1), N_k = t(\mu + 1)\}$$
$$= \frac{\binom{i}{r}\binom{j-i}{s-r}\binom{k-j}{t-s}\binom{a+b-k}{b-t}}{\binom{a+b}{b}}$$

for $1 \le i \le j \le k \le a + b$.

NOTE. If $\nu_1, \nu_2, \ldots, \nu_n$ are interchangeable random variables taking on nonnegative integers, then we have

$$\mathbf{P}\{N_r > r \text{ for } r = 1, 2, \ldots, n\} = \mathbf{P}\{N_1 > 1\} - \sum_{r=2}^{n}\sum_{j=2}^{r}\frac{(j-1)}{(r-1)}\mathbf{P}\{N_1 = j, N_r = r\}$$
$$= \mathbf{P}\{N_1 > 1\} - \sum_{r=2}^{n}\frac{1}{(r-1)}\mathbf{P}\{N_1 = 0, N_r = r\}.$$

5. In what follows we suppose that m and n are fixed, relatively prime, positive integers, and we shall consider voting records with $a = km$ votes for A and $b = kn$ votes for B where $k = 1, 2, \ldots$. Denote by $\phi(k, j), j = 1, 2, \ldots, k$, the number of voting records for which $\alpha_r \ge a\beta_r/b$ holds for $r = 1, 2, \ldots, a + b$ and $\alpha_r = a\beta_r/b$ holds for j indices $r = 1, 2, \ldots, a + b$. Furthermore, let

$$C_k = \frac{1}{(m+n)k}\binom{mk+nk}{mk}$$

for $k = 1, 2, \ldots$. Following M. T. L. Bizley [8] we can determine $\phi(k, j)$, $1 \le j \le k$, in the following way. First, we have

$$C_k = \sum_{j=1}^{k}\frac{1}{j}\phi(k, j)$$

if $k = 1, 2, \ldots$. For if we form all the $(a + b)$ cyclic permutations of all those voting records for which $\{\alpha_r \geq a\beta_r/b$ for $r = 1, 2, \ldots, a + b\}$, then on the one hand we get all the possible voting records, and on the other hand a voting record occurs exactly j times if it is a cyclic permutation of a voting record for which $\{\alpha_r \geq a\beta_r/b$ for $r = 1, 2, \ldots, a + b$ and $\alpha_r = a\beta_r/b$ holds for j indices $r = 1, 2, \ldots, a + b\}$. Accordingly

$$\binom{mk + nk}{mk} = \sum_{j=1}^{k} \frac{(m + n)k}{j} \phi(k, j)$$

which proves the statement.

Second, we have the obvious relation

$$\phi(k, j) = \sum_{k_1+k_2+\cdots+k_j=k} \phi(k_1, 1)\phi(k_2, 1) \cdots \phi(k_j, 1)$$

for $j = 1, 2, \ldots, k$. Here k_i, $i = 1, 2, \ldots, j$, are positive integers.

If we use the notation $\phi(k) = \phi(k, 1)$, then by the above two relations we obtain that

$$\sum_{k=1}^{\infty} \phi(k)\, z^k = 1 - \exp\left(-\sum_{k=1}^{\infty} C_k z^k\right)$$

for $|z| < m^m n^n/(m + n)^{m+n}$ and hence

$$\phi(k) = \sum_{j_1+2j_2+\cdots+kj_k=k} (-1)^{1+j_1+\cdots+j_k} \frac{C_1^{j_1} C_2^{j_2} \cdots C_k^{j_k}}{j_1!\, j_2! \cdots j_k!}$$

where j_i, $i = 1, 2, \ldots, k$, are nonnegative integers.

Thus if $a = km$ and $b = kn$ where $(m, n) = 1$, then

$$P_{a+b-1}(a, b) = \frac{\phi(k)}{\binom{a + b}{a}}.$$

If we use the notation $\phi^*(k) = \phi(k, 1) + \phi(k, 2) + \cdots + \phi(k, k)$, then we obtain that

$$\sum_{k=1}^{\infty} \phi^*(k)\, z^k = \exp\left(\sum_{k=1}^{\infty} C_k z^k\right) - 1$$

for $|z| < m^m n^n/(m + n)^{m+n}$ and hence

$$\phi^*(k) = \sum_{j_1+2j_2+\cdots+kj_k=k} \frac{C_1^{j_1} C_2^{j_2} \cdots C_k^{j_k}}{j_1!\, j_2! \cdots j_k!}$$

where j_i, $i = 1, 2, \ldots, k$, are nonnegative integers.

Thus if $a = km$ and $b = kn$ where $(m, n) = 1$, then

$$Q_{a+b}(a, b) = \frac{\phi^*(k)}{\binom{a + b}{a}}.$$

6. According to an unpublished result of M. T. L. Bizley, the solution can be written in the following form

$$P_j(a, b) = \frac{1}{\binom{a+b}{a}} \sum_{j/(m+n)<r\le k} \phi(r)\phi^*(k-r) \qquad (j = 0, 1, \ldots, a+b-1)$$

where $\phi(r)$ and $\phi^*(r)$ $(r = 1, 2, \ldots)$ have the same meaning as in the solution of Problem 5, and $\phi^*(0) = 1$.

7. In this case $\delta_{a,b}$ is a discrete random variable with possible values $a + b - 2j$ $(j = 0, 1, 2, \ldots, [(a + b)/2])$. First we shall show that if the distribution of $\delta_{k,k}$ $(k = 1, 2, \ldots)$ is known, then that of $\delta_{a,b}$ can easily be found. If $a > b$, then we have

$$\mathbf{P}\{\delta_{a,b} = a + b - 2j\} = \sum_{k=j}^{b} \frac{\binom{a}{k}\binom{b}{k}}{\binom{a+b}{2k}} \mathbf{P}\{\delta_{k,k} = 2k - 2j\} \frac{a-b}{a+b-2k}.$$

For if $2k$ is the greatest u in $[0, a + b]$ such that $\alpha(u) = \beta(u)$, then by Theorem 1 of Section 2

$$\mathbf{P}\{\alpha(u) > \beta(u) \text{ for } 2k < u \le a + b \mid \alpha(2k) = \beta(2k)\} = \frac{a-b}{a+b-2k}$$

if $0 \le k \le b$, and

$$\mathbf{P}\{\alpha(2k) = \beta(2k)\} = \frac{\binom{a}{k}\binom{b}{k}}{\binom{a+b}{2k}}.$$

If $a < b$, then $\mathbf{P}\{\delta_{a,b} = a + b - 2j\}$ can be expressed similarly by symmetry.

Now we shall prove that

$$\mathbf{P}\{\delta_{a,a} = 2j\} = 1/(a + 1)$$

for $j = 0, 1, \ldots, a$ and $a = 1, 2, \ldots$. It can easily be seen that

$$\begin{aligned}
\mathbf{P}\{\delta_{a,a} = 2j\} &= \mathbf{P}\{\alpha_r + \alpha_{r-1} > \beta_r + \beta_{r-1} \text{ for } 2j \text{ indices } r = 1, 2, \ldots, 2a\} \\
&= \mathbf{P}\{\alpha_r + \alpha_{r-1} > \beta_r + \beta_{r-1} \text{ for } j \text{ indices } r = 2, 4, \ldots, 2a\} \\
&= \mathbf{P}\{\alpha_r + \alpha_{r-1} > \beta_r + \beta_{r-1} \text{ for } j \text{ indices } r = 1, 3, \ldots, 2a - 1\} \\
&= \mathbf{P}\{\alpha_{2s-1} > \beta_{2s-1} \text{ for } j \text{ indices } s = 1, 2, \ldots, a\}.
\end{aligned}$$

The last probability can be expressed in the following equivalent way. Denote by ν_r $(r = 1, 2, \ldots, a + 1)$ the number of votes registered for B after the $r - 1$st and before the rth vote is registered for A. (If $r = 1$ or $r = a + 1$, then the first half or the second half of this definition should be omitted.) Then

$\nu_1, \nu_2, \ldots, \nu_{a+1}$ are interchangeable random variables taking on nonnegative integers for which $\nu_1 + \nu_2 + \cdots + \nu_{a+1} = a$. Now we have

$$\mathbf{P}\{\delta_{a,a} = 2j\} = \mathbf{P}\{\nu_1 + \cdots + \nu_r < r \text{ for } j \text{ indices } r = 1, 2, \ldots, a\}.$$

This expression can also be seen directly. If we apply Theorem 2 of Section 37 to the random variables $\gamma_r = 1 - \nu_r$, $r = 1, 2, \ldots, a + 1$, then we obtain that

$$\mathbf{P}\{\delta_{a,a} = 2j\} = 1/(a + 1)$$

for $j = 0, 1, \ldots, a$. This completes the solution of the problem.

8. Let ρ_n be that value of $j = 0, 1, \ldots, n$ for which ζ_j attains its maximum. There is only one maximal element with probability 1. Then by Theorem 6 of Section 37

$$\begin{aligned}\mathbf{P}\{\Delta_n = j\} &= \mathbf{P}\{\rho_n = j\} = \mathbf{P}\{\zeta_i \le \zeta_j \text{ for } i = 0, 1, \ldots, n\} \\ &= \mathbf{P}\{\zeta_j - \zeta_i \ge 0 \text{ for } i = 0, 1, \ldots, j\}\mathbf{P}\{\zeta_i - \zeta_j \le 0 \text{ for } i = j, \ldots, n\} \\ &= \mathbf{P}\{\Delta_j = 0\}\mathbf{P}\{\Delta_{n-j} = 0\}.\end{aligned}$$

Hence

$$\sum_{j=0}^{n} \mathbf{P}\{\Delta_j = 0\}\mathbf{P}\{\Delta_{n-j} = 0\} = 1$$

for all $n \ge 0$. If we multiply this equation by z^n and add for $n = 0, 1, 2, \ldots$, then we get

$$\sum_{j=0}^{\infty} \mathbf{P}\{\Delta_j = 0\}\, z^j = \frac{1}{\sqrt{1 - z}}$$

for $|z| < 1$ and thus

$$\mathbf{P}\{\Delta_j = 0\} = \binom{2j}{j}\frac{1}{2^{2j}}$$

for $j = 0, 1, 2, \ldots$.

9. The event $\{\alpha_k(n) = j\}$ can occur in several mutually exclusive ways: there is an r [$\max(0, j + k - n) \le r \le \min(j, k)$] such that among $\zeta_0, \zeta_1, \ldots, \zeta_{j-1}$ there are r elements less than ζ_j and among $\zeta_{j+1}, \zeta_{j+2}, \ldots, \zeta_n$ there are $k - r$ elements less than ζ_j. These two events are independent. The first event has probability $\mathbf{P}\{\Delta_j = r\}$, and the second event has probability $\mathbf{P}\{\Delta_{n-j} = k - r\}$ where these probabilities are defined in the solution of Problem 8. Accordingly

$$\begin{aligned}\mathbf{P}\{\alpha_k(n) = j\} &= \sum_{r=\max(0,j+k-n)}^{\min(j,k)} \mathbf{P}\{\Delta_j = r\}\mathbf{P}\{\Delta_{n-j} = k - r\} \\ &= \sum_{r=\max(0,j+k-n)}^{\min(j,k)} \mathbf{P}\{\Delta_r = 0\}\mathbf{P}\{\Delta_{r-j} = 0\}\mathbf{P}\{\Delta_{k-r} = 0\}\mathbf{P}\{\Delta_{n-j-k+r} = 0\}\end{aligned}$$

where

$$\mathbf{P}\{\Delta_j = 0\} = \binom{2j}{j}\frac{1}{2^{2j}}.$$

10. If $\xi_1, \xi_2, \ldots, \xi_n$ are mutually independent and identically distributed random variables having a continuous distribution function $F(x)$, then $\eta_1 = F(\xi_1)$, $\eta_2 = F(\xi_2)$, $\ldots$, $\eta_n = F(\xi_n)$ are mutually independent random variables having a common uniform distribution in the interval (0, 1). Denote by $F_n(x)$ the empirical distribution function of the sample $(\xi_1, \xi_2, \ldots, \xi_n)$ and by $G_n(x)$ the empirical distribution function of the sample $(\eta_1, \eta_2, \ldots, \eta_n)$. Then $F_n(x) = G_n(F(x))$ and

$$\delta_n = \sup_{-\infty<x<\infty} |F_n(x) - F(x)| = \sup_{-\infty<x<\infty} |G_n(F(x)) - F(x)|$$
$$= \sup_{0\le y\le 1} |G_n(y) - y|$$

which proves that the distribution of δ_n is independent of $F(x)$.

11. Let $(\xi_1, \xi_2, \ldots, \xi_n)$ and $(\eta_1, \eta_2, \ldots, \eta_n)$ be independent samples of mutually independent random variables having a common continuous distribution function. Let us combine the two samples into a single sequence and arrange its elements in increasing order of magnitude. Define the random variables $\chi_1, \chi_2, \ldots, \chi_{2n}$ as follows. $\chi_i = 1$ if the ith variable in the combined ordered sequence belongs to the first sample and $\chi_i = -1$ if the ith variable in the combined ordered sequence belongs to the second sample. Then

$$\mathbf{P}\left\{\delta^+(n, n) \le \frac{c}{n}\right\} = \mathbf{P}\{\chi_1 + \cdots + \chi_r \le c \text{ for all } r = 1, 2, \ldots, 2n\}.$$

Now the sequence $\{\chi_1 + \cdots + \chi_r\}$ describes the path of a particle performing a random walk on the x-axis. The particle starts at $x = 0$ and in $2n$ steps moves n unit distances to the right and n unit distances to the left and each path has the same probability.

By using the solution of Problem 3 in Chapter 1 we can write

$$\mathbf{P}\left\{\delta^+(n, n) \le \frac{c}{n}\right\} = 1 - \frac{\binom{2n}{n+1+c}}{\binom{2n}{n}}$$

for $c = 0, 1, \ldots, n$. If $c = [\sqrt{2n}\, z]$ in the above formula and if $n \to \infty$, then we get

$$\lim_{n\to\infty} \mathbf{P}\left\{\sqrt{\frac{n}{2}}\,\delta^+(n, n) \le z\right\} = 1 - e^{-2z^2}$$

for $z \ge 0$.

12. If we use the same notation as in the solution of Problem 11, then we can write

$$\mathbf{P}\left\{\delta(n, n) \le \frac{c}{n}\right\} = \mathbf{P}\{|\chi_1 + \cdots + \chi_r| \le c \text{ for } r = 1, 2, \ldots, n\}.$$

By using the solution of Problem 4 in Chapter 1 we obtain

$$\mathbf{P}\left\{\delta(n, n) \le \frac{c}{n}\right\} = \frac{1}{\binom{2n}{n}} \sum_k (-1)^k \binom{2n}{n + k(c+1)}$$

for $c = 0, 1, \ldots, n$. If $c = [\sqrt{2n}\, z]$ in the above formula and if $n \to \infty$, then we get

$$\lim_{n\to\infty} \mathbf{P}\left\{\sqrt{\frac{n}{2}}\,\delta(n, n) \le z\right\} = K(z) = \sum_{k=-\infty}^{\infty} (-1)^k e^{-2k^2z^2}$$

for $z \ge 0$. This is in agreement with (13) of Section 38.

13. Let $(\xi_1, \xi_2, \ldots, \xi_m)$ and $(\eta_1, \eta_2, \ldots, \eta_n)$ be independent samples of mutually independent random variables having a common continuous distribution function. Let us arrange these $m + n$ variables in a single sequence in increasing order of magnitude. In this sequence denote by α_r the number of elements among the first r elements which belong to the first sample and by β_r the number of elements among the first r elements which belong to the second sample. Then

$$\mathbf{P}\left\{\inf_{0<G_n(x)<1} [F_m(x) - G_n(x)] > 0\right\} = \mathbf{P}\left\{\frac{\alpha_r}{m} > \frac{\beta_r}{n} \text{ for } r = 1, 2, \ldots, m + n - 1\right\}.$$

If $m = n$, then by using Theorem 1 of Section 2 we get

$$\mathbf{P}\{\alpha_r > \beta_r \text{ for } r = 1, 2, \ldots, 2m - 1\} = \frac{1}{2m - 1}.$$

If $(m, n) = 1$, then by using the solution of Problem 1 of Chapter 8 we get

$$\mathbf{P}\left\{\alpha_r > \frac{m}{n}\beta_r \text{ for } r = 1, 2, \ldots, m + n - 1\right\} = \frac{1}{m + n}.$$

14. Denote by τ_r, $r = 1, 2, \ldots$, the time when the rth event occurs in the Poisson process. Then

$$\mathbf{P}\left\{\sup_{0\le u\le 1} |\nu(u) - \lambda u| \le x\sqrt{\lambda}\right\} = \mathbf{P}\{-x\sqrt{\lambda} \le \lambda\tau_r - r \le x\sqrt{\lambda} - 1$$
$$\text{for } 0 \le \tau_r \le 1 \text{ and } |\nu(1) - \lambda| \le x\sqrt{\lambda}\}$$

and consequently

$$\lim_{\lambda\to\infty} \mathbf{P}\left\{\sup_{0\le u\le 1} |\nu(u) - \lambda u| \le x\sqrt{\lambda}\right\} = \lim_{\lambda\to\infty} \mathbf{P}\left\{\sup_{0\le\tau_r\le 1} \left|\tau_r - \frac{r}{\lambda}\right| \le \frac{x}{\sqrt{\lambda}}\right\}.$$

Here τ_r is a sum of r mutually independent and identically distributed random variables having the distribution function $F(x) = 1 - e^{-\lambda x}$ for $x \ge 0$. Now $\mathbf{E}\{\tau_r\} = r/\lambda$ and $\mathbf{Var}\,\{\tau_r\} = r/\lambda^2$. By using the invariance principle of P. Erdös and M. Kac, the right-hand side of the above equality can be expressed as

$$\lim_{\lambda\to\infty} \mathbf{P}\left\{\max_{1\le r<\lambda} |\zeta_r| \le x\sqrt{\lambda}\right\}$$

where $\zeta_r = \xi_1 + \cdots + \xi_r$ for $r = 1, 2, \ldots$ and $\{\xi_r\}$ are mutually independent random variables with distribution $\mathbf{P}\{\xi_r = 1\} = \mathbf{P}\{\xi_r = -1\} = \frac{1}{2}$. By using the solution of Problem 4 in Chapter 1 we obtain easily that

$$\mathbf{P}\left\{\max_{1 \le r \le n} |\zeta_r| < a\right\} = \sum_j (-1)^j \mathbf{P}\{(2j-1)a < \zeta_n < (2j+1)a\}$$

for a positive integer a. If $a = [x\sqrt{n}]$, then by the central limit theorem

$$\lim_{n\to\infty} \mathbf{P}\left\{\max_{1 \le r \le n} |\zeta_r| \le x\sqrt{n}\right\} = \sum_{j=-\infty}^{\infty} (-1)^j [\Phi((2j+1)x) - \Phi((2j-1)x)]$$

where

$$\Phi(x) = \frac{1}{\sqrt{2\pi}} \int_{-\infty}^{x} e^{-u^2/2}\, du.$$

Accordingly

$$\lim_{\lambda\to\infty} \mathbf{P}\left\{\sup_{0 \le u \le 1} |\nu(u) - \lambda u| \le x\sqrt{\lambda}\right\} = L(x)$$

where

$$L(x) = \sum_{j=-\infty}^{\infty} (-1)^j [\Phi((2j+1)x) - \Phi((2j-1)x)].$$

This result is in agreement with (53) of Section 40.

Author Index

Subject Index